WARWICKSHIRE'S
WILDFLOWERS

WARWICKSHIRE'S
WILDFLOWERS

The wildflowers, shrubs & trees of historic Warwickshire

STEVEN J. FALK

Published on behalf of
Warwickshire Publications by:

BREWIN BOOKS

First published on behalf of Warwickshire Publications
by Brewin Books Ltd, 56 Alcester Road, Studley,
Warwickshire B80 7LG in 2009

www.brewinbooks.com

ISBN: 978-1-85858-445-4

A Cataloguing in Publication Record
for this title is available from the British Library.

Mixed Sources
Product group from well-managed
forests and other controlled sources
www.fsc.org Cert no. TT-COC-2200
© 1996 Forest Stewardship Council
FSC

Typeset in Plantin
Printed in Great Britain by
Cambrian Printers Ltd.

Frontispiece: Ramsons in flower, Copt Green.

Contents

Foreword

Pam Copson (1939-2006), nee Sturdy, worked as Natural History Assistant, Keeper of Biology, and finally Senior Keeper of Natural History at the Warwickshire Museum from 1969 to 1999. During this time she played a pivotal role in the promotion of biological recording in Warwickshire and responded to wide ranging enquiries from members of the public. She also worked tirelessly to provide ecological advice at a county and district level and played a major part in setting up the county ecology service to carry this work forward.

Plants were her primary passion, though she also worked with various invertebrate groups such as woodlice, centipedes and millipedes. For much of her time at the Museum, and several years following her retirement, she was the official Botanical Society of the British Isles (BSBI) recorder for Warwickshire, responsible for managing all the records for higher plants, and for spearheading local botanical surveys. She co-ordinated a county-wide ecological land use survey, one of the first in the country, which also provided many of the initial plant and animal distribution records through target notes. Pam recognised – ahead of her time - that there was no point recording plant and animal species without trying to safeguard them too.

Pam was held in the highest esteem by local naturalists, Women's Institute groups and churchgoers (she was a leading authority on bell-ringing), and successfully engaged large numbers of voluntary helpers. She had a special talent for transforming people from casual appreciators of the countryside into skilled and dedicated surveyors.

It was Pam's intention to produce a book entitled 'Warwickshire's Wonderful Wildflowers – Two Centuries of Change'. She was unable to complete this task, but undertook a great deal of work in preparing it. This is not the book that Pam was drafting, but it is inspired by her efforts and knowledge, and it draws heavily upon her work, particularly in the preparation of a new county checklist.

Steven Falk succeeded Pam as the natural history specialist at the Museum in 2000 and has worked closely with local botanists, such as John Roberts and the late James Partridge, to complete this project and ensure that Warwickshire's flora can be more fully appreciated into the twenty-first century.

Pam Copson, Keeper of Biology, Warwickshire Museum 1969-1999.

Acknowledgements

This book would not have been written had it not been for the original conceptual and preparation work of Pam Copson. Nor would it have been brought to publication without the generous financial assistance of the Cadbury Trust. Many other people have supported the book through their botanical fieldwork between 1970 and 2007: Martin Adkins, Alderminster Women's Institute, Chris Aldridge, Jan Andrews, Sheila Apted, Agni-Louiza Arampoglou, George Arnold, Maurice Arnold, Simon Atkinson, Juliet Bailey, E. Bainbridge, Brian Baker, Christine Baker, P. Baker, Gwen Bale, A. Banbury, D. Barnish, Dr. Linda Barnett, Lucy Bastin, Shirley Beaumont, Martin Bennett, Paul Birkin, K. Blackburn, P. Bolton, Bill Bond, Mrs. Bostock, Ann Boucher, E. Boulstridge, Nicolette Bowen, Jonathan Bowley, John Bowra, Winifred Bowra, Dr. John Box, David Boyce, Jane & John Brace, Bastiaan Brak, Brandon Marsh Nature Reserve Team, David Broughton, Jeff Brown, David Bryce, Gill Bullen, C. & Mary Burgoine, P. Burgoine, A.R. Busby, James Callow, Michael Carpenter, R. Carter, M.C. Clark, Phill Clayton, Cyril Cleaver, Eleanor Cohn, David Cole, S.M. Coles, Peter & Rachel Cooke, Val Cooper, Tom & Ro Corby, Coventry and District Natural History and Scientific Society, Robin Cure, Anne Daly, Mary Daulman, Barbara Davies, Kate Davies, Peter Davies, John Day, Liz Dinsdale, Margaret Doggett, M. Dowlen, Lorna Dudley, Robert Dunnett, Adrian Dyke, Reg Elliott, Craig Emms, Ettington Women's Institute, Gary Farmer, J.H. Field, Mike Field, Mick Finnemore, Emma Flower, Trevor Forsyth, J.E. Fortney, Harold Fowkes, B.R. Fowler, Peter Fox, B. Frankel, Prof. J.H. Fremlin, C. Fuller, N. Fuller, Ruth Gallimore, Steve Garnett, G. Garside, Suma Geeves, Ali Glaisher, Dave Green, K.M. Green, A.L. Grenfell, Halford Women's Institute, Mr.& Mrs.P.C. Hall, K. Hammant, J.A. Hardman, Jane Hardwick, Graham Harrison, Haseley Women's Institute, Prof. J.G. Hawkes, C.M.L. Haynes, Karen Headley, Sylvia Henman, Don Hildred, Michael & Myrtle Hill, Ron Hill, E. Hirons, Paul Hodges, Olga Hood, F.S. Hopkins, E. Howell, Mary Hunt, Eddie Hutchins, James Irvine, Chris Ivin, Noreen Jardine, Stella Jarman, Don Jeffray, A. Jones, D. Joan Jones, John Jones, M.A. Jones, M.D.G. Jones, Neville Jones, R.I. Jones, John H. Juckes, Roger Juckes, R.C. Kendrick, Kenilworth Women's Institute, Margaret Kingsbury, Kingswood Women's Institute, B.L. Kington, Geoffrey Kitchener, Sandra Knapton, Suman Kumar, D. Knight, R.P.H. Lamb, Steve Lane, Brian Laney, Ray Langdon, Ashley Leftwich, Richard Lester, G.E. Lewis, Caroline Lidgett, Pat & Alvar Lockett, David Long, M.M. Lowe, Mrs. Mackay, Rosemary & Ian McClenagan, Paul Marriott, Mrs.W.R.H. Marsden, John Martin, Richard Marsh, John Matthews, John Mason, Di Meakin, Barry Meatyard, D. Merry, Robert Mileto, Lee Miles, B.R. Mitchell, Ruth Moffatt, Mich & Ann Moore, Les Moore, Dr. David Morfitt, H.C. Marrall, Aaron Morris, Mrs. D.M. Napier, Mrs. Napton, Alan Newton, Ian Nex, Vanessa Nixon, Phyllis & Frank Noakes, Peter Noble, M.M. Oakes, Jane O'Dell, Steven O'Donnell, Liz Ogg, John Osley, Michael Outhwaite, J.M. Owen, Richard Palmer, Emily Partridge, James Partridge, Philip V. Partridge, Phil Parr, John Patchett, R. Pickering,

R.& D. Pitt, Michael Poulton, David Porter, J.L. Presland, William Prestwood, John Price, Tony Primavesi, A.J. Print, Prior's Marston Women's Institute, Bill Proctor, Ted & June Read, Paul Reade, Pam Reason, John Redmayne, J. Rhodes, Tim Rich, Celia & David Rickers, Jane Ricketts, Harold Roberts, John and Val Roberts, John Robbins, Sven Rufus, Sue Scott, Bill Seaby, Jane Sells, John Sells, Michael Senior, H. Shortridge, I. J. Simper, Louise Slack, Mike Slater, Mark Smith, V.C. Smith, Graham Soden, David Sollis, Jane Southey, Clive Stace, P.E. Stanley, Bob & Sue Steele, A. Stewart, Steve Stroud, Robina Stuart, Beryl & Stan Stubbs, Sutton Coldfield Natural History Society, Ian Sylvester, Ian Tanner, Sheila Tatum, Derek Thomas, Ron Thomas, M.R. Thomas, Bill Thompson, John Thompson, S. Thompson, Bob Thurston, E.S. Tonks, Les Tooby, J. Toothill, Prof. Ian Trueman, Jenny Turner, A.J. Underhill, Alison Urwick, C. Waddens, Jeff Waddell, John Wagstaffe, Simon Walden, Natalie Walker, S.M. Walters, John Walton, Monica Walton, David Wall, Keith Warmington, Warwickshire Wildlife Trust, Warwick Natural History Society, Warwickshire College of Agriculture (Moreton Morrell), Jack Watkins, Mrs. Watkins, E.C. Webster, Christopher Westall, Mike Whitecross, Dr. & Mrs.P. Whitworth, J.T. Williams, Beryl Wilson, Toby Woodhams, Neil Wyatt, Dorothy Yardley.

The following botanists provided expert plant identification: Dr. J.R. Akeroyd, Dr. C. Alexander, Dr. J.P. Bailey, P.M. Benoit, Dr. R.K. Brummitt, J.A. Camus, Dr. J.F.M. Cannon, A.O. Chater, E.J. Clement, A.P. Conolly, Prof. C.D. Cook, R.J. Cooke, Dr. T.A. Cope, H.V. Corley, J. Day, R.W. David, M. Dowlen, Dr. J.R. Edmonson, Dr. T.T. Elkington, Dr. I.K. Ferguson, Prof. J.H. Fremlin, Mrs. J. Fryer, Dr. R.J. Gornall, A.L. Grenfell, Dr. G. Halliday, Dr. D.J. Hambler, M.W.C. Hardman, R.M. Harley, Dr. B. Harold, Prof. J.G. Hawkes, Dr. N.T.H. Holmes, Dr. C.C. Haworth, Dr. C. Jeffrey, Dr. A.C. Jermy, Prof. B.E. Jonsell, G.D. Kitchener, R. Lansdown, R. Maskew, Dr. J. Mason, R.D. Meikle, Dr. A. Melderis, J.M. Mullin, A.L. Newton, Dr. C.N. Page, T.D. Pennington, Dr. F.H. Perring, Dr. A. Radley-Smith, Dr. R.C. Readett, Dr. A.J. Richards, Dr. M.C.F. Proctor, Dr. C.D. Preston, Tony Primavesi, A.W. Reid, R.H. Roberts, Dr. T.C.G. Rich, Dr. N.K.B. Robson, Dr. F.J. Rumsey, T.B. Ryves, Dr. H. Schotsman, Dr. M.J. Short, Dr. D.A. Simpson, Dr. W.A. Sledge, M.J. Southam, Prof. C.A. Stace, N.F. Stewart, Dr. E.L. Swann, Dr. P.J.O. Trist, Prof. I.C. Trueman, Dr. S.M. Walters, J.E.J. White, B.Z. Wurzell, Dr. P.F. Yeo.

The following provided assorted advice and information on other aspects of the book: Ted Copson, Gwynn Ellis, Anton Irving (Natural England), Chris Jeens (Warwickshire Publications), Alex Lockton, Helen Maclagan (Warwickshire Museum), Ken Martin, Alan Newton, Jane O'Dell, James Partridge, Dr. Jon Radley (Warwickshire Museum), Bert Reid, John Roberts, Paul Walsh (Warwickshire Publications), Warwickshire Museum Archaeological Unit (Jonathan Parkhouse, Ben Wallace, Stuart Palmer, Nick Palmer et al.), Warwickshire Museum Ecology Unit (Dave Lowe and Anna Swift), Barbara Weed, Matt Wilmott (Natural England).

I am particularly grateful to John Roberts for proof-reading the manuscript, providing constant encouragement and advice, and supplying the majority of the photographs used in the book.

All photographs were taken by John Roberts and Steven Falk with whom copyright remains.

Chapter 1

Introduction

Warwickshire has a unique mixture of northern, southern, eastern and western floristic elements. The wetlands of Sutton Park have a plant community sharing much in common with a Lake District or Scottish bog, the grassland that has developed in some of our old limestone quarries resembles the chalk grassland of areas like the South Downs, and the Sessile Oak woods of the Arden resemble those of Wales. Perhaps one should not be too surprised given Warwickshire's position in the middle of England. However, no other county in the British Midlands exhibits this pattern so strikingly. The underlying geology, with an almost perfect fifty-fifty split of calcareous underlying geology (south and east Warwickshire) versus non-calcareous underlying geology (north and west Warwickshire), can take a fair bit of credit for strengthening this pattern; so can the near fifty-fifty split of 'ancient countryside' versus 'planned countryside' (as defined by Oliver Rackham in his seminal 1986 book *History of the Countryside*) which loosely corresponds with the geology. Today, Warwickshire's diverse array of habitats includes ancient woods and meadows centuries (or even millennia) old, through to highly artificial and recently-created sites such as quarries and railway sidings, some of which are surprisingly good for wild and naturalised plants. In essence, the plantlife of Warwickshire is extremely rich and varied, reflecting the complex history, geology and modern land-use of the County. But that flora is ever-changing.

This book, which is the third major account of Warwickshire's higher plants, intends to act as a snapshot of what grows in the Vice-county of Warwickshire at the start of the twenty-first century, with an indication of what has been lost and gained prior to this period. It highlights which species might now be considered most valuable when assessing the quality of a wildlife site (an important pursuit these days), and identifies which species might be worthy of special conservation measures to prevent their further decline or extinction. But in addition to these two worthy objectives, it is hoped that this book will simply help you to enjoy and understand this attractive element of Warwickshire's biodiversity.

Work on this book was initiated by Pam Copson in the 1990s using the large amount of data gathered from various local Botanical Society of the British Isles (BSBI) surveys plus other plant surveys carried out since the 1970s. She also used information from *A Computer-Mapped Flora* (Cadbury et al., 1971) and Bagnall's *Flora of Warwickshire* (1891), which are the first two major accounts of the local flora, and from the Warwickshire Museum herbarium, which contains many important records. Given that these older sources include data from the great seventeenth century naturalist John Ray (who lived at Middleton Hall near Tamworth for part of his life), we are in the privileged position of being able to evaluate plant records covering a period of nearly four hundred years. Sadly, Pam became increasingly ill following her retirement from Warwickshire Museum in 1989 and passed away in November 2006 with a well-researched but still very incomplete manuscript. It was her dying wish that her project be completed by the author. The county checklist which Pam had prepared has been made fully up to date to the end of 2007, and a new text on the history and ecology of the various local plant habitats has been produced to allow a better understanding of the historical and ecological aspects of the local flora.

This process has been greatly facilitated by the publication of the *New Atlas of the British and Irish Flora* (Preston, Pearman & Dines, 2002), the most detailed and informative vascular plant atlas yet published for the British Isles. It enables Warwickshire's flora to be viewed in a national context, and is particularly useful in helping us to understand the changing distributions and abundances of many species. It provides particularly useful information on the native, naturalised or casual status of all species and their favoured habitats. The 1971 *A Computer-Mapped Flora*, though somewhat out of date now, still provides an excellent indication of the habitat requirements of many plants in Warwickshire specifically (which can differ from those viewed in a national context), and also has some useful accounts of the various plant habitats within its Habitat Studies chapter.

It should be stressed that trying to understand and evaluate the modern flora of Warwickshire is far more than just a botanical endeavour. It requires an understanding of ecology, landscape history, geology and soil, modern and historical land-use, geography and international trade, social history, taxonomy and even genetics. Nature conservationists tend to focus on loss of species and threats to wildlife, and there is no question that many of Warwickshire's native and naturalised plants are now much scarcer than in the past and many dozens appear to have become extinct. But for every plant species lost in the past one hundred years, several new ones have been gained. One of the most important and exciting trends in the local plant flora over the past two thousand years has been the establishment of brand new species from various parts of the globe that we call either **archaeophytes** (introduced before 1500) or **neophytes** (introduced after 1500). Initially, these were mostly introduced as contaminants of crop seeds and wool, but in more recent times they have tended to be garden escapes, contaminants of bird-seed, escapes from wildflower or vegetable seed mixtures, or arrivals as seeds carried on vehicles and imported items from abroad. Almost every year something new is reported in Warwickshire, and some real surprises have turned up. In 2006, this included the discovery of a strange stinging nettle *Urtica membranacea* growing beside a wall in the middle of Warwick, just a few yards from Warwickshire Museum (Boucher & Partridge, 2006). It was completely new to the British list! We also have a growing number of salt-tolerant, coastal plants growing along our road verges and other specialist plants colonising our old walls. Of the various plant habitats in Warwickshire, only heathland and mire remain relatively unaffected by archaeophytes and neophytes.

The geographical area covered by this book

This book covers the biological or Vice-county of Warwickshire (Vice-county 38). This 1852 boundary of the County is substantially different to that of the modern administrative County of Warwickshire, more resembling that of the old County of

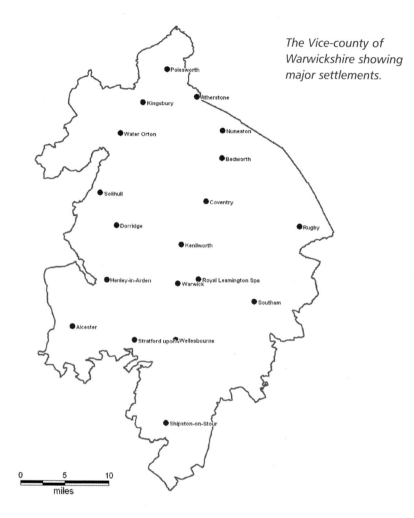

The Vice-county of Warwickshire showing major settlements.

0   5   10
miles

Warwickshire before the modern County of the West Midlands was established. This means that Coventry, Solihull, Sutton Coldfield, the eastern part of Tamworth and some of east Birmingham (including the city centre and Edgbaston) are here regarded as Warwickshire, which might please some traditionalists. However, it also means that areas like Quinton, Long Marston and Welford-on-Avon in south-west Warwickshire are ignored as they belong to Vice-county 33 (East Gloucestershire). Vice-county boundaries do not change like modern county boundaries, and tend to use natural features such as watercourses and ridges rather than roads and settlements.

The botanical scope of this book (inclusions and exclusions)

This book covers trees, shrubs and herbaceous plants, the last including grasses, rushes, sedges, ferns, horsetails and clubmosses. These are collectively termed **vascular plants** or **higher plants**. This book does not cover bryophytes (mosses and liverworts), algae (seaweeds and charophytes), lichens or fungi.

A familiar native: Bluebell (left), archaeophyte: White Dead-nettle (middle) and neophyte: Oxford Ragwort (right).

The book concentrates on native and naturalised plants. **Native** species are those that have come to grow in Britain without human assistance. Most arrived following the end of the last Ice Age, which had turned the greater part of the British Isles into an ice-covered wilderness or frozen tundra unsuitable for most of the plants that grow here today. As Britain grew warmer, plants arrived from Continental Europe assisted by the fact that no English Channel existed, sea levels being much lower than they are today. **Aliens** or **introductions** are plants that have been introduced to Britain. If they become established and grow as if they are wild plants, we term them **naturalised**. Naturalised plants are divided into **archaeophytes** (plants introduced before 1500) and **neophytes** (plants introduced after 1500). The oldest introductions are arable weeds associated with Neolithic agriculture (see Chapter 9). **Casuals** are alien plants that have not become properly established. If following its discovery a casual is subsequently recorded from at least three separate places, or if it has clearly propagated itself locally for several years, then its status will be changed to that of neophyte. We have listed casuals in the main Checklist, but have not lingered on them within the habitat chapters as they tend to say little about the character or quality of a habitat. We also exclude planted trees, garden flowers and crops that have not escaped or naturalised, or only turn up in garden waste.

These various categories are by no means trivial because they help to highlight the complex and often international inter-relationship between local plants and human activity, as reading Chapter 9 (Arable Land) or Chapter 11 (Disturbed Ground) will reveal.

Species, subspecies, microspecies, aggregates and hybrids

It is impossible to produce a detailed county flora without coming up against hybrids, subspecies, microspecies, aggregates, and other forms of variation and categorisation. These taxa can be a challenge to define and identify, but help to reveal how plants evolve and adapt.

The False Oxlip (left) is the occasionally recorded hybrid of Primrose (middle) and Cowslip (right).

Species and hybrids

We are all relatively familiar with the concept of a ***species***. A Human is not a Chimpanzee and does not interbreed with the great apes. Many plant species behave just like humans – they are genetically distinct, easily recognised, and breed true, e.g. Cow Parsley and Daisy. But plants, rather more than animals, tend to dispense with this neat conformity in a number of ways. Many closely-related species (and occasionally some rather unrelated ones) can interbreed. The result is a ***hybrid***, and it usually has characteristics of both parents. Dozens of hybrids have been recorded in Warwickshire. Some probably arrived in Warwickshire from other places already in the hybrid state, but nearly 120 are thought to have arisen spontaneously within Warwickshire. Frequent ones include crosses between Pedunculate Oak and Sessile Oak and crosses between Red Campion and White Campion. The former hybrid is called *Quercus* x *rosacea*, the latter *Silene* x *hampeana*. It is a convention to put an 'x' between the generic and specific name when quoting the scientific name of a hybrid involving two species within the same ***genus*** (a collection of closely-related species, plural ***genera***). Certain groups, such as willowherbs, willows and evening-primroses are particularly prone to hybridisation, and may even form hybrid swarms with three species involved in the parentage of some plants. ***Back-crosses*** are where hybrids interbreed with one of their parents, and these can be very difficult to identify.

    Intergeneric hybrids are those with parents belonging to two different genera and are much rarer. A Warwickshire example is the hybrid grass X *Festulolium loliaceum*, a hybrid of Meadow Fescue *Festuca pratensis* and Perennial Ryegrass *Lolium perenne*. It is a convention to put an 'X' before the scientific names of such hybrids. The reproductive barriers that prevent many animals from hybridising, such as appearance, behaviour and genetics, are seemingly poorly developed in many plants. In the wild, it is often only physical isolation that prevents hybridisation, even where two species are likely to have parted from a common ancestor many millions of years ago and ended up on different side of the Atlantic or Pacific Oceans. Human activity has been very efficient at re-introducing long-separated plant cousins and bringing about incestuous breeding! Hybrids may be sterile or fertile, but hybrid swarms and back-crosses can only arise where hybrids are fertile.

Variation

Many species exhibit variation. It may involve variation in the leaf shape or flower colour within a single population of a plant, and can be related to whether a plant is growing in the shade versus the open or within a drier or wetter piece of ground. The more distinct and regular variants are often termed *forms* or *varieties*. If there is a genetic basis to these, it will be a trivial one, like the variation in hair and eye colour that can occur within a human family. Where the variation is linked to the environmental conditions in which the plant is growing e.g. exposure, lack of key minerals or soil toxicity, the variant is often termed an *ecotype*. Variants that are deliberately created for horticultural or agricultural purposes (either to look better or grow better) are called *cultivars*. Good examples are crops such as the cultivated Carrot, which is much bigger than the wild forms of carrot (even the foreign populations from which it is derived) and has the familiar stout reddish root. Brussels Sprouts, Broccoli and Cauliflower are particularly extreme cultivars of Cabbage and look very different to their uncultivated ancestor (which resembles cabbages that have been left to go to seed).

The two Warwickshire subspecies of Anagallis arvensis, Scarlet Pimpernel (above) and Blue Pimpernel (below).

Where a species occurs across a large geographic range or in a variety of habitats, more substantive genetic variation may arise, especially if populations have become physically and genetically isolated in different environmental conditions for a long period of time. Evolution can produce what is known as a *subspecies* (abbreviated to 'ssp.') or *race*. Subspecies may look slightly different to one another and have different ecological and physiological characteristics, but not of sufficient magnitude to justify splitting them into separate species. Forty-four of Warwickshire's plants have two or more well-recognised races here. A good example is Scarlet Pimpernel, the normal (red-flowered) form of which occurs frequently in a variety of habitats, whilst the rare Blue Pimpernel (ssp. *foemina*) is a rare arable weed. It is not infrequent for one of the Warwickshire subspecies to be a native whilst the others are archaeophytes or neophytes (e.g. Common Vetch).

Microspecies are those that are deemed to have attained sufficient distinction to be deemed good species, but belong to a group (an *aggregate*) of other microspecies that are usually very difficult to separate from one another. This particularly affects plants that use **apomixis**, which is the ability to germinate unfertilised seeds, thereby producing plants that are genetically identical to the parents (e.g. many brambles, hawkweeds and dandelions). Over thousands of years these pure genetic lineages become increasingly distinct. Modern methods for studying the evolution and taxonomic relationships of plants, such as DNA analysis, are resulting in the discovery of lots of new microspecies and subspecies.

Nomenclature used

The scientific and English names used in this book are taken from the BSBI's *Vice-county Census Catalogue of Vascular Plants of Great Britain* (Stace et al., 2003). It should be pointed out that both scientific and English names can change over time for a number of reasons. During the course of writing this book Apple, until recently known as *Malus domestica*, became re-named *M. pumila*. There has been confusion over whether Tor-grass is just a single species *Brachypodium pinnatum* with a second race (subspecies *rupestre*), or two distinct species, *B. pinnatum* and *B. rupestre*, plus confusion over which is the more widespread and frequent form. Elm nomenclature and taxonomy remains the subject of much confusion, with several competing classifications in recently published literature. Fortunately, these issues only affect a relatively small proportion of the British flora, though Bagnall would be quite surprised if he saw a checklist of Warwickshire plants today, given the cumulative changes over the past 120 years.

Rarity statuses and what they mean

The presence of a rare plant, or a suite of them, can be very significant in nature conservation terms. It can bring about the designation of a site as a Site of Special Scientific Interest (SSSI) or a County Wildlife Site, or unlock funding for special land management. Care must be taken though, as not all rare plants are equal. A rare native or archaeophyte growing in its typical habitat (and therefore likely to represent an old population) is far more noteworthy in conservation terms than an equally rare casual of recent origin growing on a rubbish tip.

To flag the different levels of significance that are attached to rare and scarce plants, they are classified within different rarity categories as follows:

National rarity (Red Data List) categories

The definitions of these criteria are long and complex and can be found in '*The Vascular Plant Red Data List for Great Britain*' (Cheffings & Farrell, 2005). In descending order of threat, those categories relevant to Warwickshire are:

- **Critically endangered**
- **Endangered**
- **Vulnerable**
- **Near-threatened**
- **Nationally rare**
- **Nationally scarce**

The main checklist, plus Appendix 2, flag the Red Data List species recorded in Warwickshire. It should be noted that many national rarities only exist in Warwickshire as introduced casuals or recently established neophytes, and the checklist distinguishes these from national rarities that appear to have a long history in Warwickshire.

Warwickshire rarity categories

Warwickshire has relatively few plants falling into the national rarity categories compared with many counties. Nevertheless, many species falling outside national rarity categories are rare and vulnerable in Warwickshire and require flagging as such. This book makes the first attempt at a red data list for Warwickshire plants, using four criteria:

- **Very rare** – natives, archaeophytes and some long-established neophytes which have only been recorded at one or two sites in Warwickshire since 1969
- **Rare** – as above, but for plants that have been recorded at 3-9 sites
- **Warwickshire Notables** – scarcer native or naturalised species and more important habitat quality indicators (not used for casual, escape or planted populations)
- **Extinct** – species that have not been recorded since 1969

Difficulties arise in that some national rarities and some Warwickshire ones have been cultivated so that garden escapes and other artificially introduced specimens can obscure the true native or naturalised status of a rare species (including a species that has become fully extinct in its wild state). Where a species is thought to have become extinct in its wild form, but is now occasionally found as a non-persisting casual, it is still regarded as extinct in the checklist.

Grass-of-Parnassus, a Warwickshire Rarity only ever recorded in the Vice-county from Sutton Park.

Warwickshire rarities are not given a rarity category if already covered by a national category. The following are also excluded from rarity categories, even if they have very few records:

- hybrids (many of which arise spontaneously, may not persist, or may have non-native parentage) unless covered by the national red data list
- casuals
- very poorly defined species or subspecies which are unlikely to have been noted by recorders

Chapter 2

The History of Plant Recording in Warwickshire

A detailed account of the history of plant recording in Warwickshire up until the early twentieth century is provided by the 1971 *A Computer-Mapped Flora* (Cadbury et al., pp. 45-60) and it is not intended to repeat all the detail here. But the following highlights some of the more significant botanists of our area over the past four centuries, and their contributions.

John Ray (1627-1705) is responsible for some of our earliest published botanical records, though we do have a few from the sixteenth century. He lived at Middleton Hall in north Warwickshire from 1669 to 1675 as a tutor for the family of his friend and fellow naturalist Francis Willughby. He spent many hours botanising in the Middleton area, providing a valuable snapshot of what grew there in an age before the enclosure of heaths and drainage of mires. It would appear that the area resembled the modern Sutton Park, with many of the species now confined to that site, plus extinct species such as Great Fen-sedge and Black Bog-rush that indicate fen of great quality and antiquity was present at this time. Most of his Warwickshire records are found in his *Catalogus Plantarum Angliae et Insularum adjacentium* published in 1670. A number of these seem to represent first British records e.g. Smooth Cat's-ear, Pale Sedge and Bottle Sedge.

William Withering (1741-1799) produced some of the earliest catalogues and classifications of British plants (based on the Linnaean binomial system that we use today), and these include many important Warwickshire records, again concentrating on the north of the County. Several of these were first British records, e.g. Orange Foxtail and Bog Pondweed. He was a great friend of the **Countess of Aylesford** (1760-1832) who resided at Packington Hall (still the family seat of the Aylesford family) and was herself a keen botanist. She added about thirty new species to the County list, and also produced nearly 3000 paintings of flowers, presumably mainly Warwickshire ones. These can now be found in the Oxford University Herbarium together with important specimens gathered by her granddaughter, **Charlotte Eden Palmer** (1830-1914) who lived in Lighthorne.

In 1817 **Thomas Purton** (1768-1833) published the first two volumes of *The Midland Flora* adding over a hundred new species to the county list, many from the Alcester area. The third volume was published in 1821. This Flora is a fascinating read with much anecdotal information relating a plant's edibility, medicinal properties and other uses. It also highlights the state of plant taxonomy at the time, with some now-familiar species such as Midlands Hawthorn not yet fully recognised, and Wild Service-tree grouped with Hawthorn rather than the more closely-related Rowan. Modern rarities such as Shepherd's-needle are described as "very common". The **Rev. W. T. Bree** (1787-1863) contributed a number of records to Purton's Flora and was an excellent botanist.

1817 also saw the publication of a 'Select List of Plants' in Dugdale's *Antiquities of Warwickshire* by **William Groves Perry** (1796-1863). He was only 16 years old when he started this work. In 1820, he published *Plantae Varvicenses Selectae* (a Botanist's Guide through the county of Warwick) which contained a list of 379 species, about a quarter of which were new to Warwickshire. Many more first county records exist within his large collection of pressed plants which is now housed at Warwickshire Museum. Perry, who was Honorary Secretary of the Warwickshire Archaeological and Natural History Society, employed the assistance of various other local botanists such as **Thomas Kirk**, **Dr Lloyd** and **Dr St Brody**.

James Eustace Bagnall (1830-1918) was the most significant of the nineteenth century botanists, publishing in 1891 his *Flora of Warwickshire*, the first official county flora, and regarded as one of the foremost county floras of its day. It covered not only vascular plants but mosses, liverworts and fungi too. He was a self-taught botanist who wrote that all his work was done "in the scant leisure of a manufactory clerk", and was a key member of the Birmingham Natural History Society. In the 1870s he published important papers on the Birmingham area and Sutton Park in their *Proceedings*. His 1891 Flora contains records from a number of other fine local botanists, including the **Rev. Andrew Bloxham** (1801-1878) and **Henry Bromwich** (1828-1907). Some important records from Charlotte Palmer and the Countess of Aylesford, both mentioned earlier, and **William Baxter** (1787-1871) were bought to Bagnall's attention by George Claridge Druce too late for inclusion. These and other records were published in the *Midland Naturalist* in 1892-93.

Bagnall's herbarium was given to Birmingham Museum in 1913. Bagnall's work gives a truly fascinating snapshot of Victorian Warwickshire, with many clues to the appearance of the local countryside which clearly contained far more heathland, mire and species-rich grasslands than today. A detailed account of Bagnall is given by Price (1980).

James Eustace Bagnall, author of the first official account of Warwickshire's flora (reproduced from The Proceedings of the Birmingham Natural History Society).

Bagnall's Flora remained much used for the next fifty years. However, in 1949 members of the Birmingham Natural History and Philosophical Society and staff of the Botany Department of Birmingham University decided to start work on a new county flora. It was a truly ambitious project, one that would take twenty years to complete and a team of talented botanists to oversee, most notably the keen amateur **Dorothy Cadbury**, plus two professional botanists at Birmingham University, **Prof. John Hawkes** and **R.C. Readett**. A new county checklist was published in 1965 and the main output, *A Computer-Mapped Flora*, eventually published in 1971. It was the first flora of its kind: highly ecological, extremely detailed and wide-ranging, and based on

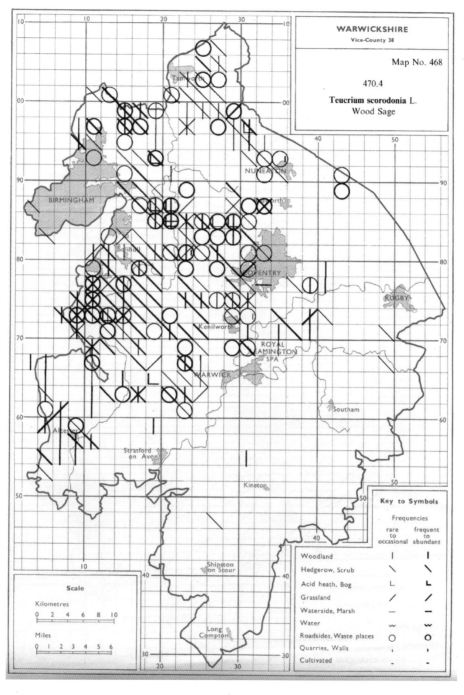

A map showing the distribution of Wood Sage in A Computer-Mapped Flora (1971). Notice the explicit depiction of both distribution and habitat preferences through the clever use of symbols.

the most stringent field recording. Every part of the Vice-county was covered, and the locations and habitats of all species, whether common or rare, were carefully noted. The data was processed by a computer, the parts of which occupied three rooms and had considerably less capacity than a modern mobile phone. The result is an extraordinary series of species maps that, using symbols for different habitats, give a very visual indication of where a plant occurred in the County and what it was doing there. The maps are complemented by species accounts (including some for scarce species not covered by the maps) which collate information in previous publications such as Bagnall's Flora or Ray's Catalogue, and also provide further information on the habitats used by individual species by quoting the percentage of records associated with particular habitats such as woods, watersides, hedges, railway banks and so on. A chapter entitled 'Habitat Studies' gives an indication of what the most frequent plant species were for several dozen habitat categories. It reveals some quite significant differences from the plant assemblages of those habitats today, some fifty years on.

A Computer-Mapped Flora laid down the foundation for one of the most intensive and structured periods of plant recording in Warwickshire's history. Over a dozen formal surveys have taken place since, and new ones are in the process of being organised at the time of writing. The more important ones include:

- 1983-84, Rediscovering Warwickshire's Rarest Flowers.
- 1984, the Warwickshire Churchyard Survey.
- 1987/88, the BSBI Local Change Survey, a national survey that covered seven 2x2km tetrads in Warwickshire.
- 1990, the Warwickshire Garden Weeds Survey, a questionnaire-based survey which gathered information for 156 sites, with results published in the journal *Professional Horticulture* (Copson & Roberts, 1991).
- 1992, the Nationally Scarce Species Project, part of a national initiative linked to the Nature Conservancy Council, Institute of Terrestrial Ecology and BSBI
- 1995-2007, the Birmingham and Black Country Flora Project, which included the Birmingham and Sutton Coldfield parts of Vice-county Warwickshire, to be published in a forthcoming book edited by Prof. Ian Trueman and Mike Poulton.
- 1996-99, Flora 2000, part of a national BSBI survey that resulted in the *New Atlas of the British and Irish Flora* (Preston, Pearman & Dines, 2002). Twenty-five 10km squares of Warwickshire were covered, with every species recorded. A 2008-09 update survey is being prepared at the time of writing.
- 2003-04, the second BSBI Local Change Survey, a repeat of the 1987/88 one, designed to compare the same sites sixteen years on. 651 plant species were reported, including 97 species not previously noted. Only 25 species were not re-encountered. Warwickshire data contributed to the BSBI publication *Change in the British Flora 1987-2004* (Braithwaite et al., 2006).
- 2005, the second Arable Weeds Survey (linked to Plantlife and BSBI) to discover arable fields with a rich weed flora. 21 fields were surveyed in Warwickshire and 6 of the 14 species targeted nationally were discovered.
- 2005-06, the BSBI Hybrids Project, part of a national survey co-ordinated by Clive Stace for a forthcoming BSBI publication.

- 2006 onwards, The Big Tree Hunt of Warwickshire, Coventry and Solihull, co-ordinated by Warwickshire Museum, which has generated a catalogue of all native, naturalised and planted tree species, plus major varieties and hybrids, found in modern Warwickshire (not Birmingham or Sutton Coldfield), also absorbing pre-existing surveys for the native Black-poplar, veteran trees and mature elms.

Through such surveys and the more general exploits of local botanists, new plants, especially casuals, are discovered in Warwickshire in most years. These discoveries and other important records have been regularly published in the *Proceedings of the Birmingham Natural History Society* since 1973 (see Further Reading section of this book for a full list). The majority of these updates were compiled by **Pam Copson** (1939-2006), Keeper of Biology at Warwickshire Museum. Pam acted as the official BSBI County Recorder for most of her time at the Museum plus several years after her retirement. She established and maintained files with species data, co-ordinated local botanical surveys, organised regular local seminars, managed the ever-growing Museum herbarium and checked material presented to the Museum. She was assisted by many local botanists with varying levels of experience and expertise. Of those, **John Bowra** (1918-2002) is noteworthy for his pioneering work on evening-primroses and their hybridisation, which he published in several articles (e.g. Bowra, 1999 & 2001). He also published many useful articles of local interest in the Warwick Natural History Society Annual Reports. **Harold Roberts** (1926-2004) was an expert on weeds and assisted Pam with the 1990 Warwickshire Garden Weed Survey. **John Price** published an account of the plants and other wildlife in the Stratford-upon-Avon area (Price, 2002) and subsequently discovered a hare's-ear new to the British list (Price & Partridge, 2007). **James Partridge** replaced Pam as the BSBI representative for Warwickshire and published papers on a variety of topics, including the discovery of a new British sowthistle in 2004 (Partridge, 2005) and hybrid dog-violets in Leamington Spa (Partridge, 2007). Sadly, James died just a few months before publication of this book. The many other amateur botanists who have contributed records in recent decades are cited in the acknowledgements section at the start of this book.

Plant surveying has also increased greatly due to the regular production of ecological impact assessments related to development proposals, and through projects such as the Habitat Biodiversity Audit (a habitat mapping project covering Warwickshire, Coventry and Solihull, based at Warwickshire Museum) and the Warwickshire, Coventry and Solihull Wildlife Sites Project (which surveys potential 'County Wildlife Sites' and 'Sites of Importance for Nature Conservation', also based at the Museum). Such work is mostly carried out by professional ecologists, including consultants and local authority ecologists.

Non-local experts have assisted significantly with our knowledge of certain difficult plant groups in Warwickshire, notably **A.L. Primavesi** for roses and **Alan Newton** for brambles.

Chapter 3

The Format of this Book
and How to Use it

This is essentially a book of two parts. The first part concentrates on the habitats of plants. It considers eight broadly-defined plant habitats, each within a chapter. It is intended that these chapters will furnish a historical and ecological context to the flora of Warwickshire that will help you to appreciate and understand it better. Each habitat chapter has an associated checklist at the end listing the plants that are strongly associated with that habitat – a register of the characteristic plants to look for. The checklists are subdivided as appropriate into trees and shrubs; grasses, sedges and rushes; other flowering plants; and ferns and horsetails. This subdivision makes the lists more digestible, and harmonises them with some of the popular identification literature available. Within these sections, the plants are arranged alphabetically by English (popular) name. If a site produces a particularly high number of species from one of these checklists, it is likely to be an important one because local loss and deterioration of wildlife sites makes it increasingly difficult to find large assemblages of characteristic plants for a particular habitat type. Species noted with a red cross are non-native archaeophytes and neophytes; those with a green tick are natives. This approach provides an indication of how some habitats are heavily dominated by non-native species (e.g. arable land and disturbed ground), whilst other habitats are still comprised essentially of native plants (notably heathland and mire). These lists were drafted by Pam Copson but have been refined in the light of new information in the 2002 *New Atlas of the British and Irish Flora* (Preston, Pearman & Dines, 2002), plus discussion with local botanists.

It has not been an intention to squeeze every Warwickshire species into a habitat checklist. For a start, only native and naturalised species are included, as casuals often have no particular affinity for the habitat in which they happen to turn up. Neither have we included species that are frequent across a variety of habitats without any clear bias. But if a species is estimated to have approximately one third or more of its sites associated with a habitat, it has been included in a checklist. A few species are listed in two or three checklists if they are overwhelmingly associated with two or three habitats, e.g. Greater Knapweed (calcareous grassland but also calcareous disturbed ground) and Stinging Nettle (woodland and hedgerows). Very little of this assignment is supported by up-to-date hard data, although *A Computer-Mapped Flora* did work out percentage splits for the habitats used by many plant species, based on data available up until the late 1960s. But with so much change in habitat coverage and habitat quality since that time, plus the changing abundances of many plants, it is likely that those percentages will be different now. *A Computer-Mapped Flora* also used a slightly different habitat classification to the one used in this book; for example, 'roadsides and waste places' (which has species that are here mostly assigned either to the Permanent Grassland or the Disturbed Ground chapters) and 'quarries and walls' (which has species assigned here mainly to the Disturbed Ground or the Built Environment chapters).

In the latter part of the book is the new checklist of the higher plants of Vice-county Warwickshire, arranged alphabetically by scientific name and annotated with rarity statuses. In effect, it provides the first red data list for the plants of Warwickshire, flagging the rarest and most threatened species. It is based on an informally published list by Copson, Partridge & Roberts, 2008. Some further modifications of the checklist were made for this book, such as the creation of a Warwickshire Notable rarity category, and refinement of the Warwickshire Rarity list. Warwickshire Museum hopes that local botanists will continue to gather data on scarce plants and update both the checklist and the red data listings at regular intervals.

Using this book to recognise a noteworthy plant

This is not an identification guide (see the Further Reading section for a list of these), but it will help you to spot whether you have found a noteworthy plant in Vice-county Warwickshire. A plant can be noteworthy on several counts. It may be a rarity at a district, county or even national level, and Warwickshire has several dozen of the last. A plant may also be a very good indicator of habitat character or quality, telling us if a woodland or hedgerow is likely to be ancient, if a watercourse is unpolluted, or if a meadow is relatively unimproved. A plant can also be noteworthy if it is a newly naturalising casual species. You may even rediscover a plant that had been considered extinct, still lingering in some isolated hedge or spinney (but beware casual specimens of 'extinct' plants that derive from bird-seed and wildflower seed mixtures, and have much lower significance). The main checklist plus the species lists at the end of each habitat chapter will help you to determine if you have found a noteworthy plant.

Visiting sites to record plants

It is important that we continue to record the plants of Warwickshire and monitor changes in the local flora. There are many fine wildflower sites that have public access, most notably the many nature reserves owned or managed by Warwickshire Wildlife Trust, featured in their guide *Discover wild Warwickshire: a guide to local nature reserves* (Vigor & Roberts, 2007), and the various other Country Parks and Local Nature Reserves managed by local authorities in our area. Some municipal parks have wildflower areas or informal water features. The extensive public footpath network provides access to many other fine areas and all of our local plant habitats. However, it is important to bear in mind that many important wildflower sites are private and some are quite hazardous, especially quarries, industrial sites and waterside or flooded locations. Always be careful when you are in the field and take an Ordnance Survey map and a mobile phone with you if possible. Each habitat chapter lists a number of sites or districts you can visit to see a good example of a particular habitat type.

The other concern, after your health and well-being, is that any recording you decide to do is accurate. Your Ordnance Survey map will allow you to produce a grid reference for a record, and the usual level of detail used is a six-figure grid reference e.g. SP304754 for Tocil Wood, where SP is the 100 km square that covers most of

Photographing plants is a great way of improving your identification skills, though you will need to collect voucher specimens for some critical species.

Warwickshire, 304 is the easting, and 754 is the northing. This places a record within a 100 metre square, which is adequate for most purposes. Geographical positioning devices can be even more accurate, allowing you to record a specimen to within a few square metres. Always note the name of the locality, the date of the visit, and your name as the recorder. A field notebook is recommended for this.

If you have a digital camera, it is recommended that you take images of anything you think is unusual. Photograph different parts of the plant to show the general growth form, the size and location of the plant, plus finer details of the flowers and leaves. You can then send these (by e-mailing or posting prints) to an expert for checking. Warwickshire Museum receives many valuable records in this way. If you have the time, you can even build up on your computer a digital image library of plants. It is one of the best ways to improve your plant identification skills, and means that you end up with 'photographic' voucher specimens that can easily be shared with others or used for printing or publishing. 'JPEG' images of about one megabyte size are ideal for this as they keep fairly good resolution even when blown up large. If the resolution setting on your camera is too small, the images will be pixellated and may not reveal enough information (as well as being substandard for printing and publishing). If the image size is too big (especially if you have a camera set for taking

'TIFF' images), you may have problems E-mailing them and larger image files are also slower to work with.

It is rarely necessary to damage a plant for identification purposes (and uprooting wildflowers is illegal), but just occasionally the aerial part of a plant, or parts of it, will need to be taken to allow critical identification by experts. Such specimens can be delivered to Warwickshire Museum as enquiries whilst still fresh, or can be pressed and dried (most easily done by placing the plant within a newspaper and then keeping it compressed under something flat and heavy for a few weeks). Warwickshire Museum is happy to accept enquiries and offers in this way, and it allows important specimens to be added to the herbarium there.

Local natural history and nature conservation groups

There are a number of local natural history groups and organisations that you can join to undertake plant recording or plant conservation in the company of others, though none of these specialise purely in botany. The main ones (with their web addresses at the time of writing) are:

- **Atherstone Natural History Society**
- **Birmingham Natural History Society** (http://freespace.virgin.net/clare.h/bnhs.htm)
- **Coventry and District Natural History and Scientific Society** (www.cdnhss.org.uk)
- **Rugby Natural History Society**
- **Sutton Coldfield Natural History Society** (www.scnhs.org.uk)
- **Warwick Natural History Society** (http://warkcom.net/live/cme1302.htm)
- **Warwickshire Wildlife Trust** (www.warwickshire-wildlife-trust.org.uk)
- **Wildlife Trust for Birmingham and the Black Country** (www.bbcwildlife.org.uk)

Contact details can change with time. Warwickshire Museum currently produces a newsletter (*Wildlife News in Warwickshire, Coventry & Solihull*) three times a year which provides up-to-date contact details for all local natural history groups, plus lists of the events they are organising. The newsletter can be downloaded from the web: www.warwickshire.gov.uk/rings.

National botanical organisations

- **The Botanical Society of Britain and Ireland (BSBI)** – for active plant recorders and researchers. It publishes many useful guides and atlases, organises regular national surveys, and puts on a variety of events. It has a regular journal called *Watsonia* and a newsletter called *BSBI News*. Web site: www.bsbi.org.uk.
- **Plantlife** – a conservation-focussed charity (part of Plantlife International), carrying out surveys and research related to conservation, purchasing and managing important wildflower sites, and lobbying for improved protection of plants and their habitats. It has a regular magazine called *Plantlife*. Web site: www.plantlife.org.uk.

- **The Wild Flower Society** – a national society specifically for amateur botanists and wildflower lovers in the UK. It aims to advance education in matters relating to wildflowers and to promote conservation of the British Flora. It holds regular field meetings throughout Britain. Web site: www.thewildflowersociety.com.

The Warwickshire Museum herbarium and local biological record centres

Warwickshire Museum acts as the official repository for specimens and records relating to the modern County of Warwickshire. The herbarium contains approximately 30,000 specimens, including many important 'voucher' specimens cited in historic literature, e.g. Bagnall's 1891 *Flora of Warwickshire* and the 1971 *A Computer-Mapped Flora*. Data for the collection is being computerised at the time of writing and it is intended that it will eventually be available on-line.

The Warwickshire Biological Records Centre housed at Warwickshire Museum holds files for several thousand individual wildlife sites in modern Warwickshire (which forms the greater part of Vice-county Warwickshire) and is managed by the County Ecologists. Site files for the Birmingham and Sutton Coldfield parts of the Vice-County are held by the Wildlife Trust for Birmingham and the Black Country's 'Ecorecord' team. Species data is jointly managed by the BSBI County Recorders in conjunction with the two biological record centres. This data is also being computerised to improve its management and accessibility, and to ensure that data for sites and for species will eventually be obtainable from a single dataset.

The Warwickshire Museum herbarium contains some 30,000 specimens including important voucher specimens that support significant records.

Chapter 4

A Brief Description of the
Vice-County of Warwickshire

Geology and topography

Geologically speaking, Vice-County Warwickshire can be divided into three regions. Firstly, the underlying geology of the south and east comprises mostly calcareous sedimentary rocks and mudstones of Late Triassic to Middle Jurassic Age. Late Triassic White Lias and Wilmcote Limestone are the oldest and form a more or less diagonal northern edge to this calcareous zone, collectively stretching from Alcester and Stratford-upon-Avon to Rugby, and resulting in escarpments (with associated quarries) near Alcester, Stratford and Ufton. The typical 'Blue Lias', an Early Jurassic succession of alternating limestone and mudstone beds, forms a broader band to the south and underlies much of south and east Warwickshire. It is an important deposit for the cement industry and has been quarried extensively in the Harbury, Stockton, Southam and Rugby areas. The dramatic north edge of the Cotswolds at places like Edge Hill, plus certain large isolated hills as at Napton and Avon Dassett, owe their existence to an ironstone bed (Marlstone), which is responsible for the tawny-coloured 'Hornton Stone' buildings in these areas. The highest point in Warwickshire, Ebrington Hill near Ilmington (259 metres), is capped by Middle Jurassic 'Cotswold' limestone. In the very south of the County, deeper into the Cotswolds, the Middle Jurassic limestones are well developed with quarries at places like Cross Hands (the very southern tip of Warwickshire). Limestone-loving ('calcicolous') plants are much in evidence in south and east Warwickshire as a consequence of these rocks, but the underlying geology is obscured in some places by river alluvium or glacial sands and clays sometimes of sufficient depth to turn the soil acidic. Gorse and Bracken are two of the best indicators of this.

Secondly, the geology of central, north and west Warwickshire which surrounds the Warwickshire Coalfield is dominated by the Mercia Mudstone. This is a Triassic deposit that gives rise to red-brown soil. The Mercia Mudstone both overlies and contains various Triassic sandstones which have been used in the construction of historic buildings, notably in Warwick. Thick layers of sand and gravel overlie the Mercia Mudstone in many places, both within river valleys and on elevated land in places like Bubbenhall. They helped produce the acidic soil conditions that once supported much of Warwickshire's heathland.

Thirdly, between Warwick and Atherstone, a broad, elongate swathe of even older rocks can be found, making up the Warwickshire Coalfield. The rocks include Carboniferous and Permian sandstones, Cambrian shales and quartzites, and even a little Precambrian rock (over 600 million years old). These also give rise to poor acidic soils that supported heathland historically. More recently the very oldest and

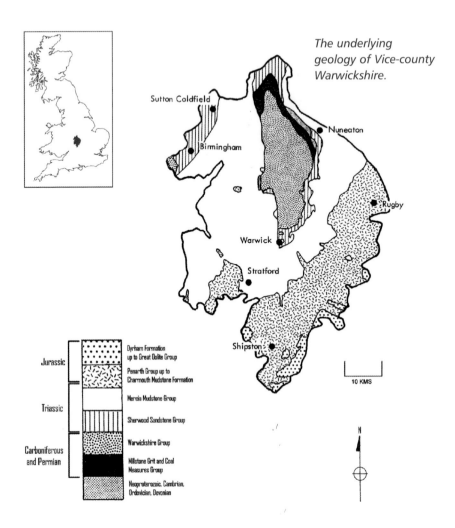

The underlying geology of Vice-county Warwickshire.

Sutton Coldfield

Birmingham

Nuneaton

Rugby

Warwick

Stratford

Shipston

10 KMS

N

Jurassic		Dyrham Formation up to Great Oolite Group
		Penarth Group up to Charmouth Mudstone Formation
Triassic		Mercia Mudstone Group
		Sherwood Sandstone Group
Carboniferous and Permian		Warwickshire Group
		Millstone Grit and Coal Measures Group
		Neoproterozoic, Cambrian, Ordovician, Devonian

hardest rocks have been subject to extensive quarrying, most notably along the Nuneaton-Atherstone Ridge which forms the highest ground in north Warwickshire. These quarries are now some of the most interesting locations in which to find plants in this part of the County.

Drainage

Drainage of Warwickshire falls mostly within two catchments. The Avon catchment, which consists of the River Avon and its tributaries such as the Sowe, Leam, Dene, Stour, Arrow and Alne, drains the south, east and middle of the County (and parts of adjoining Leicestershire and Northamptonshire) taking water into the Bristol Channel via the River Severn. Much of the water comes from intensively-farmed countryside and suffers from relatively high levels of agricultural run-off which reduces its potential to support diverse plant assemblages. Water in the north of the County and much of Birmingham flows into the River Tame and its tributaries (the

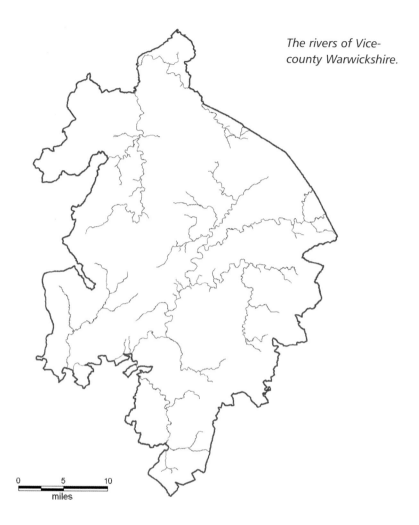

The rivers of Vice-county Warwickshire.

Blythe, Anker and Cole). These form part of the Trent catchment and flow into the North Sea via the River Trent and Humber. Some minor parts of south-east Warwickshire form part of the Thames catchment (e.g. the Priors Marston and Shotteswell areas), and take water into that great river via the Cherwell.

Warwickshire's main landscape zones

As noted earlier, Warwickshire almost perfectly straddles the two major landscape zones of lowland Britain. The north and west of the County is classic Ancient Countryside, whilst the south and east is classic Planned Countryside. The following is an account of the main landscape zones of Warwickshire as defined by the Warwickshire Landscapes Project of the early 1990s. Other landscape classification systems also exist for our area, but this one best describes what you see and feel on the ground.

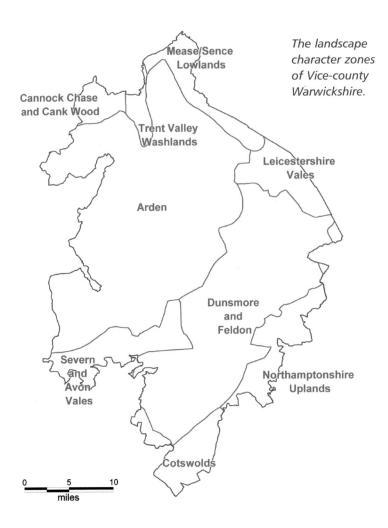

The landscape character zones of Vice-county Warwickshire.

Mease/Sence Lowlands

Cannock Chase and Cank Wood

Trent Valley Washlands

Leicestershire Vales

Arden

Dunsmore and Feldon

Severn and Avon Vales

Northamptonshire Uplands

Cotswolds

0   5   10
miles

Arden

This represents most of Warwickshire's Ancient Countryside and it occupies much of the rolling land north and west of the Avon Valley as far east as Coventry, plus much of the land north of Coventry as far north as (and including) the Nuneaton-Atherstone ridge and west towards Redditch, Birmingham and Sutton Coldfield, where it merges into what is popularly known as the Birmingham Plateau. It has extensive areas of small irregular field systems featuring ancient banked hedgerows and sunken lanes, which often date back to Anglo-Saxon times or beyond. Many, mostly small, ancient woods are present, as are veteran trees many of which originated in pasture woodland. There is a relatively high density of field ponds and much of the landscape feels enclosed by trees. The historic settlement pattern is what is known as 'dispersed' with many hamlets and ancient isolated farms (often timber-framed) but rather few classic villages. The Arden remained heavily wooded much later than other parts of the County and this is reflected in the several dozen place-names ending in '-*ley*', e.g.

A map showing place-name endings that indicate the presence of woodland into Anglo-Saxon times.

Shirley, Honiley, Allesley, Billesley and Corley; or '-*hurst*,' e.g. Burnthurst and Nuthurst. These name-endings denote settlements that once existed in heavily wooded settings, which is what the Arden was believed to be at the start of the Anglo-Saxon period. There are also many allusions to former heaths and commons within the Arden through place-names such as Balsall Common, Hockley Heath, Corley Moor and Danzey Green, and it is possible that some of these resembled a well-grazed version of the Sutton Park we see today. Ancient Countryside is strongly correlated with poorer soils, and the Arden largely overlies base-poor rocks and superficial layers of sands and gravels (which is why Silver Birch and Bracken are so frequent here).

Feldon

This is Warwickshire's most extensive area of Planned Countryside and occupies much of the south of the County. Planned Countryside is typically relatively fertile land that had much of its woodland cleared before the Anglo-Saxon period, and

Above: A classic Arden view: Church Farm, near Allesley, Coventry.
Below: A classic Feldon view: near Napton-on-the-Hill.

had a long tradition of hedgeless open field systems prior to the eighteenth century (reflected in the widespread presence of ridge-and-furrow). Ancient woodland is rare, but often takes the form of a few large woods. This landscape is called 'planned' because much of its modern character stems from the Parliamentary Enclosure Acts of the eighteenth and early nineteenth centuries. These Acts resulted in the rapid creation of large regular hedged fields plus new straight lanes, and the eviction of the 'peasants' who had occupied the open fields. The historic settlement pattern is what is known as 'nucleated', with lots of Anglo-Saxon villages, plus many farms and large houses that date from the Enclosure Acts. Feldon is gently rolling land mostly overlying calcareous clays with just a few large ancient woods such as Ufton Wood, Wellesbourne Wood and Knavenhill Wood.

Dunsmore

This is a low plateau located between Coventry, Rugby and Leamington, with settlements like Dunchurch, Ryton-on-Dunsmore and Wolston at its heart. Much of it overlies glacial sands and gravels and it was once dominated by a large area of heathland (the 'Dunsmore') which is shown on historic maps of Warwickshire and mentioned in written accounts. Place-names such as Lawford Heath and Ryton Heath reflect this history, though there is hardly any indication of such heathland today except in some sandy, bracken-dominated areas at places like Coombe Abbey Country Park and Brandon Wood. In essence, it resembles Feldon but has much poorer soils like the Arden. It has a few large ancient woods in the Binley Woods and Princethorpe areas.

Avon Valley (part of Severn and Avon Vales)

This is the lower flood-plain of the River Avon starting at Warwick and extending into Worcestershire. It is flat land overlying fertile alluvial deposits and lacks ancient woodland. There is a long history of settlement here and some fine market towns

The Avon Valley near Hampton Lucy.

Brailes Hill, at the northern edge of the Cotswolds.

featuring many old timber-framed buildings. Orchards become increasingly important towards the west end of the valley.

Cotswolds
This is the southernmost and hilliest part of Warwickshire, with limestone and ironstone uplands and some large escarpments (e.g. Edge Hill). It is rather sparsely populated with scattered villages featuring a high proportion of limestone and 'Hornton Stone' buildings. Many of the fields are enclosed by dry stone walls. A few large ancient woods are present, notably Whichford Wood and Wolford Wood. The greater part of the Cotswolds is within Gloucestershire and Oxfordshire.

High Cross Plateau (part of Leicestershire Vales)
A relatively flat, rural region located directly north of the Dunsmore characterised by large fields with much ridge-and-furrow, small nucleated villages such as Churchover, Monks Kirby and Wolvey and little obvious ancient woodland. The clay soils are more fertile than those of the Dunsmore but not as calcareous as those of the Feldon.

Mease/Sense Lowlands
This is the gently rolling, poorly-wooded rural area north of the Nuneaton-Atherstone ridge, extending into Leicestershire and South Derbyshire, with intensively farmed claylands and small nucleated villages characterised by tall church spires. It only occupies a small part of Warwickshire.

These landscape patterns have profoundly influenced the distribution of plants in recent centuries and some of those patterns remain today, albeit rather weakened by modern land-use. The Arden remains the best area in which to find ancient woodland plants (both in its woods and hedges), whilst the Feldon and Cotswolds are the areas where you are most likely to encounter a scarce arable weed.

Settlement

Vice-county Warwickshire is now one that encompasses both some of the most heavily urbanised parts of Britain and some of the most rural. Major settlements are concentrated in the north and north-west, notably Birmingham and what are now simply suburbs or close satellites such as Sutton Coldfield, Solihull, Shirley, Hampton-in-Arden, Hockley Heath, Knowle, Dorridge and Balsall Common. Nuneaton, Bedworth and Coventry form an axis through the centre of Warwickshire's northern half. Tamworth, Atherstone and the medium-sized towns of Dordon and Polesworth serve the very north. Kenilworth, Stratford-upon-Avon and the connected towns of Warwick and Leamington Spa serve the centre. Rugby and Southam are the only major towns in the east. Alcester, Bidford, Studley and Henley-in-Arden serve the west; Shipston-on-Stour is the only town in the sparsely-populated south. Villages are plenty and ever-growing; some such as Wellesbourne now approach the size of a small town.

In terms of the history of settlement, the Avon Valley appears to have been a relatively well-populated area by the Bronze Age. By the Iron Age hillforts existed in various parts of the County, which was divided between several tribes. The Romans established towns (probably by enlarging pre-existing settlements) at places such as Alcester, Mancetter, Bidford and Harbury. They also established several military roads that still serve as roads today, including the Fosse Way, Ryknield Street and Watling Street. Many villages and towns, including Warwick, can trace their origins back to the Anglo-Saxon period; they probably acted as border market towns serving both the Arden and Feldon.

The larger settlements of the north and west owe much of their growth in recent centuries to industry (especially that linked to coal and quarrying) and manufacturing. They were often world-leaders in some types of the latter. Modern globalisation is now forcing many of the County's towns and cities to re-invent themselves as local industry declines.

Most of Warwickshire's cities, towns and villages are growing at an unprecedented rate, and the part of Warwickshire that was least populated in Anglo-Saxon times (the Arden) is now overwhelmingly the most populated area. The environmental impact of this growth on the countryside is far greater than simply land-take for housing, retail parks and industry. The countryside around changes too – more golf courses, more 'horsiculture', busier roads, expanding airports, more water-abstraction from underlying aquifers, increased general disturbance, tidying up of wildflower areas, more pollution of local watercourses, and more non-native flowers escaping into the countryside and other natural greenspaces. Some interesting plants find opportunities within urbanised settings, as Chapter 11 (Disturbed Land) and Chapter 12 (Built Environment) will explain, but these tend to be non-native neophytes. But many of the County's most treasured native and archaeophyte plants are not coping well with all these changes.

Chapter 5

Woodland

*A habitat dominated by mature trees which form a canopy,
though often with discrete open areas (rides and clearings) within*

This is typically land where trees are dense and dominant, throwing much shade over the ground during summer, and also in the winter in the case of most coniferous woods (larch woods excepted). That does not mean to say that woods lack open spaces. Rides, clearings and coppiced areas (where trees are regularly cut close to the ground to yield a harvest of stems) are important features of woodland that support many plants. This chapter concentrates on the flora of typical woodland, though it should be noted that pasture woodland can be an important habitat for grassland and heathland plants. Here trees grow in a more scattered fashion out in the open, usually attaining a size and age that is impossible within a wood. But from a botanical point of view this is a very different habitat with few characteristic woodland plants, and is generally of greatest interest for the concentrations of old 'veteran' trees it supports (which are far more frequent in Britain than most other parts of northern Europe).

Primrose, Hampton Wood.

The history of Warwickshire's woodland

In twenty-first century Warwickshire we typically experience woodland as discrete and dense blocks or belts of trees, most of which you can walk through in a matter of minutes. They only occupy about five percent of Warwickshire's land surface and so stand out as something special and different. But this was not always the case. Following the end of the last (Devensian) ice age, about twelve thousand years ago, Warwickshire became dominated by a fully natural woodland known as the 'wildwood'. Pollen samples and other evidence suggest that by 6000BC Small-leaved Lime was the dominant tree over much of southern lowland Britain, with the proportion of other tree species such as oaks, Ash, Hazel, Alder, birches and Wych Elm dictated by ground conditions and climate.

There is much debate over how dense and continuous the wildwood was, though it is presumed that some areas of grassland, heathland and wetland would have existed, and these would have harboured many of the native plants that would come to dominate Warwickshire's open countryside a few millennia later as forest was cleared. However, you might have walked for many miles in Warwickshire's wildwood before you came across a significant break in the canopy.

Clearance of Britain's wildwood coincides with the start of its Neolithic period about six thousand years ago. Clearance is likely to have been slow at first, becoming progressively faster as populations of humans and their grazing stock (cattle, sheep, goats and later pigs) increased. In Warwickshire, there is no hard evidence for forest clearance before about 3000BC, and that which followed seems to have been

Small-leaved Lime (above) and Sessile Oak (below) are likely to have been dominant trees in Warwickshire's wildwood, but are relatively scarce as wild woodland trees today.

episodic, progressing more rapidly in some areas than in others, and also more rapidly in some periods than others. This may have been due to variation in climatic conditions and disease in the human population. By the end of the Romano-British period (c400AD) it is thought that much of the wildwood in the south and east of the County (the Feldon and Avon Valley landscape zones) had disappeared. Clearance was much slower on the poorer soils of Warwickshire's Arden zone which dominates the north and west of the County. This is why you find numerous place-names ending in '-ley' (e.g. Allesley, Billesley and Honiley) which represent settlements that once existed in a heavily wooded setting.

Even where woodland survived clearance, it became modified by grazing, coppicing, selective felling, and enclosure, and so stopped being a fully natural habitat. Grazing of woods seems to have had a major impact on the regeneration of Small-leaved Lime, to the extent that it is now absent from most local woods. Wych Elm also became scarcer at the onset of forest clearance in what is known as the 'Elm Decline', a Europe-wide phenomenon that probably represents an ancient epidemic of Dutch elm disease. Pedunculate Oak, Ash and Silver Birch fared much better and have replaced lime as the dominant trees of Warwickshire's ancient broadleaved woodland. Sessile Oak and Downy Birch have been less successful but remain abundant in some acidic Arden woods. The shrubby Hazel was favoured for coppicing and still survives widely, albeit rather shaded out, as a shrub layer beneath the canopies of those taller trees. Hazlenuts were an important local food in pre-Roman times, as evidenced by the large quantities of nut shells found at archaeological sites at places like Church Lawford and King's Newnham (Neolithic-early Bronze Age).

It is generally believed that the amount of woodland in lowland Britain increased during the dark ages that followed the end of the Romano-British period, and also following episodes of plague when populations would have been significantly reduced. That is why you sometimes find evidence of old settlements, roads, moats, even ridge-and-furrow within an ancient wood. However, the overall trend has been one of gradual forest clearance that has left Warwickshire with one of the lowest coverages of woodland for any county in Britain today. Fortunately, what does exist is highly varied in character, partly because of the varied geology of the County, but also because for some two hundred years or more, various types of 'plantation' woodland have appeared, comprised variously of conifers, broadleaved species or a mixture of the two. A number of recent woodland creation schemes, plus the gradual removal of conifers in some ancient woods, should result in a substantial increase in semi-natural woodland by the end of the twenty-first century.

Local woodland types
A number of distinct woodland categories can be found in Warwickshire today.

Semi-natural ancient woodland
This is woodland which has stood since at least 1600, and usually long before this, with the oldest local woods possibly representing land that has had a continuous woodland cover for nearly 10,000 years. We call it semi-natural because there has invariably been some human intervention. Very few if any examples of truly natural woodland exist anywhere in Britain today (and relatively few places globally). Ancient semi-natural woodland is typically a very rich habitat for wildlife, with the flowers, fungi and insects we most typically associate with woods. But there is much subtle variation in the tree and plant communities that is related to soil conditions, topography

Small-leaved Lime coppice at Hartshill Hayes, near Atherstone. Lime, Hazel, Alder and Sessile Oak have been the main species subject to coppicing in Warwickshire.

and site history. Pedunculate Oak, Ash and Silver Birch tend to be the dominant trees on drier soils, with Alder and Downy Birch in wetter areas. Both birches prefer woodland on poor acidic soils (lacking minerals like lime), whereas Ash becomes most dominant on lime-rich (calcareous) soils of the south and east of the County. Pedunculate Oak copes with a wide range of soil types, but the rarer Sessile Oak, like birches, avoids calcareous soils. Most local ancient woodland was managed as coppice with standards until the mid twentieth century, when it either fell into neglect or became coniferised. The intensity of coppicing is hard to imagine today. At Tile Hill Wood in Coventry, areas almost the size of football pitches were said to be cleared on regular intervals to provide the Corporation of Coventry with the stems required for fencing, and coppiced stems have long been important for charcoal manufacturing.

Wet woodland at Monks Park Wood, near Atherstone with Great Horsetail growing on deep wet silt under Alder.

Plantation broadleaved woodland

This is comprised of blocks or belts of deliberately planted trees on former farmland or heathland. This was done for various reasons, including timber production, game cover (including many local fox coverts), the aesthetic landscaping of estates (especially in the eighteenth and nineteenth centuries), and as a source of shelter and privacy. Often it involved the planting of Pedunculate Oak and Beech. In more recent times it has involved poplars, usually in regimented rows, and with a commercial objective in mind – poplar wood is suitable for matches and boxes. Similar planting was also done within cleared areas of ancient woodland, and we call this replanted ancient woodland. However, whereas replanted ancient woodland can retain many of its special ancient woodland plants, new plantation woodland tends to lack them.

An absence of Bluebell and the frequent presence of old ridge and furrow beneath the trees is one of the best clues to the fact that you are in relatively young woodland. Secondary woodland is a term generally applied to any fairly natural-looking non-ancient woodland arisen since 1600, though technically many local ancient woods are also secondary, or partially secondary, as they are thought to have arisen in medieval times on former open land, sometimes through the expansion of existing woods, following events like plague. Secondary woodland also covers the various woods that have sprung up naturally over the past 50-100 years within old quarries and gravel

Hybrid Black-poplar plantation at Ailstone, near Stratford-upon-Avon. Such plantations tend to support few true woodland plants.

workings (especially willow woods in wetter areas), and neglected patches of farmland, heathland and urban greenspace. Some of these are now very mature and would pass for ancient woodland to the untrained eye (e.g. Kenilworth Common).

Coniferous woodland

Warwickshire has only a single indisputably native gymnosperm, the Yew, which is not a tree suited to a plantation. But since the 1600s, and particularly in the Victorian period, Scots Pine and a wide variety of foreign conifers such as further pines, larches, spruces and firs have been planted. Those foreign conifers were initially European ones like European Larch and European Silver Fir, but various American and Asian species became popular in the Victorian period. The planting of such conifers in large plantations as a potential source of domestically produced timber really took off in the early and mid twentieth century, and in Warwickshire this usually took place in ancient woods with more acidic soils, such as Oversley Wood, Brandon Wood, Birchley Hays Wood and Hartshill Hayes. It has resulted in extensive damage to some particularly important woods (Oversley Wood and Hartshill Hayes appear to be especially old). The very deep shade and dense litter layer produced by most conifers means that such woods are pretty hostile to wildflowers, though rides and clearings may support some interesting plants derived from former ancient woodland. Bluebell and Pendulous Sedge can persist under conifers where they are not too densely arranged. Fortunately, conifers are being removed from some of these woods and in the long term they may well regain their original semi-natural character. Conifers can also occur at lower

Coniferous woodland at Oversley Wood with a ground cover of Bluebell.

densities within broadleaved woodland, and if there are a moderate number of them, we call it 'mixed woodland'. Conifers at low density tend to have little effect on woodland plants.

The plants of woodland

Woodland is an exclusive or major habitat for about one hundred native or naturalised plant species in Warwickshire (see plant list at end of chapter) but many other generalists can be present and *A Computer-Mapped Flora* reports 440 species growing in local woods in the 1950s and 1960s. Most true woodland herbs are adapted to cope with the dense shade that develops in woods by early summer. As a consequence, they tend to be spring-flowering perennials that do much of their growing in late winter and spring, then store the nutrients they have gathered within storage bulbs, corms, tubers and rhizomes ready for a quick start the following year. A few species, notably Dog's Mercury, Enchanter's-Nightshade, Bird's-nest Orchid and Yellow Bird's-nest can cope with deep shade without the need for a vernal growth pattern. In the case of the latter two species, chlorophyll has been dispensed with and nutrients are obtained purely from the fungal mycorrhizae that exist throughout the woodland soil. Other plants include opportunistic perennials or short-lived annuals and biennials that can take advantage of newly opened and disturbed woodland areas (e.g. newly coppiced areas) to provide a few years worth of flowering before tree regrowth or scrub shades them out, notably Marsh Thistle, Common Ragwort and Groundsel. More shade-tolerant plants such as violets, Bugle, Primrose and Foxglove can also provide fabulous blooms in temporary clearings. Enriched woodland soils, possibly stemming from the location of an ancient settlement, moat or charcoal-hearth tend to be betrayed by an abundance of Cow Parsley, Stinging Nettle and Ivy.

Woodland strata

Woodland plants occupy one of three strata. Trees provide the canopy. Species like Hazel, Holly, Elder, Rhododendron, Cherry Laurel, Portugal Laurel, Dogwood and Guelder-rose produce a shrub layer. Herbaceous plants plus brambles create a herb layer or ground layer. Climbers such as Ivy and Honeysuckle can be abundant too. Woodland is also capable of harbouring many other plants more typical of open grassland, scrub, heathland or wetland within its rides, clearing and margins, so some of Warwickshire's more varied woodland sites such as Ryton Wood, Clowes Wood, Hampton Wood and Snitterfield Bushes are exceptionally rich.

Plants of ancient woodland

Ancient woodland is the strongly preferred habitat for a number of plants which are commonly termed ***ancient woodland indicators***. Bluebell is the most familiar of these locally, but others include Wood Anemone, Primrose, Early-purple Orchid, Yellow Archangel, Common Cow-wheat, Herb-Paris, Wood Spurge, Wood Melick, Wood Millet plus trees and shrubs such as Hazel, Small-leaved Lime, Sessile Oak, Wild Cherry, Wild Service-tree, Aspen and Rowan (ignoring the more recently planted specimens of these trees that you find in parks and formal areas). Not all of these species are restricted to woodland or even ancient woodland at a national level, most also grow in open locations such as meadows and moorland in the more humid

Plants characteristic of ancient woodland

Wood Anemone

Bluebell

Aspen

Woodruff

Wood Spurge

Wood Melick

Plants characteristic of ancient woodland

Wild Service-tree

Yellow Archangel

Wild Cherry

Dog's Mercury

Hazel

Common Cow-wheat

Plants characteristic of acidic woodland

Downy Birch

Bilberry

Heather

Tormentil

Wood Sage

Bracken

Plants characteristic of acidic woodland

Greater Stitchwort

Foxglove

Sessile Oak

Rowan

Holly

Wood-sorrel

north and west of Britain. Warwickshire's drier climate makes this uncommon here, except within old hedgerows, which can act like strips of ancient woodland, or in grassland that has been subject to relatively recent woodland clearance. Woods with plentiful Small-leaved Lime and Sessile Oak (e.g. Piles Coppice, Oversley Wood, Hartshill Hayes and Rough Hill Wood) may represent primary woodland that has existed since the wildwood (albeit modified by coppicing and in some cases clay extraction). Some of the large Lime coppice stools at Oversley Wood could be between one-thousand and two-thousand years old.

Plants of acidic woodland

Because the majority of Warwickshire's woods are located within the Arden, which overlies base-poor sands, gravels, clays and sandstones, most Warwickshire woods tend to have rather acidic soils and are classified as **W10** (Pedunculate Oak-Bracken-Bramble woodland) by the National Vegetation Classification (NVC). An abundance of birches, Bracken and Holly quickly characterise such woods, also species such as Foxglove, Wood Sage, Greater Stitchwort, Bilberry, Sessile Oak and Rowan. Heather, Tormentil and Purple Moor-grass in any rides and clearings indicate the historic presence of heathland in and around such woods, and are strongly associated with woods close to locations containing 'Heath', Common' or 'Moor' in their place-names (e.g. Hay Wood and Poors Wood, both near to Balsall Common and Birchley Hays Wood near Corley Moor).

Local coniferous woodland is typically acidic too, both because it was usually established within acidic broadleaved woodland (foresters preferentially select acidic soils for better conifer growth), and because the leaf litter it produces acidifies the soil. Such woodland is generally very impoverished away from rides and clearings due to the dense litter layer, acidic soil conditions and often the deep year-round shade. Bluebell, Bracken and Wood Avens are amongst the few species that you might encounter beneath conifers.

Plants of calcareous woodland

By contrast, most of the woods in the south and east of the County have soils that are partly or wholly calcareous because they overlie limestone. They are classified as **W8** (Ash-Field Maple-Dog's Mercury woodland) by the NVC. The first thing you will tend to notice about such woods is the lack (or scarcity) of Bracken, birches or Holly and an abundance of Ash. There are a number of 'calcicolous' (limestone-loving) woodland plants that preferentially grow in our calcareous woods, including Early-purple Orchid, Herb-Paris, Spurge-laurel, Common Twayblade and Stinking Iris. Calcicolous grassland or scrub plants such as Wild Privet, Wild Parsnip, Woolly Thistle, Traveller's-joy, False Brome and Greater Butterfly-orchid may also be present in rides and clearings. Field Maple and Dog's Mercury are also more frequent, even though they are not especially calcicolous. Where these southern woods overlie a hill (e.g. Whichford and Oversley Woods), more acidic conditions featuring Bracken and birches may appear at the highest points, representing ground where a layer of clay or sand masks the underlying limestone and supports more acidic soil. Wild plants can be superb indicators of underlying geology!

Plants characteristic of calcareous woodland

Stinking Iris

Early-purple Orchid

Green Hellebore

Herb-Paris

Spurge-laurel

Wild Privet

Plants characteristic of wet and damp woodland

Alder

Greater Tussock-sedge

Hard-fern

Pendulous Sedge

Red Currant

Creeping-jenny

5. Woodland

Plants characteristic of wet and damp woodland

Wild Angelica

Goat Willow

Opposite-leaved Golden-saxifrage

Broad Buckler-fern

Ramsons

Great Horsetail

Plants of wet and damp woodland

Woodland that is prone to regular flooding from nearby water courses, or has impeded drainage, sets special challenges for woodland plants, many of which dislike water-logging. Alder, Downy Birch and Goat Willow (also White Willow and Crack-willow in younger woods) tend to form the canopy, with Stinging Nettle, Pendulous Sedge, Creeping-jenny, Opposite-leaved Golden-saxifrage, Red Currant and ferns such as Hard-fern and buckler-ferns in the ground layer. The presence of plants such as Greater Tussock-sedge, Greater Pond-sedge, Marsh-marigold, Wild Angelica, Yellow Iris, Bulrush, Great Horsetail and Skullcap in the herb layer will tend to mark the historic location of a woodland pool or marshy clearings (perhaps fed by a seepage) as these are not true woodland plants. Plants such as Indian Balsam, Hemlock Water-dropwort and Butterbur can form dense stands alongside woodland streams or wooded river margins. Lesser Celandine and Wavy Bittercress can be evident on the damp mud of small streams and wet rides when they flower in spring.

Losses and gains

The historic losses of woodland as a habitat in Warwickshire inevitably reduced the extent of all woodland-loving plants, and the long term impact of grazing on Small-leaved Lime has been noted above. Add to this the changes in management of ancient broadleaved woodland, particularly during the mid-twentieth century, and we witness the most profound impact on woodland plants in recent history. The regular coppicing of local woodlands up until the mid-twentieth century tended to result in fantastic blooms of violets, Primrose, Bugle and campions. This tailed off quickly once these woods fell into neglect or became coniferised, and many other species of half-shade or lightly disturbed woodland settings appear to have declined too, including Wood Spurge, Giant Bellflower, Narrow Buckler-fern, Broad-leaved Helleborine, Woodruff, Hairy Wood-rush, Yellow Pimpernel and Herb-Paris.

The following seven woodland plants are considered to have become extinct in the County:

- Wood Barley *Hordelymus europaeus* – recorded at Aston Grove in 1955, a species characteristic of Beech woods on calcareous soils
- Beech Fern *Phegopteris connectilis* – recorded at Berkswell in 1848, a species characteristic of Sessile Oak woodland in the north and west of Britain, especially on wet rocks and gully sides
- White Helleborine *Cephalanthera damasonium* - recorded at Farnborough in 1887, a species with similar requirements to Wood Barley
- Green-flowered Helleborine *Epipactis phyllanthes* – recorded at Charlecote in 1857, a species of woodland and other shady places on dry acidic, humus-poor substrates
- Green Hound's-tongue *Cynoglossum germanicum* – last recorded from Kenilworth and Stratford in 1875
- Yellow Star-of-Bethlehem *Gagea lutea* – last recorded at Edge Hill in 1965, a species of various sorts of shady locations and a shy flowerer (which provides hope that somebody with sharp eyes may yet rediscover it)

Extinct woodland plants

White Helleborine

Green-flowered Helleborine

Wood Chickweed

Green Hound's-tongue

Yellow Star of Bethlehem

Beech Fern

New and increasing woodland plants

Turkey Oak

Rhododendron

Cherry Laurel

Indian Balsam

Snowdrop

Sycamore

- Wood Chickweed *Stellaria nemorum* – last recorded at Honington Hall in 1891, a species most characteristic of damp areas beside woodland streams or damp hedge banks, but possibly only ever a casual here

Most of these plants were at the edge of their British range within Warwickshire, being either species more characteristic of the south, or of the north/west. Four of them had only ever been known from single sites.

Gains and increases are far more obvious. Humans have been embellishing local woods with exotic plant species for many centuries, and the Victorians pursued this with a passion. In many instances no further natural spread of those planted species has taken place e.g. most exotic conifers. But a few species have successfully naturalised and spread through either viable seeds or vegetative suckering. This includes six woody species: Sycamore, Rhododendron, Cherry Laurel, Portugal Laurel, Turkey Oak and Grey Poplar. None of these is restricted to woodland, but they thrive in it. Herbs include Snowdrop, Pink Purslane and Indian Balsam. Butcher's-broom, Beech and Hornbeam belong to a special category of species that are native to southern Britain but not Warwickshire, where they are increasing within woods having been introduced historically. Holly is a native of our woods, and has clearly increased in many Arden woods since coppicing ceased, to the point of being a major nuisance at some sites. Birches have tended to increase as neglected rides and clearings have scrubbed over, and Aspen is locally invasive in some woods (e.g. Snitterfield Bushes) following clearance or ride management. New hybrids and cultivars are also spreading within woods, including Hybrid Bluebell (a cross between our native Bluebell and Spanish Bluebell) and the variegated garden form of Yellow Archangel, which can form large patches.

Local woodland you can visit

Ancient woods
- Brandon Wood, Binley Woods SP394765 (a Friends of Brandon Wood reserve) – a partially coniferised wood with a fine system of rides and clearings that support a diverse flora with ancient woodland indicators such as Bluebell and Wood Anemone, also Heath Dog-violet, Corn Mint, Ragged-robin and Bee Orchid.
- Clowes Wood and New Fallings Coppice, near Earlswood SP101743 (a Warwickshire Wildlife Trust reserve) - a varied acidic wood dominated by Sessile Oak in many areas, also with wet woodland, marshy clearings, streams and a tiny remnant of Heather heathland. Supports a rich and varied woodland flora that includes Ramsons, Bilberry, Wood Spurge, Lily-of-the-valley, Wood Horsetail plus acid grassland species such as Heath Spotted-orchid, Meadow Thistle, Marsh Violet and Lemon-scented Fern.
- Crackley Wood, Kenilworth SP290737 (a Warwickshire Wildlife Trust reserve) – an ancient acidic wood producing superb displays of Bluebell, also some fine Downy Birch specimens alongside Silver Birch. Herbs of note include Wood Anemone, Yellow Pimpernel, Common Dog-violet and Opposite-leaved Golden-saxifrage. The nearby Glasshouse Spinney SP304714 (also a Warwickshire Wildlife Trust reserve) is a strip of ancient woodland with species

like Woodruff, Yellow Archangel, Wood Anemone, Wood Melick and Dog's Mercury.

- Hampton Wood SP254600 (a Warwickshire Wildlife Trust reserve) – an ancient wood on fairly neutral soils that was extensively cleared in the 1930s resulting in a highly diverse site with a rich flora including seven species of fern. Coppicing produces exceptional shows of spring flowers such as Primrose.
- Hartshill Hayes, Hartshill SP321944 (a Warwickshire County Council Country Park) – a partially coniferised wood still supporting much Bluebell, Small-leaved Lime coppice, Sessile Oak and Rowan, indicating its great age.
- Hay Wood, near Chadwick End SP210712 (a Forestry Commission wood) - has heather and other heathland-loving plants growing in its main ride, as does the nearby Poors Wood SP245732, possibly a reflection of their locations at the edge of the former Balsall Common.
- Oversley Wood, near Alcester SP104562 (a Forestry Commission wood) – a partially coniferised ancient wood that still has Small-leaved Lime (including some massive stools), Sessile Oak and Wild Service-tree, indicating a wood of great antiquity. The wood is located on a ridge producing more acidic conditions higher up (with species such as Wood Sage) and calcareous conditions lower down (with Spurge-laurel and Early-purple Orchid), and combined with a good ride system this produces a very rich site for wildflowers with rarities such as Narrow-leaved Helleborine.
- Piles Coppice, near Binley Woods SP385769 (a Woodland Trust reserve) – an excellent example of Small-leaved Lime and Sessile Oak coppiced woodland with giant lime coppice stools that are many centuries old. The ground flora has much Bluebell and Wood Anemone.
- Rough Hill Wood, near Redditch SP052637 (a Warwickshire Wildlife Trust reserve) – a mostly acidic wood with much Sessile Oak, also Small-leaved Lime, Bilberry, Great Woodrush, Primrose, Bilberry and Heather, though calcicoles such as Wild Privet occur at lower levels.
- Ryton Wood SP384726 (a Warwickshire Wildlife Trust reserve) one of the finest ancient woods in the West Midlands and now regularly coppiced in many places giving a good impression of how managed woodland would have looked in the past. Plants of note include Broad-leaved Helleborine, Sanicle, Common Cow-wheat and there are some fine open patches of Bluebell. The nearby Wappenbury Wood and Old Nun Wood (both Warwickshire Wildlife Trust reserves) are also excellent and together with Ryton Wood form part of the Princethorpe Woodland complex that also includes several private woods.
- Snitterfield Bushes SP200603 (a Warwickshire Wildlife Trust reserve) – a calcareous ancient wood (though largely regenerated since felling in the 1940s) with many of the specialities of this woodland type including Early-purple Orchid, Fly Orchid, Herb-Paris, Wild Privet and Wayfaring-tree; also Bird's-nest Orchid, Fragrant Agrimony, Columbine and Meadow Saffron (250 plant species in total). Active Hazel coppicing takes place in parts of the wood, and spectacular shows of Primrose and Bluebell characterise this wood in spring.
- Tocil Wood, Coventry SP304754 (a Warwickshire Wildlife Trust reserve) one of several ancient woods in Coventry with public access. Others include Tile Hill

Wood, Wainbody Wood, Willenhall Wood and Park Wood (owned and managed by Coventry City Council).
- Wolford Wood, near Moreton in the Marsh SP235334 (private but with a public footpath) – varied soils result in a very diverse flora that includes fine shows of helleborine orchids, Early-purple Orchid, Orpine, Sanicle, Pendulous Sedge and Yellow Pimpernel

Secondary woods
- Cock Robin Wood, Rugby SP493724 (a Warwickshire Wildlife Trust reserve) – a new wood created in the 1990s.
- Earlswood Moathouse, Earlswood SP116736 (a Warwickshire Wildlife Trust reserve on National Trust land) – woodland created on two former fields in the 1970s.
- Kenilworth Common, Kenilworth SP297730 (a Warwickshire Wildlife Trust reserve) – oak and birch-dominated acidic woodland that has developed on a former sand and gravel quarry that was originally a common with heathland. A little Wavy Hair-grass, Heath Bedstraw and Heather still survives, though few special woodland plants.
- Temple Balsall SP203760 (a Warwickshire Wildlife Trust reserve) – formerly a landscaped garden with pools, located next to Cuttle Brook. Now mostly wet woodland with patches of swamp, noteworthy plants include Butterbur, Opposite-leaved Golden-saxifrage and Large Bittercress.
- Ufton Fields, Ufton SP378615 (a Warwickshire Wildlife Trust reserve) – a former limestone quarry now supporting much secondary calcareous woodland that has sprung up naturally over several decades, plus some deliberately planted areas of conifers and poplars. Yellow Bird's-nest can be found in one area of woodland.
- Yarningale Common, Claverdon SP188658 – secondary woodland with open access on former grassland and heathland near Claverdon.

Woodland plant list (excluding casuals)

Trees and shrubs (in their wild or naturalised state)
- ✔ Alder *Alnus glutinosa* – wet woodland, also watersides away from woodland
- ✔ Ash *Fraxinus excelsior* – especially woods in the south, also frequent in hedgerows
- ✔ Aspen *Populus tremula* – an ancient woodland indicator
- ✘ Beech *Fagus sylvatica* – a native but probably not of Warwickshire, naturalised in many woods but widely planted elsewhere
- ✔ Downy Birch *Betula pubescens* – acid woodland, especially on wetter soils
- ✔ Silver Birch *Betula pendula* – often abundant in dry acid woodland and scrub
- ✔ Bramble *Rubus fruticosus* agg. – a dominant component of the ground layer of many woods, also frequent in hedgerows and other habitats
- ✔ Alder Buckthorn *Frangula alnus*
- ✔ Wild Cherry *Prunus avium* – an ancient woodland indicator
- ✘ Sweet Chestnut *Castanea sativa* – an archaeophyte that has become naturalised in a number of local woods

✔ Elder *Sambucus nigra* – especially associated with rabbit or badger burrows and other enriched or disturbed areas of woods, also in hedgerows and scrub

✔ Wych Elm *Ulmus glabra* – as regrowth (most mature trees killed by Dutch elm disease), also in hedgerows

✔ Guelder-rose *Viburnum opulus* – also in hedges

✔ Hazel *Corylus avellana* – a major component of the shrub layer of ancient woodland indicator, also older hedges

✔ Holly *Ilex aquifolium* – a major and invasive component of the shrub layer of acid woods, also found in older Arden hedges

✗ Hornbeam *Carpinus betulus* – a native but probably not of Warwickshire where naturalised in some woods

✗ Cherry Laurel *Prunus laurocerasus* – a neophyte that is naturalised and invasive in a number of local woods

✗ Portugal Laurel *Prunus lusitanica* – a neophyte that is naturalised and invasive in a number of local woods

✔ Spurge-laurel *Daphne laureola* – calcareous woods

✔ Small-leaved Lime *Tilia cordata* – usually in ancient woodland, frequently coppiced

✔ Pedunculate Oak *Quercus robur* – dominant in many dry woods, except the most acidic or calcareous, also frequent in hedges and fields

✗ Red Oak *Quercus rubra* – a neophyte that is introduced in a number of local woods

✔ Sessile Oak *Quercus petraea* – acid woodland, typically ancient, frequently hybridising with Pedunculate Oak

✗ Turkey Oak *Quercus cerris* – a neophyte that is naturalised and invasive in a number of local woods, also widely planted elsewhere

✗ Rhododendron *Rhododendron ponticum* – a neophyte that is naturalised and invasive in a number of local woods mostly acid ones

✔ Rowan *Sorbus aucuparia* – typically in acid ancient woodland

✔ Wild Service-tree *Sorbus torminalis* – mostly on woodbanks and the edges of ancient woodland

✗ Sycamore *Acer pseudoplatanus* – a neophyte that has formed or invaded many local woods, also widely planted elsewhere

✗ Tutsan *Hypericum androsaemum* – a neophyte grown in many gardens and occasionally naturalising in woods

✔ Yew *Taxus baccata* – clearly self-sown in many woods, but probably planted in others

Grasses, sedges and rushes

✔ Wood Fescue *Festuca altissima* – a recent discovery

✗ Broad-leaved Meadow-grass *Poa chaixii* – a rare neophyte

✔ Wood Meadow-grass *Poa nemoralis*

✔ Wood Melick *Melica uniflora* – usually in ancient woodland

✔ Wood Millet *Milium effusum* – avoids lime, usually in ancient woodland

✔ Elongated Sedge *Carex elongata* – damp woodland, rare (only Clowes Wood recently)

✔ Pendulous Sedge *Carex pendula* – damp woodland, especially on clay
✔ Smooth-stalked Sedge *Carex laevigata* – damp woodland
✔ Great Woodrush *Luzula sylvatica*
✔ Hairy Woodrush *Luzula pilosa* – possibly declining
✔ Wood-sedge *Carex sylvatica*
✔ Thin-spiked Wood-sedge *Carex strigosa* – rare

Other flowering plants
✔ Wood Anemone *Anemone nemorosa* – usually in ancient woodland
✔ Wild Angelica *Angelica sylvestris* – wet woodland, also open wetlands and water edge
✔ Yellow Archangel *Lamiastrum galeobdolon* – as a wild plant mostly in ancient woodland
✔ Water Avens *Geum rivale* (and also Hybrid Avens *Geum* x *intermedium* – a hybrid of *G. rivale* and Wood Avens *G. urbanum*)
✘ Indian Balsam *Impatiens glandulifera* – an invasive and increasing neophyte of damp woodland, also river and streambanks
✔ Giant Bellflower *Campanula latifolia* – scarce and probably declining
✔ Bilberry *Vaccinium myrtillus* – acid woods, also heathland
✔ Yellow Bird's-nest *Monotropa hypopitys* – very rare, likes deep shade (both British subspecies present)
✔ Bluebell *Hyacinthoides non-scripta* – usually in ancient woodland, also older hedgerows
✘ Butcher's Broom *Ruscus aculeatus* – a native but not of Warwickshire
✔ Lesser Butterfly-orchid *Platanthera bifolia* – very rare (just two recent sites)
✔ Lesser Celandine *Ranunculus ficaria* – also on hedgebanks (several subspecies involved)
✔ Climbing Corydalis *Ceratocapnos claviculata* – rare
✔ Common Cow-wheat *Melampyrum pratense* – acid ancient woodland, rare and declining
✔ Red Currant *Ribes rubrum*
✔ Wild Daffodil *Narcissus pseudonarcissus* (subspecies *pseudonarcissus*) – the true wild form is mostly found in woods here
✔ Early Dog-violet *Viola reichenbachiana* – the violet most confined to woods
✔ Common Dog-violet *Viola riviniana* – also in older hedgerows
✔ Alternate-leaved Golden-saxifrage *Chrysosplenum alternifolium* – damp woodland, rare
✔ Opposite-leaved Golden-saxifrage *Chrysosplenum oppositifolium* – damp woodland
✔ Green Hellebore *Helleborus viridis* – scarce
✔ Broad-leaved Helleborine *Epipactis helleborine* – scarce and probably declining
✔ Narrow-leaved Helleborine *Cephalanthera longifolia* – very rare (Oversley Wood)
✔ Violet Helleborine *Epipactis purpurata* – very rare
✔ Herb-Paris *Paris quadrifolia* – a scarce plant of calcareous woods
✔ Honeysuckle *Lonicera periclymenum* – a frequent climber in ancient woods, also in hedgerows

✔ Stinking Iris *Iris foetidissima* – especially calcareous woods and hedgebanks, rare
✔ Ivy *Hedera helix* – an abundant scrambler and climber of trees in woods, also in hedges and other habitats
✘ Leopard's-bane *Doronicum pardalianches* – a scarce neophyte
✘ Martagon Lily *Lilium martagon* – a neophyte grown in gardens and occasionally naturalising in woods
✔ Lily of the Valley *Convallaria majalis* – prefers acid woodland
✔ Dog's Mercury *Mercurialis perennis* – also in hedgerows
✔ Stinging Nettle *Urtica dioica* – especially in damp woodland, also in various other habitats
✔ Enchanter's Nightshade *Circaea lutetiana*
✔ Early-purple Orchid *Orchis mascula* – calcareous woods
✔ Bird's-nest Orchid *Neottia nidus-avis* – scarce and declining, likes deep shade
✔ Fly Orchid *Ophrys insectifera* – a calcicole, just one local wood
✔ Orpine *Sedum telephium* – rare
✔ Yellow Pimpernel *Lysimachia nemorum*
✔ Primrose *Primula vulgaris* – usually in ancient woodland, also ancient hedgerows, hybridises with Cowslip *P. veris* to produce False Oxlip *Primula* x *polyantha* which is typically encountered in or close to woods
✘ Pink Purslane *Claytonia sibirica* – an increasing neophyte
✔ Water Purslane *Lythrum portula* – wet woods, declining
✔ Ramsons *Allium ursinum* – especially damp woodland near to streams
✔ Meadow Saffron *Colchicum autumnale* – probably declining
✔ Three-nerved Sandwort *Moehringia trinervia* – especially damp woodland, also hedgebanks
✔ Sanicle *Sanicula europea*
✘ Snowdrop *Galanthus nivalis* – a neophyte that has naturalised in many woods, where it is increasing
✔ Common Twayblade *Listera ovata* – typically calcareous woods
✔ Wood-sorrel *Oxalis acetosella*
✔ Wood Speedwell *Veronica montana*
✔ Wood Spurge *Euphorbia amygdaloides* – scarce
✔ Woodruff *Galium odoratum* – declining?

Ferns and horsetails
✔ Bracken *Pteridium aquilinum* – also in hedgerows and on heathland
✔ Broad Buckler-fern *Dryopteris dilatata*
✔ Narrow Buckler-fern *Dryopteris carthusiana* – probably declining
✔ Hard-fern *Blechnum spicant* – mainly in damp acid woodland
✔ Great Horsetail *Equisetum telmateia* – wet woods
✔ Wood Horsetail *Equisetum sylvaticum* – acid woods
✔ Lady-fern *Athyrium filix-femina*
✔ Male-fern *Dryopteris filix-mas* – also in hedgerows
✔ Scaly Male-fern *Dryopteris affinis* – rare

Chapter 6

Hedgerows

*The linear strips of shrubs, trimmed trees and mature trees that
typically surround fields and help form property boundaries*

This chapter covers the woody species that form a hedge, the various climbers
that scramble over a hedge, and the herbaceous species that grow beneath a
hedge (including any associated hedgebank) or immediately beside it. It does
not include the more general grassland species that might occur along road verges
or field margins adjacent to a hedge, indifferent to whether a hedge is present or
not. Given that most hedges are deliberately planted artificial features that draw
much of their flora from other habitats such as woodland edge, one could reason
that this habitat is too contrived to dwell upon, and this chapter steers clear of the
most artificial hedgerows associated with urban areas such as those comprised of
Garden Privet, Cherry Laurel or Leylandii. But nature has played a big hand in
shaping the rural hedgerows we have today, making them a truly 'semi-natural'
habitat of considerable botanical value.

Spring flowers on an ancient banked hedge near Corley Moor.

Many woody species beyond those originally planted have infiltrated hedges, especially those with bird-spread berries and seeds, e.g. Elder, Holly and Crab Apple. English Elm, seemingly planted within many Enclosure Act hedges to produce a large hedge-tree, has managed to spread using suckering throughout great lengths of hedgerow, becoming naturalised in the process. Many sorts of herbaceous plants have also managed to colonise our hedges and some now have a high proportion of their Warwickshire populations in hedges (see plant list at end of chapter), even if they cannot be regarded as hedgerow specialists. Some ancient hedges may not even be planted at all, being perhaps strips of shrubs and trees that have developed naturally on banks. In essence, hedges produce an invaluable refuge for wildflowers often within intensively farmed rural landscapes that offer relatively few other opportunities. They produce a surprisingly varied and complex habitat type, and dazzle us with a succession of blossoms from early spring into summer.

A Blackthorn hedge at Great Alne, its blossom peaking in April between that of Cherry Plum (March) and Hawthorn (May).

The history of Warwickshire's hedgerows

Hedgerows are an intrinsic part of the modern Warwickshire landscape and understanding their history will help you to understand how the local landscape evolved. As noted earlier in the introductory section, Warwickshire almost perfectly straddles the two major landscape zones of lowland Britain as defined by Oliver Rackham in his 1986 book *History of the Countryside*. South and east Warwickshire is classic Planned Countryside. It was dominated by hedgeless open field systems prior to the Parliamentary Enclosure Acts of the eighteenth and early nineteenth centuries. The Acts resulted in hundreds of kilometres of new hedges, enclosing large regular field systems and new lanes, being rapidly established throughout this part of Warwickshire. Hawthorn ('quickthorn') was the main species used and English Elm, Pedunculate Oak and Ash appear to have been popular choices as hedge-trees, with Sycamore featuring in many Cotswold hedges and Grey Poplar becoming a popular choice for Feldon hedges later in the twentieth century. Today, such hedges are characterised by a high proportion of Common Hawthorn, Blackthorn, English Elm, Elder and Ash. They typically lack hedgebanks (though many have ditches), and their relatively young age is often betrayed by the fact that they can sometimes be seen to cut across older ridge-and-furrow plough marks.

Enclosure Act hedges with associated ridge-and-furrow, near Winderton.

6. Hedgerows

Within Warwickshire's Ancient Countryside (the Arden), some hedges resemble those of Planned Countryside, especially those that were established on former common land and in river valleys through the same series of Enclosure Acts. However, a good many are clearly much older and we term these ***ancient hedges***. They are characterised by obvious hedgebanks, an abundance of Hazel, Holly and Wych Elm, plus various herbaceous plants that are typically associated with woodland (e.g. Bluebell, Primrose and Wood Anemone). They tend to surround small, irregular field systems or to flank sunken lanes. Precisely how old these hedges are is unclear.

Primrose, Dandelion and Bluebell on an ancient Arden hedgebank near Hatton.

They probably arose as areas of woodland were 'assarted' (the process by which fields are carved out of woodland), and as such could originate from Romano-British times onwards. Anglo-Saxon charters for the Arden indicate a good number of hedges were already well-established here. Such hedges would have played a vital role in the protection and management of livestock in the Arden, where grazing and meat production complemented the grain production of the Feldon. According to Rackham, the Romans already had a tradition of establishing banked living hedges in parts of Europe before they invaded Britain.

The high proportion of woodland plants present in ancient hedges reflects two likelihoods. The first is that such hedges have their origins within a heavily wooded landscape, which is what we suspect the Arden still was at the end of the Romano-British period and the Anglo-Saxon period that followed (in strong contrast to areas like the Feldon and Dunsmore). The second is that their great age has allowed the slow spread of woodland plants over many centuries. Even where the younger hedges of Warwickshire's Planned Countryside occur near to ancient woodland there is usually little obvious spread of species such as Bluebell or Primrose. Such plants are not great colonisers of new habitat. It is possible that some ancient hedges were not planted in the way that Enclosure Act ones were, but either represent pre-existing woodbanks/woodland boundaries (that had trees and shrubs already *in situ*) or developed by woody species colonising dry hedges (formed from dead twigs and branches) or other forms of fencing around a new banked field boundary, something which can easily occur within a decade or two through natural regeneration.

Hedgerows remained a fairly stable habitat until the mid-twentieth century when many hedges, ancient and non-ancient alike, were grubbed out as Britain attempted to become self-sufficient in food production following World War II. There was also a trend for spraying out the bottoms of hedges with herbicides to kill off 'weeds'. Today, approximately 13,000 to 14,000 kilometres of rural hedgerow remains within Warwickshire, but it is far better protected. The 1997 Hedgerows Regulations make it unlawful to remove a rural hedgerow without first

A newly laid hedge near Cubbington, 2008.

having the application assessed by the local planning authority, and policies for hedgerow protection can be found in most local authority development plans. There is also funding for traditional management of hedgerows (e.g. hedge-laying) and the planting of new ones through government-funded agri-environment schemes. Many Warwickshire farmers and landowners have taken advantage of this.

Hedge grubbing at Withybrook, 1977.

Dutch elm disease

One of the most dramatic changes in our hedgerows in recent decades has been the loss of many thousands of mature elm trees through Dutch elm disease (DED), radically altering the appearance of rural Warwickshire. The disease is caused by an *Ophiostoma* fungus which blocks up the water-carrying vessels of the elm, causing it literally to wilt to death. The fungus is transported by *Scolytus* bark beetles which attack elm trees once they have become sufficiently mature. English Elm, which was the most abundant hedge-tree in Warwickshire (and many parts of lowland Britain) up until the mid-1970s, was one of the worst affected elms and not a single mature specimen survives in Warwickshire today. It was termed the 'Warwickshire weed' and is said to be responsible for the term 'Leafy Warwickshire'. Most large specimens of the other types of elm found here have been lost too, though a few old Wych Elms (which are more diverse genetically than English Elm) and hybrid elms (which often have a degree of immunity) still survive in local hedges and parks. Elms have not been lost though – they remain abundant in hedges as trimmed regrowth and will attempt to grow into new trees if not cut, usually succumbing to the disease once they attain about fifteen years of age. But the billowing shapes of huge hedgerow English Elms in Warwickshire may well be a thing of the past, never to be repeated.

A large Field Elm near Wellesbourne, one of only about twenty large elms left in Warwickshire by 2008 due to the devastating impact of Dutch elm disease.

The plants of hedgerows

Hedgerows are a major habitat for almost one hundred native and naturalised plant species in Warwickshire (see plant list at end of chapter) but many other generalists can be abundant there and *A Computer-Mapped Flora* recorded 496 species growing in Warwickshire hedges in the 1950s and 1960s. There is a good deal of variation in the conditions afforded by hedges. It can relate to their age, management history, their physical structure (e.g. whether they have a bank or ditch), the nature of adjacent habitats, whether they are shaded, soil characteristics such as pH and dampness, and whether they are subject to spray drift from adjacent farmland. All these variables affect the plants present and one can often quickly determine the underlying geology and something of the local landscape history of a location by looking at a hedge and the plants that grow in and beside it.

Plants of ancient hedges

Age is a fundamental factor. It is well-known that ancient hedges have a capacity to support more woody species than younger Enclosure Act hedges ('Hooper's Rule'). The basis for this rule seems to be founded in the fact that older hedges will have had more time in which to acquire more woody species. It more or less holds true in Warwickshire, though many ancient Arden hedges have been more or less fully taken over by Holly, and more recently, Sycamore, leaving them decidedly species-poor. Characteristic ancient hedge indicators include Hazel, Small-leaved Lime, Wych Elm, Wild Service-tree, Bluebell, Primrose, Wood Anemone, Greater Stitchwort, Goldilocks Buttercup and Yellow Archangel.

Plants of acidic hedges

The fact that many ancient hedgerows are located within the Arden with its more acidic soils somewhat obscures the effects of soil pH, though it is clear that many hedge-plants are strongly influenced by this from our knowledge of their needs elsewhere. Species favouring hedges with acidic soils include Bracken, Foxglove, Wood Sage, Greater Stitchwort, Gorse, birches and Sessile Oak.

Plants of calcareous hedges

Species strongly favouring hedges on calcareous soils in the south and east of the County include Wild Privet, Wayfaring-tree, Dogwood, Traveller's-joy, Stone Parsley, Short-styled Field-rose, Nettle-leaved Bellflower, Common Gromwell, Wild Liquorice and Hedge Bedstraw. Various plants frequent in calcareous grassland may also be present, including Wild Parsnip, Greater Knapweed, Woolly Thistle, Wild Basil and Field Scabious.

Plants of hedgebanks

Hedgebanks are important features that can substantially increase the floristic diversity of a hedge, by increasing both the area available for plant growth and the variety of conditions present. South-facing hedgebanks are typically warm and dry and can support strong colonies of Bluebell, Rosebay Willowherb, Primrose, violets, dandelions, plus grassland plants such as Cowslip and Common Knapweed. North-facing banks tend to be cooler, shaded and damper, which can suit damp-woodland or shade-loving species such as Three-nerved Sandwort, shield-ferns, Lady-fern and Snowdrop.

Plants of wet hedge-ditches

Wet hedge-ditches are equally important. In terms of woody species, they strongly influence the presence of willows (especially White Willow), Alder and Black-poplar. Herbaceous species can include Meadowsweet, Great Willowherb, Stinging Nettle, Welted Thistle, Marsh Thistle, Common Valerian, even Common Reed.

A ditched hedge near Willoughby. Great Willowherb, Meadowsweet and Willow indicate regular flooding of the ditch

Hedgerow climbers

The final category of hedge-plant is climbers. Hedgerows provide an almost perfect habitat for them. Ivy is the most conspicuous of these and is the only one that exploits large hedge-trees, though non-flowering growth can occur from the hedge base upwards. Traveller's-joy can be frequent in calcareous districts (though it is strangely rare in the Cotswolds), its fluffy seeds remaining conspicuous throughout the winter. Others include Honeysuckle, White Bryony, Black Bryony, Russian-vine, Hop and three sorts of bindweed. Russian-vine, Large Bindweed and Hairy

Plants characteristic of ancient hedges

Hazel

Wood Anemone

Bluebell

Primrose

Midland Hawthorn

Greater Stitchwort

Plants characteristic of calcareous hedges

Wayfaring-tree

Spindle

Traveller's-joy

Wild Privet

Nettle-leaved Bellflower

Common Gromwell

Hedgerow climbers

Black Bryony

Honeysuckle

White Bryony

Hop

Ivy

Hedge Bindweed

Increasing hedgerow plants

Oregon-grape

Cherry Plum

Russian-vine

Hairy Bindweed

Greater Periwinkle

Snowberry

Bindweed are most typically associated with enriched, disturbed soils in urban areas and allotments. Mistletoe is not a climber but a parasite of trees and shrubs (rooting directly into the host) and can occasionally be found in local hedges growing on Hawthorn, Apple, Common Lime and Hybrid Black-poplar.

Losses and gains

Several characteristic hedgerow plants have declined in Warwickshire, including Barberry, Stone Parsley and Catmint. In the case of Barberry, this resulted from its deliberate eradication. It is a winter host for Wheat Rust, a fungus that can devastate wheat crops throughout the world. Purton, in his 1817 *The Midland Flora* (Vol 1, p180) describes the impact of even small quantities of hedgerow Barberry in the important wheat-growing areas around Oversley and Broom. The extensive grubbing up of hedges in the latter half of the twentieth century has impacted many other species. But no plant strongly associated with hedges here is known to have become totally extinct.

Gains and increases are much more evident and mostly involve neophytes. The most noticeable increases of woody species involve Sycamore, Grey Poplar, Snowberry and Oregon-grape. Blackthorn, Elder, Field Maple, Cherry Plum, Wild Plum and Crab Apple all appear to be slowly increasing within Enclosure Act hedges, which are presumably still going through a process of colonisation even after two centuries. Holly is increasing its dominance in Arden hedges on acid soils (including many ancient ones) in the same way as it is increasing in many Arden woodlands, and this may be linked to climatic factors. Herbaceous plants on the increase include Greater Periwinkle, Russian-vine, Snowdrop, Large Bindweed and Hairy Bindweed. Short-lived casuals are also frequent in hedges, especially near to urban areas due to the fly-tipping of garden waste or the escape of garden plants.

Local hedgerows you can visit

Ancient hedges

Ancient hedgerows are easily accessible from country lanes and public footpaths in the following areas:

- The Coundon Wedge (north of Allesley village) and areas between Allesley and Corley Moor
- The Earlswood area
- The Claverdon - Lowsonford - Langley area
- The Tanworth-in-Arden area

Banked hedges with plentiful Hazel can be considered most typical.

Enclosure Act hedges

Enclosure Act hedgerows are easily accessible from country lanes and public footpaths in the following areas:

- The Napton - Priors Marston - Wormleighton area
- The Kineton - Gaydon - Tysoe area

- The Monks Kirby - Wolvey - Shilton area
- The Bishop's Itchington - Harbury area
- The Shipston-on-Stour - Halford area
- The Flecknoe - Broadwell - Willoughby area
- The floodplains of the Avon, Leam and Stour valleys

Unbanked hedges associated with ridge-and-furrow can be considered most typical.

Hedgerows plant list (excluding casuals)

Woody species

✗ Apples *Malus pumila* sens. lat. – frequently naturalised in hedges, a commonly cultivated tree

✔ Crab Apple *M. sylvestris* – most frequently encountered in hedges, but can occur in woodland and other habitats

✔ Ash *Fraxinus excelsior* – a frequent hedge-tree, also in woods and fields

✔ Barberry *Berberis vulgaris* – largely eradicated

✔ Blackthorn *Prunus spinosa* – frequent, also a scrub-former in other habitats

✗ Box *Buxus sempervirens* – a rare native, but not of Warwickshire where it can become naturalised in hedges

✔ Bramble *Rubus fruticosus* agg. – a species complex, also frequent in woodland and other habitats

✔ Buckthorn *Rhamnus cathartica* – especially on calcareous soils

✗ Dwarf Cherry *Prunus cerasus* – occasionally naturalised in hedges, an archaeophyte that used to be widely planted

✔ Cleavers *Galium aparine*

✔ Dewberry *Rubus caesius*

✔ Dog-rose *Rosa canina* agg. – a species complex that is frequent in hedges, also a scrub-species of other habitats

✔ Round-leaved Dog-rose *Rosa obtusifolia* – scarce

✔ Dogwood *Cornus sanguinea*

✔ Harsh Downy-rose *Rosa tomentosa* – rare

✔ Sherard's Downy-rose *Rosa sherardii* – rare

✔ Elder *Sambucus nigra* – frequent in hedges, also in found in woods and scrub

✔ English Elm *Ulmus procera* – still abundant as regrowth in hedges but no large trees now exist in Warwickshire following Dutch elm disease

✔ Small-leaved Elm *Ulmus minor* – scarce and very difficult to identify, especially as regrowth

✔ Wych Elm *Ulmus glabra* – frequent as regrowth in hedges, with a few mature specimens still present, also in many ancient woods

✔ Field-rose *Rosa arvensis* – frequent in hedges, also a scrub-species of other habitats

✔ Short-styled Field-rose *Rosa stylosa* – a scarce species usually of calcareous hedgerows

✔ Guelder-rose *Viburnum opulus* – also in woods

✔ Hawthorn *Crataegus monogyna* – a major hedgerow species, also a scrub-former in other habitats

✔ Midland Hawthorn *Crataegus laevigata* – prefers ancient hedgerows, also more frequent in local ancient woods than the previous species

✔ Hazel *Corylus avellana* – a major component of ancient hedgerows, also frequent in ancient woods

✔ Holly *Ilex aquifolium* – a major component of ancient hedgerows, also frequent in acid woods of the Arden (and frequently planted in gardens, parks etc)

✔ Field Maple *Acer campestre* – frequent in hedges, also woods

✘ Oregon-grape *Mahonia aquifolium* – a neophyte commonly grown in parks and gardens, increasing

✔ Pedunculate Oak *Quercus robur* – a frequent hedge-tree, also in woodland and fields

✘ Pear *Pyrus communis* sens. lat. – most frequently naturalising in hedges, a common cultivated tree and archaeophyte

✘ Cherry Plum *Prunus cerasifera* – frequently naturalised in hedgerows, an archaeophyte also widely grown in parks and gardens (usually var. Pissardii)

✘ Wild Plum *Prunus domestica* (including Damson and Bullace) – occasionally naturalised in hedges, an archaeophyte – the same species as the cultivated Plum

✘ Grey Poplar *Populus canescens* – especially frequent in Feldon hedges, where it has spread by suckering, also naturalised along various watercourses, a neophyte

✔ Wild Privet *Ligustrum vulgare* – frequent in calcareous hedgerows, also calcareous woodland edges and scrub

✘ Snowberry *Symphoricarpos albus* – an increasing neophyte, also in woods and planted elsewhere

✔ Spindle *Euonymus europaeus* – also in woods and other habitats

✘ Sycamore *Acer pseudoplatanus* – a frequent hedge-tree that is invasive in some hedges, also in woods and widely planted elsewhere, a neophyte

✔ Wayfaring-tree *Viburnum lantana* – especially hedges on calcareous soils, also woodland edge

Grasses
✔ False Brome *Brachypodium sylvaticum*
✔ Bearded Couch *Elymus caninus*
✔ Hairy-brome *Bromopsis ramosa*

Other flowering plants
✔ Wood Avens *Geum urbanum* – also in woods
✔ Hedge Bedstraw *Galium mollugo*
✔ Nettle-leaved Bellflower *Campanula trachelium* – especially calcareous hedgebanks, scarce
✘ Large Bindweed *Calystegia silvatica* – an increasing neophyte
✘ Hairy Bindweed *Calystegia pulchra* – an increasing neophyte
✔ Hedge Bindweed *Calystegia sepium*
✔ Bittersweet *Solanum dulcamara* – also in marsh and other habitats
✔ Bitter-vetch *Lathyrus linifolius* – declining

✔ Bluebell *Hyacinthoides non-scripta* – the banks of ancient hedgerows, also ancient woodland

✔ Black Bryony *Tamus communis* – a frequent climber in hedgerows

✔ White Bryony *Bryonia dioica* – a frequent climber in hedgerows

✔ Goldilocks Buttercup *Ranunculus auricomus* – older hedgerows, declining

✔ Red Campion *Silene dioica* – also woodland edge, frequently hybridising with the next species

✘ White Campion *Silene latifolia* – a neophyte

✘ Cat-mint *Nepeta cataria* – a rare and declining archaeophyte of calcareous hedgebanks

✔ Lesser Celandine *Ranunculus ficaria* – frequent on hedgebanks, also in woodland (several subspecies involved)

✔ Bur Chervil *Anthriscus caucalis* – rare

✔ Rough Chervil *Chaerophyllum temulum*

✔ Cleavers *Galium aparine* – also in various other habitats

✔ Dandelions *Taraxacum* spp.

✘ White Dead-nettle *Lamium album* – especially frequent beside hedges, but also found in various other habitats, an archaeophyte

✘ Dwarf Elder *Sambucus ebulus* – a rare archaeophyte mostly recorded in hedges

✔ Foxglove *Digitalis purpurea* – as a wild plant especially on acid hedgebanks of the Arden, also acid woods, but widely planted elsewhere

✔ Common Dog-violet *Viola riviniana*

✔ Common Gromwell *Lithospermum officinale* – especially in calcareous hedgerows

✔ Ground-ivy *Glechoma hederacea*

✔ Hedge-bedstraw *Galium mollugo* – especially on calcareous soils

✔ Upright Hedge-parsley *Torilis japonica* – especially frequent beside hedges, but also found in various other habitats

✘ Hemlock *Conium maculatum* – also watersides and other damp fertile areas, an archaeophyte

✔ Herb-robert *Geranium robertianum* – also in woodland and various other shaded habitats

✔ Hogweed *Heracleum sphondylium* – especially frequent beside hedges, but also found in various other habitats

✔ Honeysuckle *Lonicera periclymenum* – a frequent climber of hedgerows, also in woodland

✔ Hop *Humulus lupulus*

✘ Black Horehound *Ballota nigra* – an archaeophyte

✔ Stinking Iris *Iris foetidissima* – especially calcareous hedgebanks and woods, rare

✔ Ivy *Hedera helix* – an abundant climber of hedge-trees, also in woodland and various other habitats

✔ Wild Liquorice *Astragalus glycyphyllos* – calcareous hedgerows and roadsides, rare

✔ Lords-and-Ladies *Arum maculatum* – also in woodland

✘ Italian Lords-and-Ladies *Arum italicum* – a native of southern Britain but not Warwickshire where a scarce garden escape

✔ Dog's Mercury *Mercurialis perennis* – also in woodland

✔ Garlic Mustard *Alliaria petiolata* – also in woodland
✔ Stinging Nettle *Urtica dioica* – also in various other habitats
✔ Nipplewort *Lapsana communis*
✔ Cow Parsley *Anthriscus sylvestris* – especially frequent beside hedges, but also found in other habitats
✔ Stone Parsley *Sison amomum* – hedges on calcareous soils, also calcareous grassland
✘ Greater Periwinkle *Vinca major* – a neophyte
✔ Wood Sage *Teucrium scorodonia* – especially hedgebanks on acidic soils
✔ Three-nerved Sandwort *Moehringia trinervia* – frequent on hedgebanks, also in woodland
✔ Greater Stitchwort *Stellaria holostea* – also at woodland edge
✘ Duke of Argyll's Teaplant *Lycium barbarum* – an increasing neophyte
✔ Welted Thistle *Carduus crispus* – especially frequent beside hedges, but also found in various other habitats
✔ Traveller's-joy *Clematis vitalba* – a climber, especially frequent on hedges on calcareous soils
✔ Tufted Vetch *Vicia cracca* – also on disturbed land and rough grassland
✘ Russian-vine *Fallopia baldschuanica* – a neophyte climber, increasing
✔ Sweet Violet *Viola odorata*
✔ Hedge Woundwort *Stachys sylvatica*

Ferns
✔ Bracken *Pteridium aquilinum* – hedges on acid soils, also in woodland and on heathland
✔ Male-fern *Dryopteris filix-mas* – also in woodland
✔ Hard Shield-fern *Polystichum aculeatum* – also in woodland
✔ Soft Shield-fern *Polystichum setiferum* – also in woodland

Chapter 7

Permanent Grassland

Dense, low-growing vegetation covered by grasses and other herbaceous plants in areas not prone to permanent flooding and waterlogging, regular ploughing or heavy disturbance

W e use the term grassland to denote low-growing, well-established 'swards' of vegetation in open settings that usually contain a variable proportion of grasses and flowering plants. In conservation terms, the best grasslands tend to be those with less 'grass' and more 'flowers' (a loose term because grasses are just specialised flowering plants) and relatively infertile soils. Sadly, such sites are pitifully few in Warwickshire today. We exclude from this chapter the sparser vegetation that develops on sites that have experienced recent heavy disturbance, such as quarries and post-industrial sites, as these support distinct early successional plant communities with a high proportion of pioneer species not typically found in well-established grassland (see the chapter on Disturbed Ground). We also exclude the vegetation that develops on set-aside land or arable field margins that are subject to ploughing.

Draycote Meadow, Warwickshire's finest surviving hay meadow featuring an important population of Green-winged Orchid plus many other scarce plants.

The history of Warwickshire's grassland

Grassland was one of the habitats that replaced woodland following clearance of the wildwood, its expansion promoted by the grazing of stock such as cattle, sheep, horse and pig. It was probably not an instant transformation, scattered trees may have persisted in many areas in the form of a habitat we call **pasture woodland** (a habitat still found today at places like Packington Park and Charlecote Park). In other places the woodland would have given way to early arable agriculture and, on more acidic soils, heather-dominated heathland would have been favoured over grassland. Open water, marsh, mire, carr and wet woodland would have held sway in other areas such as poorly-drained river valleys.

Archaeological evidence for local grassland plants is sometimes provided by pollen grains and plant remains associated with historic human settlement from Neolithic times onwards, though the evidence is usually too sparse to draw any major conclusions. In all probability patches of grazing land (including pasture woodland) were juxtaposed with arable land from early times, with managed hay meadows as a later addition, and the plant communities of the grasslands presumably resembled those we see on the least improved grasslands today. As the human population grew and pressure on the land increased there was a constant tension between arable land and permanent pasture, with periodic shifts in emphasis from one to the other in response to economic pressures. Between 1450 and 1550, for example, much new pasture was created in the Feldon in response to the high value of wool. This often took place on ridge-and-furrow. At other times, such as following the Corn Laws of 1773 and 1815, arable reclaimed pasture.

After World War II, and especially following our joining the European Union, agricultural intensification resulted in massive losses of species-rich grassland as it became converted to arable land or species-poor improved grassland. Such grassland could produce better yields of silage grass or hay and support higher densities of grazing stock, but generally has a very impoverished flora. Much grassland has also been lost to development, notably the acid grassland of northwest Warwickshire (now largely suburban Coventry, Solihull, Sutton Coldfield and Birmingham). Shelley Green Hay Meadow is perhaps the most well-known of these losses. It produced one of the finest displays of Heath Spotted-orchid in the country, but was subject to planning permission for construction of a hypermarket in the late 1980s. Warwickshire Wildlife Trust removed the turves once it was clear that their objections had failed to overturn the planning decision, and transported them to another site several miles away. The new meadow still produces blooms of orchids, but is not of the same character as the original meadow.

Shelley Green Hay Meadow in the mid-1980s just prior to its loss to development.

Another significant agent in grassland loss has been the viral rabbit disease, myxomatosis. Since the 1950s this has suppressed the populations of these animals sufficiently for scrub to form on many grasslands and it is only through the work of organisations such as Warwickshire Wildlife Trust that certain important grasslands have been prevented from scrubbing over completely. According to the Habitat Biodiversity Audit, less than 300 hectares of relatively unimproved grassland may now exist in modern Warwickshire, which is amongst the lowest coverage for any British county.

Local grassland types

As with woodland, this is a very broad habitat category with several distinct variants that reflect soil conditions, hydrology and site history. There is no single way to classify grassland, and several distinct and complementary systems can be applied as follows.

Unimproved, semi-improved and improved grasslands

Unimproved grassland is old grassland that has never been subject to fertiliser or herbicide usage, ploughing or reseeding. It is typically very species-rich with many scarce plant species. It is unlikely that Warwickshire has any grassland that can be considered fully unimproved, though some fields have only been marginally improved and are still very species-rich, most notably Draycote Meadows, Loxley Church Meadow and Shadowbrook Meadows (all Warwickshire Wildlife Trust reserves). We classify these slightly or moderately improved examples as *semi-improved grassland*. Their character and quality is influenced by many factors, including the soil and underlying geology, management history (including the extent of agricultural improvement) and wetness of the soil.

Common Spotted-orchid and Yellow-rattle indicate that this hay meadow is relatively unimproved.

Improved grassland is that with lowest botanical interest, typically comprising a relatively small number of highly competitive grasses and flowering plants such as thistles, docks and nettles growing on fertile soils. The term 'improved' refers purely to agricultural productivity, which has been enhanced through either the use of fertilisers (targeted at certain plants to make them grow better), herbicides (to kill off unwanted plants), ploughing (to improve the soil for cultivation), reseeding (to establish favoured plant species) or a combination of these. Some improved grasslands, such as the grass leys used for silage are more akin to arable agriculture, i.e. the grass is grown as a crop and the fields involved may be subject to regular cutting and reseeding. However, there are no hard cut-off points between these three grassland types and improved grassland which has had plenty of time to recover from any of the above processes can revert to semi-improved grassland, especially once the soil loses some of its artificial fertility and has a chance to recover its subtle physical structure.

Improved and heavily grazed sheep pasture near Oxhill, very poor botanically (left). Relatively unimproved cattle pasture at Lighthorne Heath (right).

Pasture, hay meadow and amenity grassland

Pasture is grassland subject to prolonged grazing and not typically cut; the less improved examples can be fairly species-rich and (where not overgrazed) flowery. A good local example is Lighthorne Heath near Gaydon. **Hay meadow** is grassland subject to an annual mid-summer cut that produces a crop of hay (used for feeding stock), and the less improved examples, including Draycote Meadows and Loxley Church Meadow, are exceptionally rich. But, again, these categories are not exclusive as many hay meadows are subject to aftermath grazing following a hay cut, and some fields may be used for hay or silage production in certain years and grazed in others. **Amenity grassland** is that subject to regular mowing to keep it tidy and includes sports fields, much urban green space, golf courses and many churchyards and cemeteries. It is easy to think of amenity grassland as a form of improved grassland because it produces few flowers. But amenity grassland has sometimes largely escaped agricultural improvement, and can revert back to very fine species-rich grassland once regular mowing ceases (e.g. Oldberrow Churchyard near Ullenhall and Priory Park in Warwick). Overgrazing, especially that of sheep and horses, can also fool you into thinking you have improved grassland, with the true character of the pasture only becoming apparent once grazing ceases for a while.

Calcareous, acid and neutral grasslands

Grassland can also be classified according to the soil and geology-influenced plant communities that develop. **Calcareous grassland** is that which develops on thin soils containing plentiful lime and with a pH in the range of 6.5 to 8.5. It is characterised by an abundance of **calcicolous** (lime-loving) plants, and can produce some stunning displays of flowers in June and July. This grassland type is thinly scattered across the south and east of Warwickshire, most of which overlies limestones of various sorts. Two categories can be found locally, NVC classification **CG5** (Upright Brome - Tor-grass Grassland) being characteristic of the Cotswolds, with **CG2** (Meadow Oat-grass Grassland) occurring alongside CG5 on the older Triassic-Jurassic limestones of the Feldon land immediately north of the Cotswolds. Most of Warwickshire's ancient limestone grassland has been lost to intensive agriculture and the relatively unimproved examples amount to perhaps just 30

hectares. This includes relatively large patches at Oxhouse Farm, Lighthorne Heath and Grove Hill plus scraps along certain road verges. Fortunately, new patches of surprisingly high quality are developing in some of our abandoned limestone quarries, and within road, rail and canal cuttings, especially at sites where rabbits or habitat management are helping to keep scrub in check.

A rare example of old calcareous grassland at Oxhouse Farm, featuring Greater Knapweed and Hedge Bedstraw.

Acid grassland is that which has developed upon soils lacking lime, typically those overlying sand, gravel, sandstone and various igneous rocks. The soils of these locations tend to have any minerals leached from them and this causes them to become acidic (pH of 4 to 5.5), which is not strong enough to burn the skin of a human, but enough to strongly influence any plant communities. Acid grassland is characterised by an abundance of **acidophilous** (acid-loving), **calcifugous** (lime-hating) plants. It shares much in common with heathland and usually occurs in association with it or as a relict of it once heathers have been lost. It is much less species-rich than good neutral or calcareous grassland but supports many local rarities. Sutton Park still supports substantial areas of fine acid grassland, but elsewhere there is just a thin scattering of relatively unimproved acid grassland, perhaps just 13 hectares-worth in modern Warwickshire. This hectarage includes a mixture of ancient grassland sites on former heathland, plus some of the younger grasslands that have developed on colliery spoilheaps, railway sidings, in abandoned sandstone quarries, and within the rides and clearings of some acidic woodlands (e.g. Hay Wood, Grendon Wood and Clowes Wood). Acid grassland of a rather more degraded state exists along road verges, in semi-improved pasture, and around woods throughout north and west Warwickshire. It is still possible to find the odd specimen of scarcer acid grassland or heathland plants here, though the plant communities they now grow within have often become much modified by soil enrichment.

Most of Warwickshire's semi-improved grassland belongs to the **neutral grassland** category and has developed on soils that are neither strongly calcareous nor acidic (pH of 5 to 6.5). Such soils are widespread on clays and river alluviums that mask the underlying geology and buffer the formation of acidic or calcareous soil conditions. Some very rich plant communities can be present,

An acid grassland and heathland mosaic (foreground) grades into wet heath and mire at Sutton Park.

representing several distinct variants, notably NVC classifications **MG5** (Crested Dog's-tail – Common Knapweed grassland) on drier soils, **MG4** (Meadow Foxtail – Great Burnet floodplain meadow) on damper alluvial soils and **MG8** (Crested Dog's-tail – Marsh-marigold flood-pasture) on even damper soils, typically in association with marshland and swamp. About ninety-five percent of this grassland type is estimated to have been lost locally during the twentieth century leaving only about 185 hectares that can be categorised as relatively species-rich and semi-improved. MG4 and MG8 grasslands are especially scarce and special, with important concentrations beside the Sherbourne Brook near Warwick, in the Blythe Valley in Solihull District and in the Anker Valley near Polesworth. **MG1** (False Oat-grass grassland) is often neglected semi-improved rough grassland, recovering improved grassland, or the first true grassland that forms on recently disturbed, neutral soils. It can support some botanical interest, though often with a higher proportion of casuals and disturbance-loving species than other semi-improved grasslands. It is widespread along road verges and on waste ground.

Tall herb and scrub

These are regular components of grassland sites, especially where grazing or other forms of disturbance have ceased or are patchy. **Tall herb** refers to the patches of robust herbaceous plants such as nettles, umbellifers (e.g. Hogweed and Cow Parsley), willowherbs and thistles that can develop. **Scrub** refers to the shrubs or young trees that can invade grassland (plus other habitats) as it begins the slow process of reversion to secondary woodland.

Grassy road verges, motorway verges and old cuttings

Rural road verges typically support strips of permanent grassland, the quality and character of which varies enormously. The finest ones tend to be broad and sloped, and can be very species-rich. Being wide, they are largely free of roadspray which can contain oils, salt and other pollutants making conditions unsuitable for many plants, and it is often only a narrow section close to the road that receives regular cutting. Those in the south often support limestone grassland (e.g. verges along parts of the Fosse Way, the A439 at Binton and the more established parts of the Ettington by-pass). Those in the north may harbour plants characteristic of acid grassland and heathland. Narrower verges tend to suffer badly from the effects of roadspray, and also from the regular cutting of vegetation and occasional ditch clearance, which usually results in a layer of silt being spread over the verge. Not surprisingly, such verges most resemble species–poor improved grassland. Old grassy railway and canal cuttings such as Ashlawn Cutting in Rugby and Nettle Hill canal cutting near Ansty resemble deep road cuttings.

Motorway verges and newly-established by-passes can produce fine shows of flowery grassland, though these regrettably often arise from introduced wildflower seed mixtures sown on imported topsoil rather than representing naturally-developed plant communities. They usually soon revert to coarse species-poor grassland. This approach can also result in certain plant species growing in inappropriate districts (e.g. Oxeye Daisy and Kidney Vetch on non-calcareous soils in north Warwickshire). Perhaps more worryingly, it has also led to the introduction

A species-rich road verge beside the Fosse Way, near Lighthorne, Field Scabious indicating that it is calcareous.

of foreign varieties or subspecies of certain plant species into the Warwickshire countryside (ones which differ from British ones both in their genetics and subtle aspects of their appearance). If these cross-fertilise with our own indigenous varieties they can potentially change the genetics of these varieties. Fortunately, there is a growing trend for allowing some new road verges to vegetate naturally (e.g. the Southam and Ettington by-passes) and the seed mixtures used in new verges are also becoming better sourced to ensure a reasonable proportion of locally-appropriate species. A number of our most important verges are managed under contract specifications designed to preserve their botanical interest.

The plants of grassland

Grassland is a major habitat for 165 of Warwickshire's native and naturalised plant species (see plant list at end of chapter), but it can also feature many plants more typical of woodland, wetland and disturbed ground making some individual sites extremely rich. *A Computer-Mapped Flora* recorded a total of 554 species growing in grassland in the 1950s and 1960s. Short-lived populations of various casuals can also be present, though not to the extent of arable land or disturbed ground, and only 8 neophytes or archaeophytes are featured within the 165 species quoted above.

Various growth strategies are employed. The majority of species are perennials, with root systems that stake a long-term claim to a piece of soil, even if the aerial growth dies back every year. Long tap roots and storage organs such as bulbs and tubers are used by some, especially in drier grassland where drought can put plants under extreme stress. About one-fifth of our grassland specialists are annuals, typically with long-lived seeds that can germinate when some type of disturbance, such as digging by rabbits, trampling by stock, vehicle activity or emergence of a mole hill, creates an opportunity. Grasses, sedges and rushes use wind pollination, but most of the higher plants of grassland have conspicuous insect-pollinated flowers that peak in June and July. It is the diversity and abundance of these flowers in less improved grassland that can make it such a celebrated habitat. Seed dispersal mechanisms include hooks that make the seeds stick to fur or fabric (e.g. Agrimony, Cleavers, burdocks and various umbellifers), windborne seeds (willowherbs and most composites), fruit explosions (some vetches) and dispersal by ants (e.g. violets). Some species spread by vegetative means, including Creeping Thistle, Ground-ivy and Selfheal, and can form dense patches.

Whilst many grassland flowers are widespread and capable of growing in a range of grassland conditions, there are some species that are restricted to certain grassland types and geological or soil conditions. If one encounters a relatively good number of such plants at one site you have a strong indication of a site of high conservation value.

Plants of calcareous grassland

Calcicolous grassland plants have much, if not all, of their local populations concentrated upon the limestone grasslands, limestone quarries and limestone road, railway and canal cuttings of south and east Warwickshire. They occasionally turn up further north for reasons that are unclear, and sometimes occupy the rides and clearings of calcareous woodlands. Examples of calcareous grassland specialists include legumes such as restharrows and Narrow-leaved Bird's-foot-trefoil, labiates such as Marjoram, Wild Basil and Wild Thyme, composites such as Oxeye Daisy, Hoary Ragwort, Carline Thistle, Woolly Thistle, Dwarf Thistle, Musk Thistle, Greater Knapweed, Rough Hawkbit and Hawkweed Oxtongue, umbellifers such as Wild Carrot and Wild Parsnip, orchids such as Pyramidal Orchid, Greater Butterfly Orchid and Common Twayblade, also other plants such as Dyer's Greenweed, Salad Burnet, Dropwort, Autumn Gentian, Yellow-wort, Field Scabious, Clustered Bellflower, Long-stalked Crane's-bill, Hairy Violet, Fairy Flax and Wild Onion. Calcicolous grasses include Upright Brome, Tor-grass, False Brome, Crested Hair-grass and Meadow Oat-grass. Calcicolous shrubs frequently present at the edge of limestone grassland include Wild Privet and Wayfaring-tree, with Traveller's-joy much in evidence scrambling over these and any other shrubs present. The plant list at the end of this chapter gives a more complete list of calcicoles.

Some plants have fairly specific needs within calcareous grassland, perhaps drier ground, clay-rich ground or sparser areas at earlier stages of the vegetation succession. Many are equally at home on the skeletal soils of limestone quarries and new limestone cuttings. Indeed, only a relatively small number of Warwickshire's calcicolous species seem to be restricted to older limestone grassland and include scarce and much declined species such as Field Scabious, Dropwort and Clustered Bellflower. It is also worth noting that not all of Warwickshire's calcicoles are so strictly calcicolous when viewed at a national level (a situation that also arises in Warwickshire's insect fauna). The Wasp Orchid is noteworthy in that it is a variety of the more widespread Bee Orchid that is much more strongly calcicolous than the normal form, with a national stronghold that takes in the south of Warwickshire.

Plants characteristic of calcareous grassland

Yellow-wort

Pyramidal Orchid

Wild Onion

Field Scabious

Common Restharrow

Clustered Bellflower

Plants characteristic of calcareous grassland

Dropwort

Woolly Thistle

Wild Thyme

Dwarf Thistle

Dyer's Greenweed

Hawkweed Oxtongue

Plants of acid grassland

Acid grassland supports another sizeable suite of specialists only otherwise found on heathland or within the rides and clearings of acid woodland. These include Tormentil, Petty Whin, Western Gorse, Sheep's Sorrel, Heath Milkwort, Heath Bedstraw, Heath Dog-violet, Heath Speedwell, Sneezewort, Wood Sage, Oval Sedge and grasses such as Heath-grass, Wavy Hair-grass and Mat-grass.

Wetter areas (which sometimes represent relict wet heath – see the Heathland and Mire chapter) can feature Cross-leaved Heath, Heath Spotted-orchid, Purple Moor-grass, Meadow Thistle, Heath Rush, Common Cotton-grass, Fine-leaved Sheep's Fescue and Lemon-scented Fern. All have declined substantially as suitable habitat has been lost. Heather can be present as a relic of previous heathland which has been replaced by acid grassland. Gorse, Broom, Cat's-ear, Mouse-ear-hawkweed and Devil's-bit Scabious are also frequent on acid grasslands, though they can occur abundantly in other habitats too.

Plants of neutral grassland

Specialities of damp, neutral grassland such as semi-improved flood meadow include Great Burnet, Cuckooflower, Marsh-marigold, Ragged-robin, Meadowsweet, Marsh Thistle, Greater Bird's-foot-trefoil, Silverweed, Common Meadow-rue, Marsh Speedwell, Common Bistort, rushes (Hard, Soft and Compact), Carnation Sedge, Reed Canary-grass, Tufted Hair-grass and Marsh Foxtail. Some of these are only present at older grasslands.

Indicators of old grasslands

As noted above, some species can be indicators of old, relatively unimproved grassland. Other important indicators include Cowslip, Green-winged Orchid, Pignut, Pepper-saxifrage, Betony, Adder's-tongue, Lady's Bedstraw, Lady's-mantle, Meadow Saxifrage, Yellow-rattle, Greater Burnet-saxifrage, Devil's-bit Scabious, Hoary Plantain, Crested Dog's-tail, Quaking-grass and Sweet Vernal-grass. Sites with a good selection of these are very special in Warwickshire today, and the County has probably lost over 95% of its old flower-rich grassland during the last 60 years.

Plants of scrubby grassland

Many grassland plants will persist within developing scrub until it becomes too dense. But herbaceous species that seem particularly to favour scrubby grassland and scrub-edge here (as opposed to fully open grassland) include Common Agrimony, Common Spotted-orchid, Common Twayblade, Hemp-agrimony and Common Gromwell. This is also an important zone for climbers such as Traveller's-joy, bindweeds, bryonies and Honeysuckle. The main scrub-forming woody species in Warwickshire are Hawthorn, Blackthorn, Grey Willow, various roses, Gorse, Broom and young growth of larger trees such as birches, Ash and Pedunculate Oak.

Plants of grassy road verges

A good number of plants thrive on road verges, benefitting from the damp and fertile soils that characterise most of these, and managing to flower in between cuts.

Plants characteristic of acid grassland

Heath Dog-violet

Tormentil

Lemon-scented Fern

Heath Speedwell

Common Cat's-ear

Wood Sage

Plants characteristic of acid grassland

Sneezewort

Sheep's Sorrel

Heath Bedstraw

Petty Whin

Common Cotton-grass

Mat-grass

Plants characteristic of damp neutral grassland

Meadow Buttercup

Great Burnet

Cuckooflower

Silverweed

Marsh Speedwell

Common Meadow-rue

Plants characteristic of old and less improved grasslands

Lady's Bedstraw

Adder's-tongue

Green-winged Orchid

Betony

Quaking-grass

Meadow Saxifrage

Plants characteristic of old and less improved grasslands

Pepper-saxifrage

Devil's-bit Scabious

Common Lady's-mantle

Yellow-rattle

Sweet Vernal-grass

Crested Dog's-tail

A Computer-Mapped Flora recorded a total of 553 species from this habitat in the 1950s and 1960s, though the fifteen most frequently recorded plants cited suggest that verges were much more species-rich then, with less enriched soils than today. The modern roadside flora is now dominated by Cow Parsley (which did not make the earlier top-fifteen), Hogweed, Common Ragwort, Mugwort, Spear Thistle, Common Knapweed, Yarrow, dandelions, White Dead-nettle, Rosebay Willowherb and grasses like False Oat-grass, various fescues, Cock's-foot and Yorkshire-fog. Wild Parsnip, Greater Knapweed, Corn Sowthistle, Wild Mignonette, Marjoram and Woolly Thistle are some of the species that characterise road verges in southern limestone districts, whilst Bracken, Foxglove and Wood Sage the more acidic verges of the Arden. Rarities still surviving on the occasional road verge include Wild Liquorice, Pyramidal Orchid, Wasp Orchid and Spiny Rest-harrow. Neophytes and casuals are an increasing feature of road verges, partly as a consequence of fly-tipping. The more prominent ones include daffodils, michaelmas-daisies, Japanese Knotweed, and Giant Hogweed. The last two are notifiable weeds that should be reported to local authorities whenever found.

Losses and gains

As with woodland, much loss is associated with the physical reduction in the extent of the habitat, both through wholesale destruction (typically by conversion to arable or development) and the degradation or ruination of species-rich grassland as it has been converted to more improved or fully improved grassland. The following 19 grassland species are considered to have become extinct in Warwickshire:

- Slender Bedstraw *Galium pumilum* – recorded near Tredington prior to 1904, a calcicole (possibly never native to Warwickshire)
- Smith's Brome *Bromus pseudosecalinus* – several records in the period 1950-65, a neophyte
- Greater Broomrape *Orobanche rapum-genistae* – last recorded from Whitley in 1847, typically a parasite of broom and gorse in acid grassland and heathland
- Knapweed Broomrape *Orobanche elatior* – last recorded at Whichford in 1957, a parasite of the calcicole Greater Knapweed *Centaurea scabiosa*
- Lesser Calamint *Clinopodium calamintha* – recorded from Lighthorne in 1851, a calcicole
- Smooth Cat's-ear *Hypochaeris glabra* – recorded near to Middleton in the period 1670-1830 (including the first British record), acid grassland
- Chamomile *Chamaemelum nobile* – probably last recorded at Yarningale Common in 1901, dislikes calcareous soils
- Meadow Clary *Salvia pratensis* – last record as a native appears to be Birdingbury 1908, though it is an occasional garden escape
- Dodder *Cuscuta epithymum* – last recorded near Alderminster in the period 1950-65 on various plants (it is a plant parasite)
- The eyebright *Euphrasia arctica* – last recorded from Kineton in 1964 (ssp. *borealis*), a northern and western species
- The eyebright *Euphrasia micrantha* – last recorded at Olton in the period c1960, prefers acid grassland and heathland

Extinct grassland plants

Field Mouse-ear

Fragrant Orchid

Knapweed Broomrape

Frog Orchid

Smooth Cat's-ear

Chamomile

- Blue Fescue *Festuca longifolia* – last recorded in wild from Leek Wootton in 1897, but occasionally still encountered as a casual garden escape, very rare nationally
- Small Fleabane *Pulicaria vulgaris* – last recorded at Myton in 1834, likes periodically-flooded grassland
- The lady's mantle *Alchemilla xanthochlora* – last recorded in grounds of Dunchurch Lodge in 1961
- Autumn Lady's-tresses *Spiranthes spiralis* – last recorded at Kenilworth in 1873
- Field Mouse-ear *Cerastium arvense* – last recorded near Little Compton in 1960
- Nit-grass *Gastridium ventricosum* – last recorded in fields west of Alcester 1957, it used to grew both in calcareous grassland and cornfields, and is much declined nationally
- Frog Orchid *Coeloglossum viride* - last recorded at Ipsley in 1878, a calcicole
- Fragrant Orchid *Gymnadenia conopsea* – last confirmed record Snitterfield 1948 (also an unconfirmed one for Rugby 1950-65), a calcicole

Relatively recent gains to local grassland include Fox-and-cubs, Slender Speedwell, Highland Bent and Yellow Bartsia, all neophytes. Species such as Cow Parsley, Alexanders and Beaked Hawk's-beard have increased along grassy road verges over recent decades.

Local grasslands you can visit

Neutral
- Alvecote Meadows, near Tamworth SK245048 (a Warwickshire Wildlife Trust reserve) – flood meadow and marsh with a variety of damp grassland plants.
- Brook Meadow, near Dorridge SP180742 (a Warwickshire Wildlife Trust reserve) – excellent hay meadow and water meadow with acidic tendencies featuring Great Burnet, Meadow Thistle, Devil's-bit Scabious, Crested Dog's-tail, Yellow Oat-grass and Sweet Vernal-grass.
- Deans Green, near Ullenhall village SP132682 (a Warwickshire Wildlife Trust reserve) – excellent hay meadow with pronounced ridge and furrow, featuring species such as Betony, Yellow-rattle, Devil's-bit Scabious, Sneezewort, Great Burnet and Adder's-tongue Fern (over one hundred species in total).
- Draycote Meadows, near Draycote village SP448706 (a Warwickshire Wildlife Trust reserve) – the finest semi-improved grassland site in the County with fine shows of Green-winged Orchid and Cowslip in May followed by a plethora of further scarce plants later in summer including Moonwort (at its only surviving site in the County), Adder's-tongue, Meadow Vetchling; also Common Spotted-orchid and Yellow-rattle.
- Harvest Hill, near Allesley SP279283 (a Warwickshire Wildlife Trust reserve) – a field of semi-improved neutral grassland famous for its Wild Daffodils (increasingly hybrids) but also featuring Pignut, Common Bistort and Cowslip.
- Loxley Church Meadow, Loxley SP259532 (a Warwickshire Wildlife Trust reserve) – a very fine neutral to slightly calcareous hay meadow producing one of the finest Cowslip displays in the County; also Yellow-rattle, Common Spotted-orchid, Rough Hawkbit and Dropwort, plus an impressive twenty-three species of grasses.

- Oldberrow Churchyard, near Ullenhall SP121660 – the finest wildflower churchyard in the County, with a variety of old grassland indicators, including Cowslip, Betony, Devil's-bit Scabious, Lady's-mantle and Hoary Plantain.
- Radway Meadows, Edgehill SP366475 (a Warwickshire Wildlife Trust reserve) – a less improved part of the Edge Hill escarpment, with Betony, Dropwort, Adder's-tongue, Crested Dog's-tail and Sweet Vernal-grass. There is also a flushed area with wetland plants.
- Shadowbrook Meadows, near Hampton-in-Arden SP187814 (a Warwickshire Wildlife Trust reserve) – a series of wet and dry meadows with acidic tendencies, supporting many old grassland indicators such as Cowslip, Adder's-tongue, Pignut, Pepper-saxifrage, Betony, Meadow Thistle, Heath-spotted Orchid, Quaking-grass and Crested Dog's-tail.
- Stonebridge Meadows, Coventry SP348756 (a Warwickshire Wildlife Trust reserve) – possibly the finest piece of grassland within Coventry's Sowe Valley, varying from neutral flood meadow to somewhat acidic at higher levels and featuring grassland plants such as Harebell, Betony and Pignut.
- Tocil Meadow, University of Warwick, Coventry SP304755 (a Warwickshire Wildlife Trust reserve) – a damp meadow with Cuckooflower and Meadowsweet.
- Welches Meadow, Leamington Spa SP325657 (a Warwickshire Wildlife Trust reserve) – damp meadowland and marsh featuring Common Marsh-bedstraw, Silverweed and yellowcresses.
- Welcombe Hills, Stratford-upon-Avon SP205565 (a Warwickshire Wildlife Trust reserve) – extensive semi-improved grassland of varying quality, featuring plants such as Woolly Thistle (indicating more calcareous soils), Quaking-grass and Adder's-tongue. Some fine ridge-and-furrow is present.

Calcareous grassland

- Ashlawn Cutting, Rugby SP516732 (a Warwickshire Wildlife Trust reserve) – a section of the now disused Great Central Railway with moderately calcareous grassland and scrub featuring Grass Vetchling, Fairy Flax and Agrimony.
- Grove Hill, near Ardens Grafton SP112547 (a Warwickshire Wildlife Trust reserve) – a long escarpment with old calcareous grassland and scrub, rich in calcicoles such as Great Knapweed, Yellow-wort, Pyramidal Orchid, Common Gromwell, Hairy Violet, Long-stalked Crane's-bill, Fairy Flax and Traveller's-joy.
- Harbury Spoilbank, near Harbury SP384598 (a Warwickshire Wildlife Trust reserve) – calcareous grassland, scrub and disturbed ground on a spoilheap resulting from construction of adjacent railway cutting in the 1840s. Many calcicoles present including Carline Thistle, Dwarf Thistle, Woolly Thistle, Ploughman's-spikenard, Hawkweed Oxtongue, Common Twayblade, Autumn Gentian, Wild Parsnip and Yellow-wort.
- Stockton Railway Cutting, near Stockton SP437651 (a Warwickshire Wildlife Trust reserve) – calcareous grassland, scrub and disturbed ground associated with a series of old cement quarries, with calcicoles such as Dwarf and Woolly Thistles, Yellow-wort, Hairy Violet, Autumn Gentian, Blue Fleabane and Greater Butterfly-orchid .
- Ufton Fields, near Harbury SP378615 (a Warwickshire Wildlife Trust reserve) – calcareous grassland and scrub on former shallow limestone workings plus

some semi-improved neutral grassland that predates this. Many calcicoles, including Man Orchid (at its only County site), Autumn Gentian, Wild Basil, Woolly Thistle, Common Twayblade and Greater Butterfly-orchid.

Acid grassland

- Pooley Fields SK256037 (a Warwickshire Wildlife Trust reserve and Warwickshire County Council Country Park) – contains areas of acid grassland and disturbed ground that have formed on an old spoilheap and adjacent land.
- Baddesley Common SP277979 and surrounding areas – acid grassland associated with heathland and a series of spoilheaps and quarries.
- Coombe Country Park SP396799 (a Coventry City Council Country Park) features a small area of acid grassland north of the Wrautums.
- Priory Fields, Yardley SP101791 (a Warwickshire Wildlife Trust reserve) – once part of a heathy common and features a variety of acidophiles such as Heather, Broom, Western Gorse and Heath Rush.

Permanent grassland plant list (excluding casuals)

Grasses, sedges and rushes

- ✔ Meadow Barley *Hordeum secalinum* – in a range of grasslands
- ✔ Brown Bent *Agrostis vinealis* – a fairly recent discovery in Warwickshire, preferring acid grassland
- ✔ Common Bent *Agrostis capillaries* – in a range of grasslands
- ✔ Creeping Bent *Agrostis stolonifera* – in a range of grasslands
- ✘ Highland Bent *Agrostis castellana* – a neophyte sometimes introduced with grass-seed mixtures and naturalising
- ✔ Velvet Bent *Agrostis canina* – damp mostly acid grassland, rare (much confused with Brown Bent in the past)
- ✔ Meadow Brome *Bromus commutatus* - in a range of grasslands
- ✔ Smooth Brome *Bromus racemosus* – calcareous grassland, scarce
- ✔ Upright Brome *Bromopsis erecta* – calcareous grassland, probably declining
- ✔ Smaller Cat's-tail *Phleum bertolonii* – less improved grassland?
- ✔ Cock's-foot *Dactylis glomerata* – in a range of grasslands
- ✔ Crested Dog's-tail *Cynosurus cristatus* – less improved grassland
- ✔ Meadow Fescue *Festuca pratensis* – in a range of grasslands
- ✔ Red Fescue *Festuca rubra* – in a range of grasslands
- ✔ Meadow Foxtail *Alopecurus pratensis* – in a range of grasslands
- ✔ Crested Hair-grass *Koeleria macrantha* – calcareous grassland, also disturbed calcareous sites, probably declining
- ✔ Tufted Hair-grass *Deschampsia cespitosa* – damp grassland, also marsh
- ✔ Wavy Hair-grass *Deschampsia flexuosa* – acid grassland and heathland (often persisting in the woodland that invades this)
- ✔ Heath-grass *Danthonia decumbens* – prefers acid grassland
- ✔ Mat-grass *Nardus strictus* – damp acid grassland
- ✔ Narrow-leaved Meadow-grass *Poa angustifolia* – in a range of grasslands
- ✔ Smooth Meadow-grass *Poa pratensis* – in a range of grasslands

- ✔ Spreading Meadow-grass *Poa humilis* – damp grassland
- ✔ Purple Moor-grass *Molinia caerulea* – damp acid grassland plus wet heath
- ✔ False Oat-grass *Arrhenatherum elatius* – in a range of grasslands
- ✔ Downy Oat-grass *Helictotrichon pubescens* – preferring calcareous grassland
- ✔ Meadow Oat-grass *Helictotrichon pratense* – calcareous grassland
- ✔ Yellow Oat-grass *Trisetum flavescens* – in a range of grasslands
- ✔ Quaking-grass *Briza media* – less improved grassland
- ✔ Compact Rush *Juncus conglomeratus* – damp grassland, also wetlands
- ✔ Heath Rush *Juncus squarrosus* – damp acid grassland, also wet heath and mire, rare
- ✔ Round-fruited Rush *Juncus compressus* – prefers damp grassland, also marshes
- ✔ Perennial Rye-grass *Lolium perenne* – in a range of grasslands
- ✔ Carnation Sedge *Carex panicea* – damp grassland, also wetlands
- ✔ Distant Sedge *Carex distans* – wet grassland, also wetlands, rare
- ✔ Glaucous Sedge *Carex flacca* – in a range of grasslands, but especially common on calcareous clays
- ✔ Hairy Sedge *Carex hirta* – wet grassland, also wetlands
- ✔ Oval Sedge *Carex ovalis* –acid grassland
- ✔ Pill Sedge *Carex pilulifera* – acid grassland and heath, rare
- ✔ Spiked Sedge *Carex spicata* – prefers grasslands on damp calcareous clay
- ✔ Spring Sedge *Carex caryophyllea* – probably declining
- ✔ Sheep's-fescue *Festuca ovina* – especially on poorer more acidic soils
- ✔ Fine-leaved Sheep's-fescue *Festuca filiformis* – acid grassland and heathland, rare and declined
- ✘ Slender Soft-brome *Bromus lepidus* – more improved grasslands, a neophyte
- ✔ Timothy *Phleum pratense* – in a range of grasslands
- ✔ Tor-grass *Brachypodum pinnatum* – calcareous grassland
- ✔ Sweet Vernal-grass *Anthoxanthum odoratum* – less improved grassland
- ✔ Field Wood-rush *Luzula campestris*
- ✔ Yorkshire-fog *Holcus lanatus* – in a range of grasslands

Other flowering plants
- ✔ Agrimony *Agrimonia eupatoria*
- ✘ Alexanders *Smyrnium olusatrum* – a scarce but increasing archaeophyte of road verges
- ✔ Red Bartsia *Odontites verna* – mostly calcareous grassland, also disturbed calcareous land
- ✔ Heath Bedstraw *Galium saxatile* – acid grassland and heathland
- ✔ Lady's Bedstraw *Galium verum*
- ✔ Clustered Bellflower *Campanula glomerata* – calcareous grassland, rare and much declined
- ✔ Betony *Stachys officinalis*
- ✔ Common Bird's-foot-trefoil *Lotus corniculatus* – dry grassland, also disturbed sites
- ✔ Narrow-leaved Bird's-foot-trefoil *Lotus glaber* – calcareous grassland, also disturbed calcareous land

✔ Great Burnet *Sanguisorba officinalis*
✔ Salad Burnet *Sanguisorba minor* – calcareous grassland, also disturbed calcareous land
✔ Lesser Burnet-saxifrage *Pimpinella saxifraga*
✔ Bulbous Buttercup *Ranunculus bulbosus* – prefers drier grasslands
✔ Creeping Buttercup *Ranunculus repens* – prefers damper grasslands
✔ Meadow Buttercup *Ranunculus acris*
✔ Common Calamint *Clinopodium ascendens*
✔ Common Cat's-ear *Hypochaeris radicata*
✔ Wild Clary *Salvia glomerata* – calcareous grassland, rare and much declined
✔ Knotted Clover *Trifolium striatum* – rare
✔ Strawberry Clover *Trifolium fragiferum* – possibly declining
✔ Subterranean Clover *Trifolium subterraneum* – rare, recently recorded from Sherbourne only
✔ White Clover *Trifolium repens*
✔ Zigzag Clover *Trifolium medium*
✔ Cowslip *Primula verum* – less improved grassland
✔ Long-stalked Crane's-bill *Geranium columbinum* – a calcicole
✘ Autumn Crocus *Crocus nudiflorus* – a rare neophyte, mainly in the Warwick area (formerly grown as a substitute for saffron)
✔ Crosswort *Cruciata laevipes* – probably declining
✔ Cuckooflower *Cardamine pratensis* – damp grassland, also wetlands
✔ Daisy *Bellis perennis*
✔ Oxeye Daisy *Leucanthemum vulgare* – calcareous ground, also disturbed calcareous ground
✔ Dandelions *Taraxacum* spp – a complicated group, many of them seem to favour grassland, especially pasture
✔ Fiddle Dock *Rumex pulcher*
✔ Heath Dog-violet *Viola canina* – acid grassland
✔ Dropwort *Filipendula vulgaris* – calcareous grassland, probably declining
✔ The eyebright *Euphrasia confusa* – a fairly recent discovery in Warwickshire
✔ The eyebright *Euphrasia nemorosa* – less improved grassland only
✔ Fairy Flax *Linum catharticum* – a calcicole
✔ Changing Forget-me-not *Myosotis discolor* – a fairly recent discovery in Warwickshire
✘ Fox-and-cubs *Pilosella aurantiaca* – a widely naturalised garden escape neophyte
✘ Fritillary *Fritillaria meleagris* – a British native but probably introduced to Warwickshire where scarce and usually a casual
✔ Field Garlic *Allium oleraceum* – rare and probably declining
✔ Autumn Gentian *Gentianella amarella* – calcareous grassland, also disturbed calcareous land
✔ Goat's-beard *Tragopogon pratensis*
✔ Gorse *Ulex europaeus* – especially on acid grassland and that on Cotswoldian hillside pasture, often forming thickets
✔ Dyer's Greenweed *Genista tinctoria* – calcareous grassland, scarce

✔ Common Gromwell *Lithospermum officinale* – a scarce and declining species of calcareous scrub, also hedgerows

✔ Harebell *Campanula rotundifolium* – less improved grassland, declining

✔ Autumn Hawkbit *Leontodon autumnalis*

✔ Lesser Hawkbit *Leontodon saxatilis*

✔ Rough Hawkbit *Leontodon hispidus*

✘ Beaked Hawk's-beard *Crepis vesicaria* – increasing, esp. along grassy road verges, a neophyte

✔ Rough Hawk's-beard *Crepis biennis* – calcareous grassland, rare

✔ Smooth Hawk's-beard *Crepis capillaris* – in a range of grasslands

✔ Hawkweeds *Hieracium* spp – a complicated group, some of them seem to favour rough grassland

✔ Common Knapweed *Centaurea nigra* – in a range of grasslands

✔ Greater Knapweed *Centaurea scabiosa* – calcareous grassland, also disturbed calcareous land

✔ Lady's-mantle *Alchemilla filicaulis* – prefers less improved meadows

✔ Spotted Medick *Medicago arabica*

✔ Common Milkwort *Polygala vulgaris*

✔ Heath Milkwort *Polygala serpyllifolia* – acid grassland, also heathland

✔ Common Mouse-ear *Cerastium fontanum*

✔ Sticky Mouse-ear *Cerastium glomeratum*

✔ Green-winged Orchid *Orchis morio* – less improved grassland

✔ Pyramidal Orchid *Anacamptis pyramidalis* – calcareous grassland, also more disturbed calcareous sites

✔ Hawkweed Oxtongue *Picris hieracioides* – calcareous grassland

✔ Stone Parsley *Sison amomum*

✔ Pepper-saxifrage *Silaum silaus* – probably declining

✔ Pignut *Conopodium majus* – less improved grassland

✔ Hoary Plantain *Plantago media* – less improved meadows

✔ Ribwort Plantain *Plantago lanceolata*

✔ Common Ragwort *Senecio jacobaea* – also on disturbed ground and woodland rides etc

✔ Hoary Ragwort *Senecio erucifolius* – calcareous grassland, also disturbed calcareous ground

✔ Common Restharrow *Ononis repens* – mostly calcareous grassland

✔ Spiny Restharrow *Ononis spinosa* – calcareous grassland, probably declining

✔ Common Rockrose *Helianthemum nummularium* – calcareous grassland, rare

✔ Saw-wort *Serratula tinctoria* – declining

✔ Meadow Saxifrage *Saxifraga granulata* – probably declining

✔ Field Scabious *Knautia arvensis* – calcareous grassland, probably declining

✔ Small Scabious *Scabiosa columbaria* – calcareous grassland, rare and probably declining

✔ Selfheal *Prunella vulgaris*

✔ Sheep's-bit *Jasione montana* – acid grassland, very rare (Middleton only)

✔ Sneezewort *Achillea ptarmica* – prefers damp acid grassland, also wet heath

✔ Common Sorrel *Rumex acetosa*

✔ Sheep's Sorrel *Rumex acetosella* – prefers acid grassland
✔ Germander Speedwell *Veronica chamaedrys*
✔ Heath Speedwell *Veronica officinalis* – prefers acid grassland and also heathland, probably declining
✘ Slender Speedwell *Veronica filiformis* – an increasing neophyte
✔ Thyme-leaved Speedwell *Veronica serpyllifolia*
✔ Heath Spotted-orchid *Dactylorhiza maculata* – damp acid grassland, also wet heath, scarce
✔ Squinancywort *Asperula cynanchica* – calcareous grassland, rare
✔ Lesser Stitchwort *Stellaria graminea*
✔ Hairy St John's-wort *Hypericum hirsutum*
✘ Star-of-Bethlehem *Ornithogalum angustifolium* – an increasing neophyte
✔ Creeping Thistle *Cirsium arvense*
✔ Dwarf Thistle *Cirsium acaule* – calcareous grassland, also disturbed calcareous land
✔ Marsh Thistle *Cirsium palustre* – damp grassland, also wetlands
✔ Meadow Thistle *Cirsium dissectum* – damp acid grassland, also mire and wet heath, rare
✔ Musk Thistle *Carduus nutans* – mostly calcareous grassland
✔ Spear Thistle *Cirsium vulgare*
✔ Woolly Thistle *Cirsium eriophorum* – calcareous grassland
✔ Wild Thyme *Thymus polytrichus*
✔ Tormentil *Potentilla erecta* – acid grassland and heathland
✔ Hop Trefoil *Trifolium campestre*
✔ Lesser Trefoil *Trifolium dubium*
✔ Slender Trefoil *Trifolium micranthum*
✔ Common Vetch *Vicia sativa*
✔ Horseshoe Vetch *Hippocrepis comosa* – considered extinct until rediscovered at Little Compton in 1994, a calcicole
✔ Spring Vetch *Vicia lathyroides* – considered extinct until rediscovered at Piles Coppice in the late 1990s
✔ Kidney Vetch *Anthyllis vulneraria* – calcareous grassland, also calcareous ruderal
✔ Grass Vetchling *Lathyrus nissolia*
✔ Meadow Vetchling *Lathyrus pratensis*
✔ Hairy Violet *Viola hirta* – calcareous grassland
✔ Yarrow *Achillea millefolium*
✔ Yellow-rattle *Rhinanthus minor* – less improved grassland

Ferns
✔ Adder's-tongue *Ophioglossum vulgatum* – less improved grasslands
✔ Lemon-scented Fern *Oreopteris limbosperma* – mainly on acid grassland, scarce
✔ Moonwort *Botrychium lunaria* – rare (just Draycote Meadow now)

Chapter 8

Water Courses and Wetlands

Flowing and standing water and more or less permanently waterlogged land

This chapter features the plants of wet places, excluding wet woodland and mire which are covered in other chapters. It covers plants that grow in water, beside water and on waterlogged land. By waterlogged, we do not simply mean land that gets temporarily flooded in winter or following heavy rainfall, but land that remains wet throughout much of a typical year, perhaps only drying out following a period of drought. Many characteristic plants are associated with such conditions, some with very exacting requirement, others more adaptable and able to exploit a range of conditions. Some can colonise remarkably small, isolated and young patches of suitable habitat, others are associated with very old wetland sites such as fen.

River Itchen at Long Itchington.

The history of Warwickshire's water courses and wetlands

Natural water courses such as streams and rivers are some of the most ancient features of our local landscape. Their origins predate the last ice age (which did not cover Warwickshire with ice) and stretch to the end of the Anglian Ice Age some 425,000 years ago. This was the most severe glaciation in British geological history, producing a deep and slow-moving ice sheet that covered most of Britain north of the London area. The southern edge of the ice sheet is partly indicated by the modern course of the River Thames (which had previously followed a more northerly route) and the ice sheet radically altered the drainage pattern of all the land it covered by eroding hills, creating new valleys and depositing thick deposits of clays, gravels and silts. The River Bytham, which had flowed through mid Warwickshire towards East Anglia prior to the Anglian glaciation, was obliterated and replaced by two new river systems, the Avon and the Tame. The Avon and its tributaries flow towards the Bristol Channel via the River Severn. The Tame and its tributaries, which belong to a different catchment, flow into the North Sea via the Rivers Trent and Humber. These water courses have now witnessed nearly half a million year's worth of local climate change including eleven smaller ice ages and associated interglacials, plus the constantly changing flora and fauna associated with these. At times they would have flowed through frozen tundra and resembled the rivers and streams one now finds in the arctic. At other times they would have passed through a warm savannah-type landscape, and between about 10,000 and 5,000 years ago they would have meandered through the heavily forested wildwood that covered most of Britain prior to forest clearance by Neolithic people.

Wetlands are areas with a more or less permanently high water table and are strongly associated with river valleys. They share many plants with river and stream margins and this is also a habitat with a long history in our area. In the mild, damp climate we experience in Britain, river valleys tend to become waterlogged if not subject to artificial drainage and it is likely that swamp, fen and patches of open water were widespread until humans started to drain the land to increase the area of productive farmland. Wetlands are also natural features of unmodified rivers, forming in old ox-bows, and along river sections that are shallow and not subject to strong flow (e.g. on the sand and shingle deposits associated with meandering rivers). Sutton Park (covered more fully in the Heathland and Mire chapter) now contains the only valley in our area with its original valley wetlands. Almost every other valley in Warwickshire has been substantially drained and modified, with rivers, streams and any associated wetlands now typically confined to narrow corridors that are ecologically disconnected from the farmland or urban development that they pass through. The only significant exception to this situation occurs in valleys subject to gravel extraction,

Wormleighton Reservoir – a high proportion of Warwickshire's wetlands are artificial and of relatively recent origin.

such as sections of the Avon, Tame, Blythe and Arrow. Here, a number of large wetlands of recent origin have developed in flooded gravel workings (e.g. Brandon Marsh and Kingsbury Water Park). These now support many of the plants that would have been associated with ancient valley wetlands and allow rivers and streams to resume the complicated interplay they historically had with their valleys.

Wetlands can also occur away from river valleys through the flooding of old quarries (e.g. Ufton Fields and Bishops Bowl Quarry, near Harbury) and in association with ornamental lakes, reservoirs, ponds, ditches, fishing pools, canals and moats. Springs and seepages can also produce small wetlands, and some of these may be thousands of years old, though most local ones are in wooded settings.

Local types of water courses and wetlands

Rivers and streams

These are natural drainage features, in the sense that they exist for the most part where nature put them, though many stretches have been straightened, deepened, channelised or culverted to reduce the risk of flooding to properties and roads, and to permit increasing amounts of floodplain development. Warwickshire's rivers and streams mostly fall into two catchments. The Avon catchment is based upon the river Avon (which rises near Rugby and flows into the River Severn at Tewkesbury) plus its tributaries, notably the Leam, Dene, Stour and Arrow. The River Trent catchment includes the River Tame and its tributaries, notably the Blythe, Cole and Anker. It drains the north of the County, taking water to the North Sea via the Trent and Humber.

Unmodified rivers and streams can be physically complex with varied water depths and flow rates, meanders (curved stretches of river), areas of bank erosion (usually on the outside of a meander where the water is faster and more erosive) and areas of deposition (usually on the inside of a meander where slower water flow can deposit silt, sand or gravel). The bottom (or 'bed') can be comprised of silt, clay or gravel. Small islands can develop where the channel is broad and the water shallow. Banks are often perpendicular, but can become shallow where stock such as cattle come to drink or where there is landslippage. All these various factors affect the flora. Another strong influence on the plants is water quality. Rivers and streams have become increasingly polluted since the onset of the industrial revolution. This is mainly due to the run-off of various effluents from the land, including agricultural fertilisers and slurry, untreated sewage and household discharges, road run-off (full of oils plus salt in winter) and industrial effluent (often full of solvents and heavy metals). This has been a major factor behind the decline of many aquatic

The River Avon at Barford, a particularly natural stretch of river featuring different depths of water, natural erosion and deposition, and a varied flora.

river-plants. Fortunately, new legislation such as the Water Resources Act 1991 and the Land Drainage Act 1994 has reduced the discharge of pollutants into water courses (with polluters now facing heavy fines) and compels landowners to look after watercourses and to "further the conservation of any special flora". The British Waterways Act 1995 provides similar coverage to canals.

Ponds and lakes

Open standing water comes in many forms. Ponds are the most numerous, and modern Warwickshire is reckoned to have nearly 7000 of them (excluding garden ponds or tiny ponds smaller than 1.6 square metres), mostly within farmland. Field ponds are approximately four times more frequent in fields of north-east Warwickshire (the Arden) than fields in the south and east, reflecting the division of the county into ancient countryside and planned countryside. Field ponds were mostly created to serve livestock, but other pools represent old marlpits or small quarries, and many modern ones are balancing pools (used to prevent flooding or to act as small reservoirs) or ornamental landscape features. Because many ponds are no longer used for stock, they have tended to become shaded out by trees and shrubs, which reduces their value for other plants and increases the rate at which they silt up.

Larger water bodies include reservoirs like Draycote, Shustoke, Olton and Edgbaston, the ornamental lakes associated with historic properties (e.g. Coombe Abbey, Warwick Castle Park, Charlecote Park, Packington Park and Compton Verney), those of flooded gravel workings (notably Brandon Marsh and several sites

A large subsidence pool at Alvecote Pools, near Tamworth, featuring Bulrush and Common Club-rush, surrounded by swamp and carr.

within the Tame and Blythe valleys), flooded quarries (e.g. Bishops Bowl near Harbury and Newbold Quarry, Rugby) and canal feeder lakes (e.g. Earlswood Lakes and Wormleighton Reservoir). In addition to these, several large subsidence pools have formed where floodplain land overlying coal mines has collapsed by a few feet (e.g. Alvecote Pools, Wyken Slough and Stoke Floods). The pools of Sutton Park result from damming and used to drive mills. Most local water bodies are 'eutrophic' in that the water they contain has relatively high nutrient levels (nitrates and phosphates). Those of Sutton Park, Alvecote Pools, Keresley Mere and a few other places in former heathland districts of the Arden are more 'mesotrophic' with much lower nutrient levels and a lower pH (i.e. more acidic). As in rivers and streams, water chemistry has an important influence on the plants present.

Marsh, fen and swamp

This is land with a permanently high water table which means plants are either growing in shallow water or in waterlogged soil. It can occur in old gravel pits and quarries, at the edges of lakes and reservoirs, on the banks of rivers (and in any old oxbows), in silted-up ponds and balancing pools, in the clearings of wet woodland, and in wet meadows with damp hollows. Approximately 116 hectares occurs in modern Warwickshire. The water of marsh, fen and swamp is both rain-fed and ground-fed, and not infrequently fed by flooding from any adjacent rivers or streams that have burst their banks after heavy rain. The nomenclature covering these habitats is somewhat complex. **Swamp** is the term used for well-vegetated areas that are usually permanently covered by shallow water, and a typical reedbed is a good example. **Marsh** and **fen** are drier, with the water level fluctuating at around ground level, sometimes just below and sometimes above during periodic flooding, but they intergrade with swamp at many sites. The term marsh technically refers to wetlands that have formed on mineral soils such as river alluvium, gravel, and lake or pond silts. Fens are characterised by peat (the partially decomposed remains of plants), and are older wetlands that typically originated as marshes many centuries ago. Fens can have considerable botanical interest and support many scarce species. **Bog** also forms on peat but is more acidic (pH typically 3.5) and nutrient-poor, and its peat almost entirely derived from Sphagnum moss. It is covered in the Heathland and Mire chapter, though it often intergrades with fen and marsh at a site. A number of wetlands in the north and west of Warwickshire represent **poor-fen**, which is moderately acidic (pH of 4-5) wet peatland on base-poor rocks such as sandstone. Warwickshire does not have any **rich-fen** which is typically found in flat, poorly drained areas overlying chalk, such as the Norfolk Broads and Cambridgeshire Fens. But the County may well have had in the distant past in poorly-drained areas overlying limestone.

Marsh vegetation featuring Yellow Iris, Ragged-robin, Marsh-marigold and Bogbean.

Fen and swamp is rarely uniform, and typically features a **hydrosere** (or at least part of one) in which one finds a succession of plants ranging from those that grow in open water through to those growing in swamp, marsh or fen, and eventually wet scrub (known as *carr*), wet woodland, or drier open habitats such as wet grassland (which often features marsh plants) and scrub. Wet woodland is what most marsh, fen and swamp will eventually succeed to in the absence of management or grazing.

Ditches

These are typically features of agricultural landscapes, designed to assist drainage of farmland (but sometimes to irrigate meadows) and are often associated with hedgerows. Many stem from the Enclosure Acts of the eighteenth and early nineteenth centuries, though they would have been used at least as far back as the Bronze Age. They often support narrow strips of shallow wetlands, the character of which depends on water depth, duration of flooding, water quality and local sources of wetland plants. The water in ditches generally flows after rain, but can become standing at other times, and may disappear in dry periods. Because of the nature of their surroundings, ditches are particularly prone to pollution such as eutrophication.

A well-vegetated ditch in Willoughby featuring abundant Great Willowherb, Reed Canary-grass and Marsh Woundwort.

Canals

Canals are artificial corridors of standing water that date from the late eighteenth century, when they acted as important transportation routes for industry, including local quarries. There are seven canals in Vice-county Warwickshire, of which the most important botanically are the Oxford, Grand Union, Stratford-upon-Avon and Coventry. As with rivers and streams, the water quality has improved significantly in recent decades and greater effort is made to conserve aquatic and marginal plant communities, which can be very rich. Unused canal backwaters and

Flowering-rush and Sweet-flag line the Birmingham & Fazeley Canal near Kingsbury Water Park.

spurs at places like Cathiron, the Swift Valley Nature Reserve in Rugby and Onley can be especially important. Today most canals are primarily used for amenity and their towpaths can provide excellent opportunities for recording aquatic and marginal plants.

Seepages (flushes)

These are small-scale wetlands, often of great antiquity, that typically emerge from hillsides or river terraces where porous deposits such as sands and gravels overlie non-porous clays. Most flushes and seepages in Warwickshire tend to occur in woodland, but a few exist in more open conditions, such as the faces of quarries. They can support small assemblages of wetland plants or patches of willow carr. Those in limestone areas are typically highly calcareous and often give rise to limestone streams. The Long Compton, Ilmington and Napton areas are particularly important for these features. A few spring-fed saline pools occur near Southam and Flecknoe.

The plants of wetland and water courses

211 native or naturalised species currently rely entirely or heavily upon water courses or wetlands for their presence in Warwickshire (see plant list at end of chapter). It is a highly diverse assemblage that includes some extremely specialised plants, particularly the free-floating or fully-submerged ones. Others, such as Angelica, Marsh-bedstraw, Greater Bird's-foot-trefoil and Marsh Ragwort more closely resemble fully-terrestrial species. Like grassland and woodland, a very high proportion of the species are perennials, presumably to maintain a footing in what can be a very competitive environment that is prone to fluctuating water levels and other stresses. Also, like woodland, vegetative reproduction is used by many species, and includes budding (e.g. duckweeds), fragmentation (many submerged plants) and spread by underground stolons (most swamp plants).

In terms of species, the flora is dominated by native plants, with a relatively modest number of neophytes. However, those neophytes include some highly invasive species (notably, Indian Balsam, New Zealand Pigmyweed and Least Duckweed) that are profoundly affecting the abundance of those native species. The only archaeophytes are amongst the willows, which appear to have been introduced in pre-Roman times as a source of twigs for basketry.

Free-floating aquatics

This is a small assemblage with some of our most specialised higher plants, often with highly adapted morphology. Most duckweeds consist of just a few small flat leaves called 'fronds' from which one or several tiny roots hang. Much of their reproduction is by vegetative budding, but they produce tiny flowers that use 'contact pollination' (where the flowers of two different plants literally touch each other to fertilise one another). Warwickshire has five sorts of duckweed, one of which, Least Duckweed, is a recent arrival. Water Fern (an introduction from North America) resembles duckweeds, but has tiny scale-like leaves called 'thalli' which contain a blue-green alga that can fix atmospheric nitrogen. It also reproduces by budding, and any sexual reproduction involves a swimming sperm (like typical ferns). Duckweeds and Water-fern occur on both standing and slow-moving water and can entirely cover the surfaces of a nutrient-rich pool. Larger free-floating plants include Bladderwort and Frogbit. The former is a predatory plant of mesotrophic water-bodies such as those of Alvecote Pools. It has tiny underwater bladders that trap small invertebrates. Swamp plants such as Bulrush and Reed Sweet-grass sometimes form floating mats.

Submerged and floating aquatics

This is a much larger and varied assemblage, and one that has been seriously impacted by the pollution of watercourses in the twentieth century. Most species are anchored to the water-bed and the majority can cope with both standing and slow-flowing water. Relatively few local species can cope with fast-flowing water. Permanently submerged species include water-milfoils, hornworts, some pondweeds and some water-starworts. These species have waterborne pollen, but much reproduction can take place by simple breakage of a plant into two or more individuals. Various other aquatics have some foliage and/or flowers that rest on the water surface or project a short way above it, at least for part of the year (though these plants may be fully submerged at other times). The most conspicuous of these are the water lilies, of which Warwickshire has two true sorts, plus the unrelated look-alike, Fringed Water-lily. Others include the water-crowfoots (essentially aquatic buttercups), several pondweeds and water-starworts, and the various waterweeds, which are fully submerged except for the tiny flowers they project above the water surface. In water-crowfoots and pondweeds, the floating leaves are very different-looking to the submerged ones (a condition known as 'heterophylly'), which can make identification challenging. Water-soldier, a bromeliad-like native of East Anglia now much spread thanks to garden centres, rises to the surface in summer for flowering, descending to the depths by winter. The now-notorious New Zealand Pigmyweed, a native of Australia and New Zealand, can entirely choke up a water body, growing densely from the surface down to a depth of 3 metres, and even muscling in on damp ground beside the waterbody. It is one of the most seriously invasive aquatics in Britain and an increasing problem in Warwickshire.

Plants of swamp and water margins

There can be much competition in this part of a wetland or water feature. Species such as Arrowhead and Amphibious Bistort try to side-step this by growing as far out as their roots and stems will let them. But the dominant species of swamp in Warwickshire tend to be Bulrush, Reed Sweet-grass, Common Reed, Common Club-rush and pond-sedges, which are densely-growing, often tall plants that can form pure stands around lakes, sheltered river edges and in ponds. They spread by underground rhizomes and can tolerate flooding, drought and periodic pollution. Other species that grow at lower densities in swamp with fairly deep water include water-plantains, Sweet-flag, bur-reeds and, at mesotrophic sites, Bulbous Rush and Bogbean. In shallower water, you can find Yellow Iris, Greater Spearwort, Flowering-rush, watercresses, Fool's-water-cress, Water Mint, Mare's-tail and some more generalised marsh and fen species. There are slight differences in the proportions of such species according to whether you are dealing with a pondside, lakeside, riverside or canalside, and *A Computer-Mapped Flora* gives a good

Examples of aquatic plants

a water-crowfoot

Water-soldier

Bladderwort

Bog Pondweed

Fringed Water-lily

White Water-lily

Examples of aquatic plants

Greater Duckweed

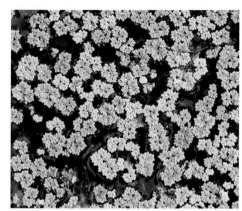

Water Fern

Canadian Waterweed

Common Water-starwort

Amphibious Bistort

Spiked Water-milfoil

Examples of swamp and marsh plants

Yellow Iris

Arrowhead

Sweet Flag

Soft-rush

Greater Pond-sedge

Wild Angelica

Examples of swamp & marsh plants

Bogbean

Great Willowherb

Meadowsweet

Ragged-robin

Marsh-marigold

Common Reed

indication of this from work carried out in the late 1960s (though proportions may have changed since then).

Plants of marsh and fen

Marsh and fen is generally the richest part of a wetland for plants, especially where there is variable depth of water. A high proportion of the plants listed in the species list at the end of this chapter can be found here, with the more frequent ones including Marsh Foxtail, Hard Rush, Soft-rush, Jointed Rush, Reed Canary-grass, Meadowsweet, Greater Bird's-foot-trefoil, Angelica, Bog Stitchwort, Brooklime, Marsh Thistle, Ragged-robin, Marsh-marigold and Hairy Willowherb. Some species prefer less waterlogging then others, with plants like Reed Canary-grass, Great Willowherb and Silverweed often concentrated in the drier parts of a marsh. Woody species can include Grey Willow, Crack-willow, Osier and Alder and these can invade marsh and replace it with carr in the absence of management, especially following drought years. Warwickshire has very little peat fen, but what does exist is generally poor-fen, which is covered in the Heathland and Mire chapter.

Plants of carr

Many wetland species cannot cope with the shade and leaf litter produced by carr, and pond-sedges, Great Horsetail and Stinging Nettle are sometimes the only plants found in the ground layer of more deeply shaded areas. But carr edge or any gaps between shrubs may still hold some interest. At Claybrookes Marsh in Coventry, one of the finest populations of Common Spotted-orchid in the County is associated with the interface of Grey Willow carr and drier grassland.

Part of a spectacular bloom of Common Spotted-orchid in carr at Claybrookes Marsh, Coventry.

Plants of damp riverbanks and ditch-sides

A number of species that cannot necessarily be considered classic wetland plants nevertheless have a high proportion of their Warwickshire populations on damp riverbanks, streamsides or associated with ditches. This may arise because they like the periodically-flooded and enriched soils here or perhaps because the flowing water helps them to propagate themselves by allowing detached fragments to re-root in wet soil. Native species include Butterbur (which forms a particularly impressive stand beside the River Dene at Oxhouse Farm) and Purple-loosestrife. Neophytes include the highly invasive Indian Balsam, and more slowly-spreading Orange Balsam and Giant Hogweed. Stinging Nettle, Hemlock, Hogweed, Common Comfrey and Cow Parsley also tend to thrive in such locations. Trees and shrubs here include Alder, willows (notably White and Crack-willow), Grey Poplar (which has formed large suckering stands beside sections of the River Stour and River Dene) and Black-

Examples of riverside plants

Purple-loosestrife

Orange Balsam

Butterbur

Grey Poplar

Alder

Crack-willow pollard

Black-poplar

A Black-poplar growing beside the River Leam at Jephson Gardens, Leamington Spa (left). The spiral-galls on the leaf-stalk allow easy separation from similar hybrid poplars (below).

poplar. The latter has been widely planted, but older specimens growing randomly near rivers, streams and ditches, may be self-set, either from detached twigs that have rooted, or from fertile seed where a rare female tree occurred near enough to a male to produce fertile wind-blown seed. The valleys of the Alne, Arrow, Blythe and Tame are the best locations for seeing such specimens.

Plants of seepages

This is not a well-recorded habitat, but Great Horsetail is one of the most characteristic species, and Water Mint, Water Figwort and rushes can also be present. A couple of our saline pools support remarkable inland populations of Sea Club-rush.

Losses and gains

Over the course of the twentieth century, there has been a considerable decline in many of the aquatic species of rivers, lakes and canals, largely because of pollution and channelising of watercourses. Our pondweeds and water-crowfoots have been particularly badly affected, also species such as Marsh Arrowgrass, River Water-dropwort, Intermediate Water-starwort and Greater Duckweed. The loss of much old marsh over the past two centuries or more has affected species such as Marsh Valerian, Marsh Speedwell, Fleabane, Tubular Water-dropwort and Common Spike-rush, plants that seem slow to colonise new wetlands. 19 species of water courses and wetlands are now considered extinct in Warwickshire:

- Black Bog-rush *Schoenus nigricans* – last recorded at Coleshill Bog in 1817, typically found in fens, but much declined in central Britain
- Least Bur-reed *Sparganium natans* – last recorded from Arbury Hall and the road from Coton House to Cave's Inn in 1854, typically found at water margins
- Great Fen-sedge *Cladium mariscus* – recorded from Tamworth in 1670
- Marsh Fern *Thelypteris palustris* – last recorded at Sutton Park in 1877, a species of fen, carr and wet woods
- Royal Fern *Osmunda regalis* – formerly at water margins in heathland districts but probably extinct as a native plant, with a few modern records representing escapes or introductions
- Small Fleabane *Pulicaria vulgaris* – last recorded near to Myton Road, Warwick in 1834, it likes winter-flooded areas and is much declined nationally
- Marsh Hawk's-beard *Crepis paludosa* – last recorded near Stratford-upon-Avon in 1960, typically found in wetlands and streamsides in north and west Britain
- Rough Horsetail *Equisetum hyemale* – last recorded at Middleton in 1695, a species most characteristic of river banks in north and west Britain
- Grass-wrack Pondweed *Potamogeton compressus* – last recorded in the Oxford Canal at Napton in 1965, a submerged aquatic of still and slow-flowing water
- Loddon Pondweed *Potamogeton nodosus* – the only local record is for the River Stour at Alderminster in 1856, a very rare submerged aquatic of unpolluted rivers with gravelly bottoms
- Long-stalked Pondweed *Potamogeton praelongus* – last recorded in a Rugby canal in about 1960, a submerged aquatic that likes deep water of unpolluted lakes and slow-flowing rivers

Examples of extinct wetland plants

Rough Horsetail

Small Fleabane

Water-violet

Great Fen-sedge

Royal Fern

Lesser Water-plantain

- Red Pondweed *Potamogeton alpinus* – last recorded in a pool at Newton in 1967, a submerged and floating aquatic that likes still and slow-flowing water where silt accumulates
- Sharp-leaved Pondweed *Potamogeton acutifolius* – last recorded in a canal at Rugby before 1895, a submerged aquatic of unpolluted water
- Marsh Stitchwort *Stellaria palustris* – last recorded at Spernall in 1884, a plant of wetlands and winter-flooded areas
- Narrow-leaved Water-dropwort *Oenanthe silaifolia* – last recorded near Stratford-upon-Avon in 1854, it likes calcareous marsh and wet meadows
- Whorled Water-milfoil *Myriophyllum verticillatum* – last recorded in Rugby in 1955, a submerged aquatic of unpolluted still or slow-moving water
- Tasteless Water-pepper *Persicaria mitis* – recorded from Bourton in 1892, a plant of water margins and damp hollows
- Lesser Water-plantain *Baldellia ranunculoides* – last recorded at Monks Kirby in 1957, likes shallow water margins, widely declined
- Water-violet *Hottonia palustris* – last recorded as a native at Allesley in 1878, though some were introduced to Kingsbury Water Park in 1991

There are also a number of extinct hybrid pondweeds of note (see main Checklist), most notably 'Cadbury's Pondweed' *Potamogeton* x *cadburyae*, a hybrid between Shining Pondweed and Curled Pondweed which was discovered at Seeswood Pool, Nuneaton in 1948 and is unknown from any other site in the world.

But gains and increases are also much in evidence. The relatively recent creation of many new wetlands and waterbodies through quarrying, gravel extraction and the creation of ornamental lakes and pools, has offset historical habitat loss to some extent, allowing many species to increase. Swamp species have done particularly well. The most dramatic increases, however, relate to a relatively small number of invasive neophytes that include New Zealand Pigmyweed, Least Duckweed, Curly Waterweed, Nuttall's Waterweed and Fringed Water-lily. These have escaped from garden ponds and aquatic plant suppliers and are rapidly spreading. Wetland and water margin species on the increase include Indian Balsam, Orange Balsam, Galingale, Giant Hogweed and Grey Poplar.

New Zealand Pigmyweed choking up a pond.

Local wetland and water courses you can visit

Wetlands and waterbodies
- The Alvecote Pools and Pooley Fields complex, near Tamworth SK242045 to SK257040 (partly a Warwickshire Wildlife Trust reserve) – a series of mesotrophic lakes, poor-fen and carr lying north of the Coventry Canal, with Bladderwort, Hemlock Water-dropwort, Sneezewort and Southern Marsh-orchid. The nearby Alvecote Meadows SK245048 (a Warwickshire Wildlife

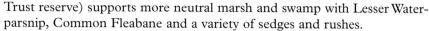

Trust reserve) supports more neutral marsh and swamp with Lesser Water-parsnip, Common Fleabane and a variety of sedges and rushes.

- Brandon Marsh SP386761 (a Warwickshire Wildlife Trust reserve) – a large and complex wetland system in former gravel workings beside the River Avon, with several waterbodies, swamp (including large beds of Common Reed, Reed Sweet-grass and Common Club-rush), marsh and carr.
- Claybrookes Marsh, Coventry SP380769 (a Warwickshire Wildlife Trust reserve) – formerly a railhead serving Binley Colliery, now with fine swamp (including reedbeds), marsh and carr in lower-lying areas, featuring Yellow Loosestrife, Common Spotted-orchid and a variety of sedges.
- Coombe Country Park, near Coventry SP400797 (a Coventry City Council Country Park) – has a large ornamental lake (Coombe Pool) with associated marsh and swamp.
- Eathorpe Marsh SP389687 (a Warwickshire Wildlife Trust reserve) – a small block of marsh and swamp beside the River Leam in Eathorpe village with Reed Sweet-grass, Bulrush, Angelica, Marsh Woundwort, Lesser Water-parsnip and Water Mint.
- Kingsbury Water Park, near Kingsbury SP205960 (a Warwickshire County Council Country Park) and the adjacent Middleton Hall SP193980 – a series of waterbodies and associated wetlands in former gravel workings in the Tame Valley.
- Newbold Quarry, Rugby SP497770 (a Warwickshire Wildlife Trust reserve) – the lake margin features Lesser Bulrush and Spiked Water-milfoil can be found in the lake.
- Stoke Floods, Coventry SP370785 (a Warwickshire Wildlife Trust reserve) – a subsidence pool beside the River Sowe with well-developed swamp and marsh supporting species like Reed Canary-grass, Nodding Bur-marigold and Purple-loosestrife.
- The Swift Valley Nature Reserve, Rugby SP505775 (a Warwickshire Wildlife Trust reserve) features marsh with plants such as Meadowsweet, Angelica, Gipsywort, Water Figwort and Skullcap.
- Ufton Fields SP378615 (a Warwickshire Wildlife Trust reserve) – contains calcareous pools and associated swamp, marsh and carr with much Greater Pond-sedge, Common Reed, Bulrush and Grey Willow.
- Whitacre Heath SP209931 (a Warwickshire Wildlife Trust reserve) – pools, swamp, marshland and carr in former gravel workings beside the River Tame.
- Whitnash Brook Local Nature Reserve near Leamington Spa SP334642 (a Warwickshire Wildlife Trust reserve) – pools, wetlands and the brook featuring beds of Greater Pond-sedge, also Brooklime and Lesser Water-parsnip.
- Wyken Slough, Coventry SP362835 (a Warwickshire Wildlife Trust reserve) – a subsidence pool and associated wetland with beds of Reed Sweet-grass, also Angelica and Gipsywort.

Rivers and streams

- The River Alne at Wootton Wawen and Great Alne.
- The River Arrow Nature Reserve, near Alcester SP086581 (a Warwickshire Wildlife Trust reserve), also the river near Studley Church SP080636 which features natural erosion/deposition and a fine Black-poplar.

- The River Avon at King's Newnham SP448770, Ashow SP312701, Warwick SP288646, Hampton Lucy SP259571, Stratford-upon-Avon SP211558, Welford SP144530 and Bidford SP099517.
- The River Blyth at Brueton Park, Solihull SP160786 and Bradnock's Marsh, near Hampton-in Arden SP216794.
- The Leam Valley Nature Reserve, Leamington Spa SP330658 – features a fine stretch of the River Leam and associated wetland with plants such as Reed Sweet-grass, Yellow Iris, Purple-loosestrife, Flowering-rush, Greater Tussock-sedge and Ragged-robin. Welches Meadow nearby SP325657 also has marshland with Marsh Bedstraw, Angelica and Reed Canary-grass.
- The River Sowe at Stoke Floods SP370785 and Stonebridge Meadows SP348756.
- The Swift Valley Nature Reserve, Rugby SP505775 (a Warwickshire Wildlife Trust reserve).
- The River Tame at Whitacre Heath SP209931 and Kingsbury Water Park SP213962.

Canals
- The Birmingham and Fazeley Canal beside Kingsbury Water Park SP199965.
- The Coventry Canal at Alvecote Pools SK255035 and where it runs through Nuneaton and Coventry.
- The Grand Union Canal where it runs through Shrewley, Hatton, Warwick, Leamington Spa and Long Itchington.
- The Oxford Canal where it runs through Ansty, Brinklow, Rugby, Napton and Wormleighton, plus a disused branch on the Swift Valley Nature Reserve (see above).
- The Stratford-upon-Avon Canal where it runs through Lowsonford, Wootton Wawen, Wilmcote and Stratford-upon-Avon.

Seepages
- Goldicote Cutting near Ettington SP247505 (a Warwickshire Wildlife Trust reserve) – a disused railway cutting with seepage-fed calcareous wetland featuring much Great Horsetail, plus Water Figwort and Common Fleabane.
- Radway Meadow, Edgehill SP366475 (a Warwickshire Wildlife Trust reserve) features a wet flush within old meadows with plants such as Opposite-leaved Golden-saxifrage, Ragged-robin and Water Figwort.

Water courses and wetlands plant list (excluding casuals)

Trees and shrubs (in their wild or naturalised state)
- ✔ Alder *Alnus glutinosa* – especially watersides, also wet woodland
- ✘ Crack-willow *Salix fragilis* – wetlands and watersides where it is frequently pollarded, an archaeophyte
- ✘ Osier *Salix viminalis* – wetlands, watersides and osier-beds, an archaeophyte
- ✔ Black-poplar *Populus nigra* ssp. *betulifolia* – native or naturalised beside streams, rivers and ditches (also widely planted elsewhere)

✗ Grey Poplar *Populus canescens* – naturalised beside various streams and rivers, sometimes forming woodland strips, an increasing neophyte, (also widely planted elsewhere)

✗ Almond Willow *Salix triandra* – wetlands, watersides and osier-beds, an archaeophyte

✔ Bay Willow *Salix pentandra* – wetlands and watersides, rare

✔ Eared Willow *Salix aurita* – wetlands and watersides, also in drier locations, rare

✔ Grey Willow *Salix cinerea* – the greater part of its local population is associated with wetlands, especially on formerly disturbed ground such as quarries and gravel pits; two subspecies are present, the frequent ssp. *oleifolia* and the scarce ssp. *cinerea*

✔ Purple Willow *Salix purpurea* – wetlands and watersides

✗ White Willow *Salix alba* – watersides and also ditched hedgerows where it is frequently pollarded, an archaeophyte

Grasses, sedges and rushes

✔ Bladder-sedge *Carex vesicaria* – wetlands and watersides, rare

✔ Reed Canary-grass *Phalaris arundinacea* – watersides and other marshy areas

✔ Bristle Club-rush *Isolepis setacea* – watersides and other wet places, preferring acidic areas

✔ Common Club-rush *Schoenoplectus lacustris* – an emergent of riverside and lakeside swamp

✔ Grey Club-rush *Schoenoplectus tabernaemontani* – an emergent of riverside and lakeside swamp, increasing

✔ Sea Club-rush *Bolboschoenus maritimus* – an emergent of saline swamp associated with Lias springs, rare

✔ Wood Club-rush *Scirpus sylvaticus* – wetlands and watersides, declining

✔ Flat-sedge *Blysmus compressus* – watersides, rare and declining

✔ False Fox-sedge *Carex otrubae* – wetlands and watersides

✔ Marsh Foxtail *Alopecurus geniculatus* – wetlands and watersides

✔ Orange Foxtail *Alopecurus aequalis* – wetlands, especially on drying mud

✗ Galingale *Cyperus longus* – a rare native of the coast, but spreading throughout wetlands inland (first reported in Warwickshire in 1973)

✔ Tufted Hair-grass *Deschampsia cespitosa* – also wet grassland

✔ Lesser Pond-sedge *Carex acutiformis* – an emergent of swamp, watersides, also wet woodland

✔ Greater Pond-sedge *Carex riparia* – an emergent that often dominates swamp and watersides, also frequent in carr and wet woodland

✔ Common Reed *Phragmites australis* – typically an emergent that often dominates riverside and lakeside swamp, also some ditches and sometimes drier riverbanks

✔ Blunt-flowered Rush *Juncus subnodulosus* – marshes and watersides

✔ Bulbous Rush *Juncus bulbosus* – acidic wetlands and mesotrophic shallow water, often an emergent

✔ Compact Rush *Juncus conglomeratus* – wetlands, and also damp grassland

✔ Hard Rush *Juncus inflexus* – various wetlands, especially on clays

✔ Jointed Rush *Juncus articulatus* – various wetland types

✔ Round-fruited Rush *Juncus compressus* – marshes, also wet grassland
✔ Sharp-flowered Rush *Juncus acutiflorus* – watersides and marshes
✔ Slender Rush *Juncus tenuis* – a neophyte, watersides and damp areas, increasing
✔ Toad Rush *Juncus bufonius* – a species complex, associated with various wet habitats
✔ A sedge *Carex viridula* – various wet habitats, the subspecies *brachyrrhyncha* is probably extinct here
✔ Bottle Sedge *Carex rostrata* – an emergent of swamp and watersides, rare
✔ Brown Sedge *Carex disticha* – wetlands and watersides
✔ Carnation Sedge *Carex panicea* – wetlands and damp grassland
✔ Common Sedge *Carex nigra* – various wetlands
✔ Cyperus Sedge *Carex pseudocyperus* – an emergent of swamp and watersides
✔ Distant Sedge *Carex distans* – wetlands, also wet grassland, rare
✔ Elongated Sedge *Carex elongata* – rare
✔ Hairy Sedge *Carex hirta* – various wetlands, also wet grassland
✔ Pale Sedge *Carex pallescens* – especially watersides
✔ Remote Sedge *Carex remota* – water margins, also wet woodland
✔ Tawny Sedge *Carex hostiana* – various wetlands, rare
✔ Purple Small-reed *Calamagrostis canescens* – wetlands and carr, rare
✔ Soft-rush *Juncus effusus* – various wetland types
✔ Common Spike-rush *Eleocharis palustris* – swamp and watersides, declining
✔ Needle Spike-rush *Eleocharis acicularis* – swamp and watersides, rare
✔ Slender Spike-rush *Eleocharis uniglumis* – marshes, rare
✔ Floating Sweet-grass *Glyceria fluitans* – a floating aquatic of standing and slow-flowing water and watersides, sometimes forming floating rafts
✔ Plicate Sweet-grass *Glyceria notata* – watersides, ditches etc
✔ Reed Sweet-grass *Glyceria maxima* – an emergent that often dominates riverside and lakeside swamp and ponds, sometimes forming floating rafts
✔ Small Sweet-grass *Glyceria declinata* – watersides and other marshy areas
✔ Slender Tufted-sedge *Carex acuta* – wetlands and watersides
✔ Greater Tussock-sedge *Carex paniculata* – an emergent of swamp, carr, also wet woodland
✔ Lesser Tussock-sedge *Carex diandra* – poor-fen, also mire, rare
✔ Whorl-grass *Catabrosa aquatica* – an emergent and floating aquatic of standing and flowing water, rare

Other flowering plants
✔ Wild Angelica *Angelica sylvestris* – wetlands, watersides, also wet woodland
✔ Marsh Arrowgrass *Triglochin palustre* – wetlands, declining
✔ Arrowhead *Sagittaria sagittaria* – an emergent aquatic of standing and flowing water
✘ Indian Balsam *Impatiens glandulifera* – river and streambanks, also wet woodland, a highly invasive and increasing neophyte
✘ Orange Balsam *Impatiens capensis* – watersides, an increasing neophyte
✔ Fen Bedstraw *Galium uliginosum* – wetlands and watersides

✔ Common Marsh-bedstraw *Galium palustre* – wetlands and watersides

✘ Beggarticks *Bidens frondosa* – damp ground, also disturbed ground, an increasing neophyte,

✔ Greater Bird's-foot-trefoil *Lotus pedunculatus* – wetlands, ditches and watersides

✔ Amphibious Bistort *Persicaria amphibia* – a floating aquatic and emergent of standing and slow-flowing water (but with a terrestrial form that occurs on roadsides, disturbed ground etc.)

✔ Large Bitter-cress *Cardamine amara* – wetlands and watersides, also wet woodland

✔ Wavy Bitter-cress *Cardamine flexuosa* – wetlands and watersides

✔ Bittersweet *Solanum dulcamara* – marshes, also hedgerows and woodland

✔ Bladderwort *Utricularia australis* – a free-floating aquatic of standing and slow-flowing water

✔ Bogbean *Menyanthes trifoliata* – an emergent of watersides and shallow water, especially associated with mire and mesotrophic water in Warwickshire, rare

✔ Brooklime *Veronica beccabunga* – an emergent of shallow standing and flowing water

✔ Brookweed *Samolus valerandi* – wetlands and watersides, especially in calcareous districts, rare

✔ Bulrush *Typha latifolia* – an emergent that often dominates watersides and swamp, sometimes forming floating mats, fairly pollution-tolerant

✔ Lesser Bulrush *Typha angustifolia* – an emergent of watersides and swamps, sometimes forming floating mats, not pollution tolerant

✔ Nodding Bur-marigold *Bidens cernua* – wetlands and watersides

✔ Trifid Bur-marigold *Bidens tripartita* – wetlands and watersides (increasing beside canals)

✔ Branched Bur-reed *Sparganium erectum* – an emergent of swamp and river margins

✔ Unbranched Bur-reed *Sparganium emersum* – an emergent of swamp and river margins that prefers deeper water than the previous species

✔ Butterbur *Petasites hybridus* – mostly watersides and ditches, also wet woodland

✘ Giant Butterbur *Petasites japonicus* – riversides and other damp places, a neophyte

✔ Celery-leaved Buttercup *Ranunculus sceleratus* – wetlands and watersides

✔ Greater Chickweed *Stellaria neglecta* – wetlands and watersides

✔ Water Chickweed *Myosoton aquaticum* – wetlands and other damp places

✔ Marsh Cinquefoil *Potentilla palustris* – watersides and shallow water, also mire, rare

✔ Common Comfrey *Symphytum officinale* – especially watersides and ditches

✔ Creeping-jenny *Lysimachia nummularia* – wetlands and other damp areas

✔ Ivy-leaved Crowfoot *Ranunculus hederaceus* – a floating aquatic of small water bodies, sheltered river sections, scarce and declining

✔ Cuckooflower *Cardamine pratensis* – wetlands, also damp grassland

✔ Clustered Dock *Rumex conglomeratus* – watersides and wet areas

✔ Golden Dock *Rumex maritimus* – watersides and wet areas, increasing

✔ Water Dock *Rumex hydrolapathum* – an emergent of watersides and swamp

✔ Common Duckweed *Lemna minor* – a free-floating aquatic of still or slow-flowing water

✔ Fat Duckweed *Lemna gibba* – a free-floating aquatic of still or slow-flowing water

✔ Greater Duckweed *Spirodela polyrhiza* – a free-floating aquatic of standing and slow-flowing water, rare and declining

✔ Ivy-leaved Duckweed *Lemna trisulca* – a free-floating aquatic of still and slow-flowing water, declining

✘ Least Duckweed *Lemna minor* – a free-floating aquatic of still and slow-flowing water, a recently-arrived and increasing neophyte, highly invasive

✔ Green Figwort *Scrophularia umbrosa* – especially watersides, rare

✔ Water Figwort *Scrophularia auriculata* – watersides and wetlands

✔ Common Fleabane *Pulicaria dysenterica* – wetlands, ditches and watersides, declining

✔ Flowering-rush *Butomus umbellatus* – an emergent of swamp and watersides

✔ Fool's-water-cress *Apium nodiflorum* – a low-growing emergent of shallow water and watersides

✔ Creeping Forget-me-not *Myosotis secunda* – watersides of peaty acidic streams and pools, also mire, rare

✔ Tufted Forget-me-not *Myosotis laxa* – wetlands, watersides and other wet areas

✔ Water Forget-me-not *Myosotis scorpioides* – an emergent of swamp and watersides

✔ Gipsywort *Lycopus europaeus* – wetland and watersides

✔ Marsh Helleborine *Epipactis palustris* – wetlands, rare

✔ Hemlock *Conium maculatum* – especially riversides and enriched wetlands, sometimes in drier places

✔ Hemp-agrimony *Eupatorium cannabinum* – mostly wetlands and watersides, also wet woodland and occasionally dry locations

✘ Giant Hogweed *Heracleum mantegazzianum* – an increasing neophyte, mostly found on the banks of streams and rivers

✔ Rigid Hornwort *Ceratophyllum demersum* – a submerged aquatic of water bodies and slow-flowing water

✔ Soft Hornwort *Ceratophyllum submersum* – a submerged aquatic of water bodies, rare

✔ Yellow Iris *Iris pseudacorus* – an emergent of swamp and watersides

✔ Yellow Loosestrife *Lysimachia vulgaris* – fen and watersides

✔ Mare's-tail *Hippuris vulgaris* – an emergent of swamp and watersides

✔ Marsh-marigold *Caltha palustris* – wetlands, watersides and carr

✔ Early Marsh-orchid *Dactylorhiza incarnata* – wetlands and damp grassland, very rare

✔ Southern Marsh-orchid *Dactylorhiza praetermissa* – wetlands and other damp areas

✔ Lesser Marshwort *Apium inundatum* – a submerged and floating aquatic of shallow standing and flowing water, rare (Seeswood Pool, 1984)

✔ Common Meadow-rue *Thalictrum flavum* – wetlands and watersides, scarce

✘ Lesser Meadow-rue *Thalictrum minus* – a native, but not to Warwickshire, where it is a garden escape that occasionally naturalises

✔ Meadowsweet *Filipendula ulmaria* – wetlands, ditches and damp areas
✔ Water Mint *Mentha aquatica* – an emergent of wetlands and watersides
✘ Monkeyflower *Mimulus guttatus* – watersides and wet areas, a neophyte
✘ Monk's-hood *Aconitum napellus* – watersides and other damp places, probably not a native of Warwickshire where very rare (only Cherington)
✔ Mudwort *Limosella aquatica* – muddy watersides, rare
✘ Parrot's-feather *Myriophyllum aquaticum* – a rare submerged aquatic of shallow water and watersides, a neophyte
✔ Pennyroyal *Mentha pulegium* – various wet and damp places, rare in its wild state but increasing as an alien
✘ New Zealand Pigmyweed *Crassula helmsii* – a highly invasive submerged and floating aquatic neophyte of standing water, increasing
✔ Blunt-leaved Pondweed *Potamogeton obtusifolius* – a submerged aquatic of standing water, rare
✔ Bog Pondweed *Potamogeton polygonifolius* – a submerged and floating aquatic of acidic water bodies, also boggy pools in mire, rare
✔ Broad-leaved Pondweed *Potamogeton natans* – a submerged and floating aquatic of standing and slow-flowing water
✔ Curled Pondweed *Potamogeton crispus* – a submerged aquatic of still and slow-flowing water
✔ Fennel Pondweed *Potamogeton pectinatus* – a submerged aquatic of still or slow-flowing water, pollution-tolerant
✔ Flat-stalked Pondweed *Potamogeton friesi* – a submerged aquatic of still or slow-flowing water, rare and declining
✔ Hairlike Pondweed *Potamogeton trichoides* – a submerged aquatic of still and slow- flowing water, rare
✔ Horned Pondweed *Zannichellia palustris* – a submerged aquatic of unpolluted standing and flowing water, declining
✔ Lesser Pondweed *Potamogeton pusillus* – a submerged aquatic of still and slow-flowing water, declining
✔ Opposite-leaved Pondweed *Groenlandia densa* – a submerged aquatic of still and flowing unpolluted water, rare and declining
✔ Perfoliate Pondweed *Potamogeton perfoliatus* – a submerged aquatic, typically of larger waterbodies, declining
✔ Shining Pondweed *Potamogeton lucens* – a submerged aquatic of standing and slow-flowing calcareous and unpolluted water, declining
✔ Small Pondweed *Potamogeton berchtoldii* – a submerged aquatic of still and slow-flowing water, rare
✔ Purple-loosestrife *Lythrum salicaria* – wetlands and watersides
✔ Ragged-robin *Lychnis flos-cuculi* – wetlands and other damp areas
✔ Marsh Ragwort *Senecio aquaticus* – wetlands
✔ Shoreweed *Littorella uniflora* – an aquatic and marginal, mainly of standing acidic water, especially associated with mire and mesotrophic water in Warwickshire, rare
✔ Skullcap *Scutellaria galericulata* – wetlands, also wet woodland
✔ Greater Spearwort *Ranunculus lingua* – an emergent of wetlands and watersides

✔ Lesser Spearwort *Ranunculus flammula* – an emergent of wetlands and watersides, generally avoiding calcareous sites

✔ Marsh Speedwell *Veronica scutellata* – an emergent of wetlands and watersides, rare and declining

✔ Square-stemmed St John's-wort *Hypericum tetrapterum* – wetlands and watersides

✔ Bog Stitchwort *Stellaria alsine* – wetlands and watersides

✘ Sweet-flag *Acorus calamus* – an emergent of swamp and watersides, a neophyte

✔ Marsh Thistle *Cirsium palustre* – wetlands of various types, also damp grassland

✔ Common Valerian *Valeriana officinalis* – wetlands, watersides, ditches etc

✔ Marsh Valerian *Valerian dioica* – wetlands, declining

✔ Water-cress *Rorippa nasturtium-aquaticum* – a low-growing emergent of watersides and shallow water

✔ Narrow-fruited Water-cress *Rorippa microphylla* – a low-growing emergent of watersides

✔ Common Water-crowfoot *Ranunculus aquatilis* – a submerged and floating aquatic of standing and flowing water

✔ Fan-leaved Water-crowfoot *Ranunculus circinatus* – a mostly submerged aquatic of standing and slow-flowing water, rare and declining

✔ Pond Water-crowfoot *Ranunculus peltatus* – a submerged and floating aquatic of standing and flowing water, scarce

✔ River Water-crowfoot *Ranunculus fluitans* – a mostly submerged aquatic of flowing water, rare

✔ Stream Water-crowfoot *Ranunculus penicillatus* – a mostly submerged aquatic of flowing water, scarce

✔ Thread-leaved Water-crowfoot *Ranunculus trichophyllus* – a submerged and floating aquatic of pools in calcareous areas

✔ Fine-leaved Water-dropwort *Oenanthe aquatica* – an emergent of standing or slow-flowing water, rare

✔ Hemlock Water-dropwort *Oenanthe crocata* – wetlands and watersides; also wet woodland

✔ Parsley Water-dropwort *Oenanthe lachenalii* – wetlands, rare

✔ River Water-dropwort *Oenanthe fluviatilis* – an emergent of standing and flowing water, rare and declining

✔ Tubular Water-dropwort *Oenanthe fistulosa* – typically an emergent of wetlands and watersides, declining

✘ Fringed Water-lily *Nymphoides peltata* – a floating aquatic of standing and slow-flowing water, a native but not of Warwickshire where an increasing garden escape

✔ White Water-lily *Nymphaea alba* – a floating aquatic of water bodies and slow-flowing water

✔ Yellow Water-lily *Nuphar lutea* – a floating aquatic of water bodies and slow-flowing water

✔ Spiked Water-milfoil *Myriophyllum spicatum* – a submerged aquatic of standing and slow-flowing water

✔ Lesser Water-parsnip *Berula erecta* – typically an emergent of standing and flowing water, sometimes in marsh

✔ Water-pepper *Persicaria hydropiper* – watersides and other wet areas
✔ Small Water-pepper *Persicaria minor* – watersides and other marshy areas, Sutton Park only (but not a bog or mire specialist)
✔ Water-plantain *Alisma plantago-aquatica* – an emergent of still and slow-moving water and watersides
✔ Narrow-leaved Water-plantain *Alisma lanceolatum* – an emergent of still and slow-moving water and watersides
✘ Water-soldier *Stratiodes aloides* – a submerged or free-floating aquatic of unpolluted standing water, a native but not of Warwickshire, where scarce but increasing
✔ Blue Water-speedwell *Veronica anagallis-aquatica* – an emergent of shallow standing and flowing water, rare and declining
✔ Pink Water-speedwell *Veronica catenata* – an emergent of shallow standing and flowing water
✔ Autumnal Water-starwort *Callitriche hermaphroditica* – a submerged aquatic of standing water, rare
✔ Blunt-fruited Water-starwort *Callitriche obtusangula* – a submerged and floating aquatic of standing and slow-flowing water
✔ Common Water-starwort *Callitriche stagnalis* – a submerged aquatic of standing water, also watersides
✔ Intermediate Water-starwort *Callitriche hamulata* – a submerged and floating aquatic of still and flowing water, rare and declining
✔ Pedunculate Water-starwort *Callitriche brutia* – a submerged and floating aquatic, especially in temporary pools, rare
✔ Various-leaved Water-starwort *Callitriche platycarpa* – a submerged and floating aquatic of standing water, rare
✔ Water-violet *Hottonia palustris* – a submerged and floating aquatic of shallow standing water, rare
✘ Canadian Waterweed *Elodea canadensis* – a submerged aquatic of waterbodies, a declining neophyte
✘ Curly Waterweed *Lagarosiphon major* – a submerged aquatic neophyte of waterbodies, increasing
✘ Nuttall's Waterweed *Elodea nuttallii* – a submerged aquatic neophyte of waterbodies, increasing
✔ Great Willowherb *Epilobium hirsutum* – wetlands and watersides, sometimes drier places
✔ Hoary Willowherb *Epilobium parviflorum* – wetlands and watersides, sometimes drier places
✔ Marsh Willowherb *Epilobium palustre* – wetlands, preferring more acidic sites including mire, declining?
✔ Pale Willowherb *Epilobium roseum* – typically wetlands and watersides
✔ Short-fruited Willowherb *Epilobium obscurum* – wetlands and watersides, sometimes drier places
✔ Winter-cress *Barbarea vulgaris* – wetlands and watersides, sometimes drier places
✔ Marsh Woundwort *Stachys palustris* – wetlands and watersides

✔ Creeping Yellow-cress *Rorippa sylvestris* – watersides and damp ground
✔ Great Yellow-cress *Rorippa amphibia* – an emergent of watersides and swamp
✔ Marsh Yellow-cress *Rorippa palustris* – watersides and wet mud

Ferns and horsetails

✘ Water Fern *Azolla filiculoides* – a free-floating aquatic of water bodies and sluggish river sections, a neophyte
✔ Great Horsetail *Equisetum telmateia* – especially flushes and seepages, including those in carr and wet woodland
✔ Marsh Horsetail *Equisetum palustre* – wetlands and watersides
✔ Water Horsetail *Equisetum fluviatile* – an emergent that grows in a variety of wetlands and water bodies

Chapter 9

Arable Land

Land used primarily for the cultivation of herbaceous crops such as cereals and vegetables

This is land typically subject to annual ploughing, annual re-seeding with a chosen crop species, regular input of fertiliser and herbicide (except where organic) and annual harvesting. The density and structure of the crop varies between crop species, and may be very dense (e.g. grains and Oil-seed Rape) or relatively sparse (e.g. Onion). Irrigation and pesticide-usage is also common and soils may be manipulated to reduce soil acidity, which is why you now find crops growing in parts of north and west Warwickshire that would have been almost impossible for medieval farmers to cultivate there. Most arable land is subject to a fallow period every few years (a year in which no crops are grown) or a 'break' whereby a physiologically different crop is inserted into the main cropping plan. Both approaches are designed to break the cycle of weeds, pests and diseases associated with crops. In 2002 the Habitat Biodiversity Audit recorded 57,000 hectares of modern Warwickshire under cereal and a further 77,000 hectares under other crops, basically about half of the County's land surface.

Poppies in a Nebsworth wheat field.

Rape (left) and Wheat (right), the dominant arable crops in Warwickshire.

Whilst modern farming practices attempt to buffer extremes of soil condition, there remains a fair deal of variation in arable land, depending on the pH of the soil, whether it has high content of sand, lime or clay, the degree of waterlogging or drying, the aspect of the land (i.e. whether it is south-facing or north-facing) and the disposition of the farmer towards wildlife conservation and agri-environment funding. This variation, plus the choice of crop species, can have a strong influence on the so-called 'arable weeds' present. Typical Warwickshire crops today include Wheat, Barley, Oil-seed Rape and Maize. Onions, Broad Bean, Flax and Borage can also be locally frequent, and energy crops such as Miscanthus are gaining popularity. Silage grassland can also be considered here as it is often grown intensively like a cereal crop.

The dominant habitat of arable farmland is the crop-growing part of the field. This initially consists of bare newly ploughed and fertilised soil, followed by the growing and maturing crop, and finally by the stubble that remains. Traditionally, this was a major habitat for arable weeds, especially the edges of the crop where competition from the crop was slightly less. Under modern farming regimes opportunities for arable plants now mainly exist within uncultivated field margins, headlands, and fallow areas. Such areas can remain relatively undisturbed for several months if not years and may escape ploughing, herbicide usage and fertiliser usage, especially if managed as part of an agri-environment agreement.

There are several dozen plants nationally that can be regarded as specialists of arable land and these are of high conservation concern. Of the 30 vascular plant species showing the greatest declines across Britain during the twentieth century, no fewer than 18 are characteristic of arable and other cultivated ground (Byfield & Wilson, 2005).

The history of Warwickshire's arable farmland

The history of arable farming in Warwickshire is a mystery-shrouded one stretching back some five to six thousand years. Arable farming evolved in various parts of the world on several independent occasions about ten thousand years ago. That which arose in the Middle-east's Fertile Crescent (perhaps in the Jericho area) was mostly based on Wheat (a series of hybrids involving *Triticum* and *Aegilops* grasses) and Barley. It gradually spread across Europe, West Asia and North Africa, becoming

Examples of some early crop species

Barley

Wheat

Flax

Broad Bean

adapted to the widely differing climatic and soil conditions of this vast and varied area (see Ammerman & Cavalli-Sforza, 1971), and evidence for British arable activity by 5000BC exists at various localities.

The Neolithic period

The first evidence of arable farming in Warwickshire has been dated back to about 3000BC and is associated with the Middle Neolithic period. The Neolithic period marks a gradual transition from a nomadic hunter-gatherer lifestyle to a more settled one that involved forest clearance, the keeping of livestock such as sheep and cattle, and the cultivation of grains and certain other crops. Whether it involved a mass influx of new people into Britain or simply the spread of new farming methods within indigenous people (or a balance of the two) is unclear. That early arable farming would have been very different to what we see today, probably involving simple tilling and hand-sowing of relatively small patches of land that could only be used for short periods before the soil became depleted. The Avon Valley and Cotswolds appear to have been some of the first areas of Warwickshire to host arable farming, the loamy, relatively well-drained and fertile soils being more easily cultivated.

Archaeological checking of pollen, seeds and plant remains from the Neolithic period suggests that species like Common Poppy, Common Fumitory, Charlock, Wild Radish, Penny-cress, Corn Spurrey, Smooth Tare, Pale Persicaria, Small Nettle, Ivy-leaved Speedwell and Field Madder were amongst the first British arable weeds. Some of these species are likely to have been natives that were able to move into arable settings from naturally disturbed areas of grassland, woodland or coastal habitat (pollen or seed evidence for their presence in Britain from pre-Neolithic times provides the strongest evidence for this). But others seem to represent some of our first archaeophytes. They would most probably have been accidentally introduced from Europe with imported grains, goods and on clothing. Some were exploited for their medicinal properties (e.g. poppies) or as a source of dye (Field Madder). Evidence for Neolithic arable weeds in Warwickshire is very poor, though remains of Emmer (a primitive form of Wheat) and Barley give some indication of what the crops were.

The Bronze Age, Iron Age and Romano-British period

The period stretching from about 2000BC to 410AD saw more intensive arable farming in Warwickshire's Feldon, Dunsmore and Avon Valley zones. It now involved the use of animal-drawn ploughs that permitted land to be cultivated more rapidly and increased the productivity of that land. Farming communities had become more complex and new crops were added to the portfolio, including Hemp, Flax and Rye during the Iron Age (700BC to 43AD) and Opium Poppy, Lentil, Broad Bean and Pea by the Romans. Each arable crop is likely to have had its own particular weed assemblage. Rye and Flax seem to have been especially weedy crops. Regular importation of seed batches from Europe contaminated by European arable weeds would have supplied Britain with an ever-increasing number of new archaeophytes. Major arable weeds recorded during this period nationally include Corn Marigold, Corn Gromwell, Scarlet Pimpernel, Darnel, Corncockle, Corn Buttercup and Corn

Examples of some early arable weeds, most now much declined

Corn Gromwell

Corn Buttercup

Sharp-leaved Fluellen

Cornflower

Pale Persicaria

Corn Marigold

Examples of some early arable weeds, most now much declined

Field Madder

a fumitory

Small Nettle

Shepherd's-needle

Night-scented Catchfly

Prickly Poppy

Chamomile. New species included Broad-fruited Cornsalad, Shepherd's-needle, Prickly Poppy and Night-flowering Catchfly. Corncockle, Rye Brome and Cornflower were probably introduced with imported Flax seed. Some of the weeds were themselves edible – their seeds could be made into a form of unleavened bread. Most of these weed species have now been identified from local archaeological surveys at places like Church Lawford, Long Itchington, Tiddington and Billesley, though the data available for Warwickshire is relatively poor compared with many counties. The Arden zone of Warwickshire, with its poorer soils, appears to have remained extensively wooded during this period, with any farming predominantly pastoral utilising the various heaths and other clearings there. A strong economic interplay had developed between the non-wooded and largely arable parts of Warwickshire and the Arden, the latter being a better source of timber, charcoal, rough pasture and game, and this persisted for many centuries.

The Anglo-Saxon and medieval periods

Much farmland was abandoned during the dark ages that followed the end of the Romano-British period. The Saxon open field system of farming (*strip farming*) seems to have become established in the eighth and ninth centuries. This involved the dividing of land into ploughed units known as *strips*, typically with a three-year rotation of crops within a strip, involving spring-sown Barley in one year, winter-sown Wheat in another, plus one fallow year to allow the soil to recover. It is the ploughing from this period that has resulted in the ridge-and-furrow earth patterns that so characterise parts of south and east Warwickshire. By the medieval period, new forms of Wheat were being grown, Rye, Oat, Flax and Hemp were popular, and arable weeds continued to flourish. The most frequent ones nationally included Rye Brome, Scented Mayweed, Wild Radish, Charlock, Corncockle, Corn Marigold, Darnel, Cleavers, thistles, docks, nettles and various vetches. Local archaeological surveys at sites such as Warwick Castle Park, Cawston and Dunchurch have recorded most of these. Early legislation to bring about control of certain weeds was introduced from the twelfth century and published reference to specific weed species increases, including occasional references to what might well be Warwickshire's arable weeds within the works of Shakespeare. It is hard for us today to appreciate the extent to which certain arable weeds reduced the yield of crops and contributed to hardship in those times. Farming was still very simple and labour-intensive by today's standards with relatively little change between Romano-British times and the late medieval period.

Ridge-and-furrow such as this fine example near Halford represents the old plough marks associated with strip farming and is often much older than the hedges and modern field boundaries now associated with it.

The first agricultural revolution

The eighteenth century saw the introduction of horse-drawn seed drills and harrows, threshing machines, improved ploughs and new crop rotations. The Parliamentary Enclosure Acts of the eighteenth and early nineteenth centuries bought about the eviction of peasant farmers and the reorganisation of their open field systems and commons into large regular fields bounded by new hedges (the birth of what Oliver Rackham terms 'planned countryside'). Enclosure enabled the land to be cultivated in new ways with far greater productivity for the ever-increasing populations of towns and cities. The Corn Laws of 1773 and 1815 encouraged the expansion of arable land onto grassland. Arable weeds were still common and those noted by William Pitt as being especially troublesome in neighbouring Leicestershire in 1809 included Common Couch, Black Bent, Creeping and Spear Thistle, Chickweed, Ivy-leaved Speedwell, Fat-hen, Knotgrass, Shepherd's-purse, Black Mustard, Charlock, Wild Radish, Corn Chamomile, Corn Marigold, Corn Buttercup and sowthistles. By the latter part of the nineteenth century, artificial nitrogen-based fertilizer was being used to supplement manure, and steam power was starting to mechanise activities such as ploughing.

The second agricultural revolution

This was a response to Britain's need to become self-sufficient following World War II. The impact on arable weeds and farmland wildlife generally has been devastating. The 1947 Agricultural Act and the Common Agricultural Policy that we entered into in 1973 promoted highly efficient and mechanised farming involving increased use of pesticides, herbicides, non-traditional or genetically-modified crops, new sowing and harvesting schedules, also improved drainage, widespread hedge removal, stubble-burning and an increasing shift towards expansive crop monocultures in featureless settings. Not only had it now become more difficult for arable weeds to physically cope with arable farmland, but the rapidly increasing soil-fertility of arable land rendered soils unsuitable for many species. Modern threshing processes and liberal use of herbicides started to result in much cleaner harvesting of cereals. This meant that when grains were stored and re-sown they lacked the contaminating seeds of arable weeds that were previously present. Arable weeds thus stopped being re-introduced to the arable landscape or spread around the countryside as they used to be. As a consequence of all these recent changes, specialised arable weeds have declined nationally and locally more than any other group of plants in the last sixty years.

Crop spraying. Herbicides and pesticides both radically reduce the biodiversity of arable land.

A third agricultural revolution?

This book coincides with an awareness of what we have lost and a desire to undo some of the damage. Government-funded agri-environment schemes, underpinned by

Redshank thriving along an uncultivated field margin at Haseley.

the UK Biodiversity Action Plan process, are attempting to restore more favourable conditions for arable weeds, and botanical surveys by the BSBI are helping to monitor the success (or otherwise) of these. Warwickshire has contributed actively to all these opportunities and challenges. Set-aside was introduced by the European Union in 1992 to curb over-production and had some benefits for wild plants (though much was sprayed with herbicide) but in 2007 global wheat shortages saw it withdrawn. However, the growing organic food market is resulting in increasing areas of herbicide-free arable land, and stubble burning (which tended to kill off arable weeds) has now ceased. So as arable weed conservation loses out on one front it advances on another. It is unclear at the time of writing quite what the future holds, though scarce arable weeds and field margins are both subject to regularly-reviewed action plans in the Local Biodiversity Action Plan for our area, and many local farms receive agri-environment funding specifically targeted at the needs of arable plants.

The plants of arable land
Approximately 100 native or naturalised plant species in Warwickshire are strongly or entirely associated with arable farmland (see plant list at end of chapter) and the vast majority of these are archaeophytes and neophytes, with relatively few natives. About half of these can be considered specialist arable weeds i.e. species that rarely grow in any other habitat in Britain. Other plants more characteristic of disturbed ground, grassland and tall herb can also occur at field margins, on fallow land, and sometimes within the crop, especially if there is a nearby seed source. This is why the 1971 *A Computer-Mapped Flora* recorded a total of 351 species from this habitat in the 1950s and 1960s. Short-lived populations of casuals are also frequent and include the crops themselves e.g. Wheat, Barley, Oats, Rape, Pea, Borage and Radish, which can persist for several years following cropping.

Arable weed life cycles
Most true arable weeds are rather specialised opportunists that need to fit their growth cycle into that of the crop they are growing within, and need to have survival

strategies to cope with periods lacking suitable growth conditions. About 80% of Warwickshire's arable weeds are annuals and species such as Shepherd's-purse and Groundsel can produce seeds as quickly as six weeks after germination. All species can over-winter as seed, and most are programmed so that a proportion of the seed will remain dormant for long periods and help to form a persistent seed bank that gives a better chance of long-term survival within an area (hence the old adage "*one years' seeding, seven years weeding*"). However, this is not the case with some of our more declined species such as Corncockle, Corn Marigold, Shepherd's-needle and Gold-of-pleasure, which have very short-lived seeds. The seeds of Common Poppy are able to survive for several centuries and this species produces an average of 16,500 seeds per plant. Not surprisingly it has coped quite well with all the changes. Some of the least successful arable weeds, such as Thorow-wax, are characterised by relatively low seed production. The size of the seed has also influenced the success of certain species in the past. Where the seed is a similar size and weight to that of the crop within which it is growing (e.g. Corncockle and Rye), old-fashioned threshing and winnowing failed to separate them efficiently, which meant that when the crop was re-sown, the weed was re-sown along with it.

Most species have fairly specific germination periods, typically either late autumn-early winter (e.g. Corn Cleavers, Corn Buttercup and Spreading Hedge-parsley) or spring (e.g. Weasel's-snout, Narrow-fruited Corn-salad and fluellens). This can dictate which crops best suit a given arable weed, though both strategies tend to fall foul of the autumn drilling and spring harvesting associated with some modern crops. Autumn crop-sowing also tends to involve high levels of nitrogen and herbicide usage which is bad news for most arable weeds. Flowering periods vary greatly, with species like Corn Buttercup, Shepherd's-needle and Spreading Hedge-parsley flowering relatively early (May or June), whilst others such as Night-flowering Catchfly and the two fluellens typically flower in the post-harvest stubble of spring-sown crops.

Species such as Black-grass, Barren Brome and Cleavers still manage to thrive deep within modern arable crops due to having life cycles that fit in well with modern crop cycles plus a tolerance to nitrogen-rich soils. The popularity of wildflower seed mixtures and bird seed means that some arable weeds are now turning up in new habitats as short-lived casuals e.g. Corn Marigold, Cornflower and Corncockle, though it is important to distinguish such populations from more ancient ones associated with arable land.

The effects of soil conditions on local arable weeds

Many arable weeds grow on a range of soil types, but a significant proportion have clear preferences, and this can result in distinct assemblages associated with the calcareous soils of south and east Warwickshire, the neutral or acidic soils of the central and Arden zone, or the well-drained alluvial soils of river valleys such as the Avon, Stour and Dene. Calcicoles include Round-leaved Fluellen, Sharp-leaved Fluellen, Dense-flowered Fumitory, Spreading Hedge-parsley, Corn Gromwell, Red Hemp-nettle, Cornfield Knotgrass, Dwarf Spurge, Slender Tare and Venus's-looking-glass. By contrast, Corn Spurrey, Annual Knawel and Marsh Cudweed are strongly calcifugous and scarcely recorded anywhere in the south and east of the County. Mousetail and Marsh Cudweed require areas subject to winter flooding.

Some of the more familiar modern arable weeds

Common Poppy

Redshank

Scented Mayweed

Field Pansy

Corn Sow-thistle

Shepherd's-purse

Herbicide-resistance

Not all arable weeds are equally susceptible to all herbicides, and Black-grass has been observed to develop new resistance to certain pesticides in recent decades. Perennials with deep root systems or deep stolons such as Corn Sowthistle, Creeping Thistle and Common Couch can be notoriously difficult to eradicate with herbicides.

Plants at field margins and on fallow land

Arable land that has not been subject to recent usage can still support some of the arable weeds listed at the end of this chapter, but quickly becomes invaded by generalists and hedge-margin species such as Stinging Nettle, Spear Thistle, Common Ragwort, Greater and Lesser Burdock, Hogweed, Cow Parsley, Hemlock, White Dead-nettle, Ground-ivy, Field Bindweed and various speedwells, forget-me-nots, vetches and clovers. On more calcareous soils expect to find plants like Wild Mignonette, Woolly Thistle, Greater Knapweed, Field Scabious and Musk Thistle.

A calcareous field margin in south Warwickshire featuring Field Scabious and Greater Knapweed.

Plants of allotments and gardens

These are worthy of a brief mention here as they are another form of cultivated land, although they have not been used in assembling the arable land plant list at the end of this chapter. In their botanical character, they have much in common with both arable land and disturbed ground. Unlike arable land grains do not feature in the crop (except maize), so certain arable weeds have never become established. Herbicides are typically used in a more targeted way too, also more regular hoeing and weeding of plots by allotment-holders. The commonest allotment weeds recorded by the 1971 *A Computer-Mapped Flora* included Shepherd's-purse, Groundsel, Sun Spurge, Petty Spurge, Red Dead-nettle, Fat-hen, Common Chickweed and Annual Meadow-grass. Because many allotments are also used for garden plants or are subject to the import of garden waste for compost, the number of casuals can be very high.

A study was carried out of the garden weeds of Warwickshire in 1990 (Copson & Roberts, 1991) based on a questionnaire survey. This covered 156 sites, relating to 151 flower gardens and 93 vegetable plots. The ten most abundant annual weeds (with their % occurrence) were Groundsel (93), Chickweed (81), Cleavers (69), Shepherd's-purse (67), Annual Meadow-grass (62), Smooth Sow-thistle (58), Hairy Bitter-cress (54), Petty Spurge (53), Red Dead-nettle (51) and Common Field-speedwell (46). The ten most abundant perennials were dandelions (91), Common Couch (76), Creeping Buttercup (71), Broad-leaved Willowherb (52), Broad-leaved Dock (49), Lesser Celandine (45), Field Bindweed (42), Ground-elder (37), Hedge Bindweed (32) and Rosebay Willowherb (29). In many gardens no problem was

Some familiar 'weeds' of allotments and gardens

Groundsel

Fat-hen

Creeping Buttercup

Red Dead-nettle

Sun Spurge

Common Chickweed

Just a few square metres of unweeded garden can attract flowers such as buttercups and forget-me-nots.

experienced with cultivated plants becoming a nuisance, yet altogether some 120 species were mentioned in this context and included violets (especially Common Dog-violet), Foxglove and Feverfew.

Local gardens occasionally produce interesting plant records. The hare's-ear *Bupleurum longifolium* was added to the British list from a garden in Stratford-upon-Avon (Price & Partridge, 2007), and a study of the hybrid violet *Viola* x *bavarica* was made in a Leamington Spa garden (Partridge, 2007).

Odibourne Allotments, Kenilworth - even the best-tended allotments provide some opportunities for wildflowers.

Losses and gains

It perhaps appears ironic to lament the declines and losses of plants that are mostly non-native archaeophytes, neophytes and casuals. But many of these arable weeds are declining globally at a dramatic rate, and some are now unknown anywhere in the world away from arable settings, possibly because their original habitats have been lost over recent millennia. It has been suggested that in conserving rare arable weeds, we should consider national boundaries irrelevant and attempt to conserve them at an international level. In a sense, this is already happening as several species are included in the UK Biodiversity Action plan, even though they are archaeophytes rather than natives. The Warwickshire Local Biodiversity Action Plan has an action plan for Scarce Arable Plants, which selects the following declined species, plus one subspecies, for particular action:

- Corn Buttercup *Ranunculus arvensis*
- Night-flowering Catchfly *Silene noctiflora*
- Stinking Chamomile *Anthemis cotula*
- Corn Gromwell *Lithospermum arvense*
- Spreading Hedge-parsley *Torilis arvensis*
- Large-flowered Hemp-nettle *Galeopsis speciosa*
- Red Hemp-nettle *Galeopsis angustifolia*
- Corn Marigold *Chrysanthemum segetum*
- Wild Pansy *Viola tricolor*
- Blue Pimpernel *Anagallis arvensis* subspecies *foemina* (a rare subspecies of the Scarlet Pimpernel)
- Prickly Poppy *Papaver argemone*
- Shepherd's-needle *Scandix pecten-veneris*
- Dwarf Spurge *Euphorbia exigua*
- Corn Spurrey *Spergula arvensis*
- Field Woundwort *Stachys arvensis*

For twelve species this has come too late as they are already considered extinct here (excluding the odd recent record of some that probably represent casual population originating from bird-seed or wildflower seed mixtures):

- Small Bur-parsley *Caucalis platycarpos* – a neophyte last recorded at either Binton in 1895 or Alcester in 1875, now considered nationally extinct
- Wild Candytuft *Iberis amara* – probably last recorded in 1847 at Exhall, near Coventry, a rare native of chalk grassland in the Chilterns, but a much declined arable weed of neophyte status elsewhere
- Small-flowered Catchfly *Silene gallica* – an archaeophyte last recorded in the wild in 1913, though a rare casual of bird-seed since
- Corn Cleavers *Galium tricornutum* – an archaeophyte last recorded in 1964 near Newbold-on-Stour
- Corncockle *Agrostemma githago* – as an archaeophyte arable weed last recorded in cornfields at Edge Hill in 1954 and Upper Brailes in 1955, but with a few casual records since derived from wildflower seed mixtures, bird-seed and imported vegetable seed
- Darnel *Lolium temulentum* – extinct as an archaeophyte arable weed (though historically one of the most frequent arable weeds), but also a rare casual, last recorded in 1965 at Rugby, and much declined nationally
- Gold-of-pleasure *Camelina sativa* – an archaeophyte last recorded at Hams Hall in 1939
- Larkspur *Consolida ajacis* – a neophyte once associated with imported grain, but now a rare garden escape, last recorded as a possible arable weed at Studley in 1817

- Nettle-leaved Goosefoot *Chenopodium murale* – nineteenth century records possibly represent archaeophyte arable weed populations, but also one record of it as a casual in the period 1950-65
- Nit-grass *Gastridium ventricosum* – last recorded in fields west of Alcester 1957, it used to grew both in cornfields and calcareous grassland, and is much declined nationally
- Corn Parsley *Petroselinum segetum* – last recorded at Newbold-on-Stour in 1950
- Thorow-wax *Bupleurum rotundifolium* – as an archaeophyte arable weed last recorded from farmland near Aston Cantlow, Wilmcote and Moreton Morrell in the period 1950-65, with more recent casual records probably from bird-seed; considered extinct nationally as an arable weed

Despite the above losses, arable farmland is also an important habitat for the gain of newly naturalised species and casuals, most of which are general species of disturbed locations that can turn up at field margins and on fallow land. Examples include Green Nightshade, False Thorow-wax, Procumbent Yellow-sorrel, Bulbous-Canary-grass and Pale Cabbage.

Local sites you can visit
There are few specific farms where you can guarantee to see rare arable weeds in a given year. The best strategy for finding arable weeds is to select public footpaths that cross arable farmland, perhaps especially farmland on lighter and more calcareous soils in the Feldon and Cotswolds zones of Warwickshire. In recent years, local hotspots for arable weeds have included farmland in the Combrook, Milverton, Newbold-on-Stour, Ettington, Ilmington and Wellesbourne areas.

Arable land plant list (excluding casuals)
An asterix * denotes an arable land specialist

Grasses
- ✗ Black Bent *Agrostis gigantea* – an archaeophyte, also on disturbed ground
- ✗ *Black-grass *Alopecurus myosuroides* – an archaeophyte that is probably increasing
- ✗ Green Bristle-grass *Setaria viridis* – a rare neophyte, also on disturbed ground
- ✗ Barren Brome *Anisantha sterilis* – an archaeophyte, also on disturbed ground
- ✗ *Rye Brome *Bromus secalinus* – a rare and much declined archaeophyte
- ✗ Bulbous Canary-grass *Phalaris aquatica* – a neophyte fairly recently discovered in Warwickshire
- ✗ Cockspur *Echinochloa crus-galli* – a neophyte that is probably increasing
- ✗ *Loose Silky-bent *Apera spica-venti* – a rare archaeophyte
- ✗ Winter Wild-oat *Avena sterilis* – a neophyte
- ✗ Wild-oat *Avena fatua* – an archaeophyte, also on disturbed land

Other flowering plants
- ✗ Sweet Alison *Lobularia maritima* – a neophyte
- ✗ Common Amaranthus *Amaranthus retroflexus* – a neophyte that is probably increasing, often in nurseries

Some extinct arable weeds (at least as naturalised populations)

Corncockle

Small Bur-parsley

Wild Candytuft

Small-flowered Catchfly

Thorow-wax

Nettle-leaved Goosefoot

✗ Creeping Bellflower *Campanula rapunculoides* – a neophyte garden escape

✗ *Black-bindweed *Fallopia convolvulus* - an archaeophyte

✗ Buckwheat *Fagopyrum esculentum* – a scarce neophyte (an ancient crop)

✗ Buffalo-bur *Solanum rostratum* – a neophyte fairly recently discovered in Warwickshire

✗ Bugloss *Anchusa arvensis* – an archaeophyte that is probably increasing

✗ *Corn Buttercup *Ranunculus arvensis* – an archaeophyte that is much declined

✔ Hairy Buttercup *Ranunculus sardous* – rare (only recent record Wellesbourne, 1992)

✔ *Small-flowered Buttercup *Ranunculus parviflorus* – rare

✗ Pale Cabbage *Brassica tournefortii* – a neophyte fairly recently discovered in Warwickshire

✗ *Night-flowering Catchfly *Silene noctiflora* – a rare and much declined archaeophyte

✗ *Corn Chamomile *Anthemis arvensis* – a rare and much declined archaeophyte

✗ Stinking Chamomile *Anthemis cotula* – an archaeophyte that is probably declining

✗ Charlock *Sinapis arvensis* – an archaeophyte, also on disturbed ground

✔ Common Chickweed *Stellaria media* – abundant

✗ Crimson Clover *Trifolium incarnatum* – a rare neophyte

✗ *Cornflower *Centaurea cyanus* – a rare archaeophyte, plus a casual of wildflower seed mixes

✗ *Narrow-fruited Cornsalad *Valerianella dentata* – a very rare and much declined archaeophyte of calcareous soils

✔ Marsh Cudweed *Gnaphalium uliginosum* – especially waterlogged arable areas away from calcareous soils

✗ *Cut-leaved Dead-nettle *Lamium hybridum* – an archaeophyte that is probably increasing

✗ Henbit Dead-nettle *Lamium amplexicaule* – an archaeophyte that is probably declining

✗ Red Dead-nettle *Lamium purpureum* – an archaeophyte, also on disturbed land

✔ Fat-hen *Chenopodium album* – abundant, also disturbed ground

✗ Common Field-speedwell *Veronica persica* – a neophyte

✗ *Green Field-speedwell *Veronica agrestis* – an archaeophyte

✗ *Grey Field-speedwell *Veronica polita* – a neophyte that is possibly declining

✗ *Round-leaved Fluellen *Kickxia spuria* – an archaeophyte of calcareous soils

✗ *Sharp-leaved Fluellen *Kickxia elatine* – an archaeophyte of calcareous soils

✗ *Common Fumitory *Fumaria officinalis* – an archaeophyte

✗ *Dense-flowered Fumitory *Fumaria densiflora* – an archaeophyte of calcareous soils

✗ Gallant-soldier *Galinsoga parviflora* – a neophyte; also on disturbed ground

✗ *Many-seeded Goosefoot *Chenopodium polyspermum* – an archaeophyte that is probably increasing

✗ *Corn Gromwell *Lithospermum arvense* – a rare archaeophyte of calcareous soils

✔ Groundsel *Senecio vulgaris* – also on disturbed ground

✗ *Spreading Hedge-parsley *Torilis arvensis* – a rare and much declined archaeophyte of calcareous soils

✔ Bifid Hemp-nettle *Galeopsis bifida* – fairly recently discovered in Warwickshire

✘ *Large-flowered Hemp-nettle *Galeopsis speciosa* – considered extinct until rediscovered at Maxstoke in 2004, an archaeophyte

✘ *Red Hemp-nettle *Galeopsis angustifolia* – a rare and much declined archaeophyte of calcareous soils

✔ *Annual Knawel *Scleranthus annuus* – much declined, avoids calcareous soil in Warwickshire

✔ Knotgrass *Polygonum aviculare* – also disturbed ground

✘ *Cornfield Knotgrass *Polygonum rurivagum* – a rare archaeophyte of calcareous soils

✔ Larkspur *Consolida ajacis* – a neophyte, rare

✔ *Field Madder *Sherardia arvensis*

✘ *Corn Marigold *Chrysanthemum segetum* – an archaeophyte, plus a casual of wildflower seed mixes

✘ Rough Marsh-mallow *Althaea hirsuta* – a rare neophyte

✘ Scented Mayweed *Matricaria recutita* – an archaeophyte that is probably increasing

✔ Wild Mignonette *Reseda lutea* – usually on calcareous sites

✔ Corn Mint *Mentha arvensis*

✔ *Mousetail *Myosurus minimus* – prefers damp areas

✘ White Mustard *Sinapis alba* – an archaeophyte, also on disturbed ground, the source of commercial mustard

✘ Small Nettle *Urtica urens* – an archaeophyte that is probably increasing

✘ Black Nightshade *Solanum nigrum* – an increasing species, possibly native to SE England but probably not Warwickshire

✘ Green Nightshade *Solanum physalifolium* – a neophyte fairly recently discovered in Warwickshire

✔ Common Orache *Atriplex patula* – also on disturbed ground

✘ *Field Pansy *Viola arvensis* – an archaeophyte

✔ *Wild Pansy *Viola tricolor* – much declined

✘ Fool's Parsley *Aethusa cynapium* ssp. *agrestis* – this scarce subspecies is probably an archaeophyte and prefers arable land (ssp. *cynapium* is the more frequent one and occurs in a range of habitats)

✔ Parsley-piert *Aphanes arvensis* – possibly declining

✘ *Field Penny-cress *Thlaspi arvense* – an archaeophyte

✘ Field Pepperwort *Lepidium campestre* – an archaeophyte

✔ Pale Persicaria *Persicaria lapathifolia* – also disturbed ground

✘ *Pheasant's-eye *Adonis annua* – an archaeophyte possibly now extinct in Warwickshire as a true arable weed but still encountered as a rare casual

✔ Scarlet Pimpernel Anagallis arvensis ssp. *arvensis* – also found on disturbed ground

✘ *Blue Pimpernel *Anagallis arvensis* ssp. *foemina* – a rare archaeophyte of arable land

✘ *Common Poppy *Papaver rhoeas* – an archaeophyte, also on disturbed land

✘ *Long-headed Poppy (including Babington's Poppy) *Papaver dubium* – an archaeophyte, also on disturbed ground

✘ *Prickly Poppy *Papaver argemone* – an archaeophyte

✗ *Rough Poppy *Papaver hybridum* – a very rare archaeophyte (Wellesbourne, 1990)

✗ Wild Radish *Raphanus raphanistrum* – an archaeophyte, probably increasing

✔ *Common Ramping-fumitory *Fumaria muralis* – rare, also tips and allotments

✔ Redshank *Persicaria maculosa* – abundant, also disturbed land

✗ *Shepherd's-needle *Scandix pectin-viridis* – a rare and much declined archaeophyte (it was relatively frequent in the 1950s and 1960s)

✗ Shepherd's-purse *Capsella bursa-pastoris* – an archaeophyte, also on disturbed ground

✗ Ivy-leaved Speedwell *Veronica hederifolia* – an archaeophyte

✔ Wall Speedwell *Veronica arvensis*

✗ Springbeauty *Claytonia perfoliata* – a neophyte that is probably increasing

✗ *Broad-leaved Spurge *Euphorbia platyphyllos* – a rare archaeophyte of calcareous ground

✗ *Dwarf Spurge *Euphorbia exigua* – a declining archaeophyte of calcareous soils

✗ Petty Spurge *Euphorbia peplus* – an archaeophyte, also on disturbed ground

✗ *Sun Spurge *Euphorbia helioscopia* – an archaeophyte, also on disturbed ground

✗ *Corn Spurrey *Spergula arvensis* – avoids calcareous soil in Warwickshire, an archaeophyte on the British mainland

✔ *Slender Tare *Vicia parviflora* – rare, a much declined calcicole

✔ Smooth Tare *Vicia tetrasperma* – also on disturbed ground

✗ Turnip *Brassica rapa* – an archaeophyte crop that can become naturalised on arable land, also on disturbed land and roadsides

✗ *Venus's-looking-glass *Legousia hybrida* – a rare and much declined archaeophyte of calcareous soil

✗ *Weasel's-snout (Lesser Snapdragon) *Misopates orontium* – very rare, an archaeophyte

✗ Weld *Reseda luteola* – an archaeophyte

✗ American Winter-cress *Barbarea verna* – a neophyte that is probably increasing

✗ Medium-flowered Winter-cress *Barbarea intermedia* – a neophyte that is probably increasing

✗ *Field Woundwort *Stachys arvensis* – a much declined archaeophyte

Chapter 10

Heathland and Mire

*Acidic land dominated by dwarf shrubs of the heather family,
plus the peaty wetland that is often associated with it*

Heathland is a special type of vegetation dominated by dwarf-shrubs (usually heathers) that typically forms on nutrient-poor, acidic mineral soils overlying sandstone or thick layers of glacial sands or gravels. Soil pH can be as low as 3.5, which is considerably more acidic than neutral grassland (pH 5 to 6.5) and calcareous grassland (pH 6.5 to 8.5). Mire is the waterlogged peaty wetland that is frequently associated with heathland, the most acidic areas of which are called 'bog'. These are much declined habitats in Warwickshire that have international significance. Britain holds a surprisingly high proportion of all the world's dry *Calluna vulgaris* (Heather/Ling) heathland, and our mire communities tend to be different from those of other countries due to our milder, damper climate.

Baddesley Common, near Atherstone.

Two of the most characteristic plants of heathland and mire, Heather or Ling (left) which tends to dominate the drier areas and Cross-leaved Heath (right) which prefers wetter areas.

The history of Warwickshire's heathland and mire

Prehistoric heathland

Heathland and mire akin to what we see in Britain today almost certainly dominated parts of the tundra landscape that covered our area during, and immediately after, the last ice age. We are less certain how these habitats fared within the forested wildwood that followed as we do not know exactly how dense or continuous the forest cover was. It is conceivable that a heathland-type ground layer, with many of the plants we consider typical of local heathland today, could have been present in more open parts of the wildwood where this coincided with the poorest and most acidic soils. Mire species may well have been present in wet acidic woodland or the clearings of such woodland.

The rise of local heathland

Woodland clearance from Neolithic times onwards almost certainly permitted an increase of local heathland and mire. Woodland cover tends to protect infertile acidic soils, maintaining what is technically known as **acid brown soil**, a soil less harsh for plant growth than typical heathland soil or the peat of mire. Once woodland is removed and grazing or burning introduced, the upper layers of the soil become leached of minerals, increasingly acidic, and develop a complex series of layered horizons to form what is known as a **podsol**. One of the most important characteristics of a podsol is the development of a hard, impervious, iron-rich layer known as an **iron pan** usually a foot or more below the surface. This pan prevents any minerals below it from rising upwards, exacerbating soil acidity and infertility and enhancing the formation of fully expressed heathland and mire. So, following woodland clearance on acid brown soil, heathland would have been more strongly favoured than grassland. This process may have been occurring up until the

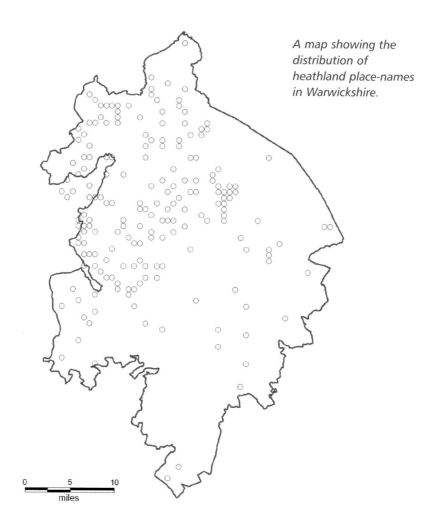

A map showing the distribution of heathland place-names in Warwickshire.

0   5   10

miles

seventeenth century when improvements in agricultural technology (such as new ploughs and the use of fertilisers and lime) and the enclosure of common land saw heathland increasingly converted to arable.

It is clear that by medieval times heathland was very widespread in the Arden zone of north and west Warwickshire, and also on the Dunsmore Plateau between Coventry, Leamington and Rugby. It is referred to in dozens of local place names containing 'heath', 'moor' or 'common', including Hockley Heath, Dunsmore Heath, Bentley Heath, Balsall Common and Corley Moor to name just a few. Many of these sites represent former expanses of common land used for rough grazing. There is also archaeological evidence for past heathland in the pollen and plant remains associated with early human settlement. At Ling Hall Quarry near Church Lawford (in a part of the Dunsmore that came to be known as Lawford Heath), an excavation of a Romano-British settlement produced evidence of heathers, Heath-grass and Sheep's Sorrel. Medieval evidence of heather is also known from the

Cawston and Dunchurch area. Heaths are also indicated in some early local maps (e.g. Walpole's maps of 1794) and in Bagnall's 1891 *Flora*, which shows that acidophilous plants (those liking heathland and bog) really did once occur at Feldon locations like Bascote Heath and Lighthorne Heath. These areas are now characterised by calcareous soils due to years of deep ploughing over Lias geology, though it would seem that in pre-Enclosure times patches of leached acidic soils masked the underlying geology sufficiently for plants like Bracken and certain bog-loving species to grow (a situation that can still be observed in various chalk and limestone areas of Britain).

The decline of local heathland

Within Warwickshire, the transformation of heathland to farmland has been so efficient that very little visual evidence is left anywhere to suggest heathland was ever present, except the presence of Bracken, birches and Gorse in hedges or along certain road verges. Whatever heathland has not been ploughed up has generally been lost to urban development, which has been concentrated in various parts of north-west Warwickshire that heathland once occupied rather than the more productive farmland in south and east Warwickshire. This is why you will find suburbs of

Coventry and Birmingham called Small Heath, Stoke Heath, Little Heath and Westwood Heath. Several other former heaths such as Kenilworth Common and Yarningale Common have reverted to secondary woodland in the absence of grazing. The net result of all the above is that heathland has experienced the highest levels of loss of any habitat in Warwickshire.

Mire was more difficult to convert to agriculture or development but, aside from that at Sutton Park, it has virtually all reverted to wet woodland or been drained. Examples of wet woods that were previously mire include Coleshill Pool, Bannerley Pool, Bickenhill Plantation and Birmingham's Moseley Bog.

A small area of relic mire at Bickenhill Plantation within the grounds of Birmingham's National Exhibition Centre.

Today, only two local sites in Watsonian Warwickshire currently support enough heather-rich vegetation to be meaningfully honoured with the title heathland and only one of these contains mire. Sutton Park, located in the northern suburbs of Birmingham (within the modern county of the West Midlands), supports about 465 hectares of dry heathland, wet heathland, mire and bog, and is a National Nature Reserve of great importance. Grendon and Baddesley Common near Atherstone only supports a meagre 15 hectares of dry heathland, and whilst it represents the only true heathland in modern Warwickshire, it is unexceptional by West Midlands standards. Other smaller patches of Heather can be found at Rough Hill Wood near Redditch, Clowes Wood near Earlswood, Priory Fields near Yardley Wood, Alvecote Pools near Tamworth and the odd woodland ride and clearing in the Arden zone.

However, a loss of heather does not automatically result in a loss of all heathland-loving plants, and you can still find some of these persisting within patches of acid grassland and within woodland rides and clearings. It is also possible to find some of the plants associated with bog and mire in the clearings and pools of wet woods such as Tile Hill Wood in Coventry and Clowes Wood.

Heather in a ride of Poors Wood, near Balsall Common.

Local heathland and mire types

Heathland can take the form of ***dry heath*** (typically where it overlies sand) or ***humid heath*** and ***wet heath*** (where the ground has impeded drainage and gains peat). ***Peat*** comprises the remains of plant material that has not fully decomposed due to soil acidity inhibiting the invertebrate, bacterial and fungal activity that would normally take place in soil. In humid and wet heath, the peat layer is shallow. Where a thicker layer of more permanently waterlogged peat and associated pools is present, it becomes ***mire***, the most acidic areas of which are termed ***bog*** in the true ecological sense (as opposed to 'boggy ground' in the loose sense which is a term applied to many wetlands). The definition of mire also includes the transitional phases between bog and more species-rich fen that are often termed ***poor-fen*** (pH of about 5). Nationally, poor-fen has a number of distinctive plants and plant communities and is a valuable habitat in its own right.

Bog and poor-fen frequently occur together within a valley mire system, bog typically at the head of a valley or along the sides, and poor-fen lower down the valley axis where more mineral enrichment of the ground water occurs (a situation that can be observed at Sutton Park). Acid grassland, covered in the Permanent Grassland section of this book, is intimately associated with heathland and shares many species with it. It is in the grassy interstices between Heather and can also replace heathland if Heather disappears. As with so many local habitats, there are

Dry heathland at Sutton Park (left). Little Bracebridge Pool at Sutton Park, lying within a waterlogged area of bog and poor-fen (right).

Characteristic plants of dry heathland

Broom

Heath Bedstraw

Bell Heather

Wavy Hair-grass

Western Gorse

Heath Milkwort

no neat cut-off points between heathland and mire, or between them and other habitats such as acid grassland, rich fen or acidic ruderal habitat, but typical heathland and typical bog are very distinctive habitats.

The plants of heathland

56 native and naturalised species currently rely entirely or heavily upon heathland, mire and bog for their presence in Warwickshire (see plant list at end of chapter). No archaeophytes or neophytes fall into this category, other than Heart-leaved Willow. Nearly all are declining and most are rare or restricted by virtue of the scarcity of their habitats. Many other plants can turn up on heathland too, especially the more fertile edges or beside paths. *A Computer-Mapped Flora* recorded a total of 299 species from acid bog and heath in Warwickshire during the 1950s and 1960s.

Plants of dry heath

Dry heath is typically dominated by Heather, though Gorse, Western Gorse, Bracken, Broom and patches of acid grassland featuring Wavy Hair-grass, Creeping Soft-grass, Heath Bedstraw, Heath Milkwort and Heath Cudweed may be present too. These are all drought-tolerant (xerophytic) plants that can cope with soil that may hold little moisture for much of the summer. Soil enrichment from dog-fouling along footpaths or fly-tipping and road spray along road verges, can result in coarse grassland of a more mesotrophic nature infiltrating dry heath. This can be much more species-rich than traditional dry heathland, but the encroachment of thistles, brambles, Common Ragwort, Rosebay Willowherb, Hogweed, Cow Parsley and a variety of common grasses are sure indications of heathland degradation, and such plants will eventually out-compete the more valuable Heather. Bracken, Gorse and birches can also be very invasive in the absence of management such as grazing, cutting or burning.

Expanses of bright pink heather blossom in late summer are the annual highlight of dry heath, and at Sutton Park this is augmented by the yellow of Western Gorse flowers, a delightful combination.

Plants of wet heath

Wet heath has darker soils that experience periodic waterlogging. Whilst Heather may persist here, it is joined by Cross-leaved Heath, Purple Moor-grass, Heath Rush, Common Cotton-grass, Heath Spotted-orchid, Deergrass, Marsh Pennywort, Meadow Thistle, Bog Pimpernel, Crowberry, Cowberry, Cranberry and Dioecious Sedge. More generalist damp-ground species such as Marsh Thistle and Devil's-bit Scabious can also be common, and mosses are much in evidence. Wet heath can be invaded by Downy Birch and Grey Willow in the absence of grazing and cutting.

Plants of mire and bog

Bog and mire is characterised by the presence of waterlogged peat (which can be up to several feet deep) extensively covered by spongy sphagnum moss, within which you will find tussocks of Purple Moor-grass, Round-leaved Sundew, White Sedge, Marsh Lousewort, Common Butterwort plus the species of wet heath (but usually at lower frequency than in wet heath proper). Boggy pools may contain Floating Club-rush,

Characteristic plants of wet heathland

Cowberry

Crowberry

Meadow Thistle

Bog Pimpernel

Heath Spotted-orchid

Heath Rush

Characteristic plants of bog and mire

Common Sundew

Marsh Lousewort

Marsh Cinquefoil

Bog Pondweed

Common Butterwort

Shoreweed

Six-stamened Waterwort, Bog Pondweed, Bladderwort and Round-leaved Crowfoot. The margins of the larger pools at places like Sutton Park and Earlswood have a number of marginal plants such as Bogbean and Shoreweed that do not ordinarily occur in the more eutrophic waterbodies that are typical of Warwickshire.

The lack of nutrients in bog and mire has resulted in some very interesting feeding strategies by some of the plants that grow there. Sundews and butterworts have become insectivorous, digesting insects that get trapped on their sticky leaves. Bladderworts, which inhabit boggy pools, trap tiny creatures in underwater bladders as an alternative approach. Marsh Lousewort is a hemiparasite of sedges, tapping the hosts' roots with its own to gain valuable nutrients (though it is still capable of photosynthesis). Lousewort does the same thing on grasses in drier parts of a heath. As mire transforms into poor-fen, transitional species such as Bog-bean, Marsh Cinquefoil and Blinks appear, also more generalised wetland species such as Water Mint, Angelica, Bulrush, Common Spike-rush, Sharp-flowered Rush and spearworts. In the absence of management, and particularly following drought periods, bog and mire can be invaded by Downy Birch and Grey Willow, also Alder alongside any streams.

Losses and gains

No other local habitat features such a high proportion of declining species, though the declines have taken place much more slowly than those of specialist arable weeds or the flowers of less improved grasslands. These declines stem variously from habitat loss, fragmentation and deterioration, and this appears to have been happening since local plant recording began, so it cannot just be attributed to twentieth century factors. Heathland and mire are complex habitats, with much subtle variation, and mire and wet heath are both vulnerable to changes in hydrology which might arise from drainage, depletion of local aquifers, changes in water quality and drought. Habitat fragmentation has a major impact on heathland and mire ecology, allowing invasive species to exert progressively greater pressure on specialist species, weakening the populations of those specialists and deleting some of the subtle habitat variation that tends to be associated with a large and continuous heathland or mire system. A mire or heathland one hectare in area could never hope to support the same number of specialist species as one of a hundred hectares, and history suggests that a one-hundred hectare site cannot support the range of species of a one-thousand hectare site either. Sixteen species are considered to have become extinct:

- Allseed *Radiola linoides* – last recorded at Cornet's End in 1893, likes damp acid grassland and wet heath, much declined nationally
- Bog Asphodel *Narthecium ossifragum* – a bog and mire specialist last recorded at Coleshill Bog in 1962
- White Beak-sedge *Rhynchospora alba* – a wet heath and mire species last recorded at Packington in 1885
- Ivy-leaved Bellflower *Wahlenbergia hederacea* – last recorded at Arbury Hall in 1872, a plant of wet heath, bogs and other acidic habitats
- Lesser Bladderwort *Utricularia minor* – a free-floating aquatic of boggy pools, last recorded at Sutton Park in 1934

Extinct heathland and mire plants

Upright Chickweed

Marsh St John's-wort

Marsh Clubmoss

Lesser Skullcap

Allseed

Bog Asphodel

- Upright Chickweed *Moenchia erecta* – last recorded at Yarningale Common in 1898, likes heathland and associated acid grassland
- Fir Clubmoss *Huperzia selago* – last recorded at Coleshill Bog in 1846 and much declined in England
- Marsh Clubmoss *Lycopodiella inundata* – a wet heath, bog and mire specialist last recorded from Coleshill in 1842
- Stag's-horn Clubmoss *Lycopodium clavatum* – last recorded at Sutton Park in 1884
- Pillwort *Pilularia globulifera* – last recorded from Sutton Park in 1898, it likes peaty water margins in Warwickshire
- Lesser Skullcap *Scutellaria minor* – a plant of bogs, mire and damp acidic woodland, last recorded at Ryton Wood in 1962
- Many-stalked Spike-rush – *Eleocharis multicaulis* – a bog and wet heath specialist last recorded from Bickenhill in 1945
- Marsh St John's-wort *Hypericum elodes* – a bog and mire specialist last recorded at Coleshill Pool in 1959
- Alternate Water-milfoil *Myriophyllum alterniflorum* – last recorded at Sutton Park, Bracebridge Pool in 1968, a submerged aquatic that likes boggy pools and streams
- Creeping Willow *Salix repens* – occurred on wet heath at Sutton Park, where last recorded in about 1960 (though a population introduced with sea sand has been recorded at Emscote, near Warwick subsequently)
- Common Wintergreen *Pyrola minor* – a wet heath and wet acid woodland species last recorded at Meriden in 1873

Most of these are mire specialists that were at the edge of their national range in Warwickshire, and most have declined throughout the marginal parts of their range. But it says a great deal about the subtle needs of these plants that even the great Sutton Park has been unable to hang on to them. There is always the hope that somewhere in the depths of Coleshill Bog or Arbury Park (both poorly surveyed by comparison to Sutton) they might still be persisting, though both these sites have lost most of their open mire.

There are no increasing species within the specialist flora of heathland or mire, though a number of expanding neophytes, plus the odd casual, can turn up.

Local heathland and mire sites you can visit
- Sutton Park SP099975 – a large National Nature Reserve owned and managed by Birmingham City Council. Superb dry heath, wet heath, mire, acid grassland plus various woodland types. Many of the rare and unusual plants listed in the plant list below are present.
- Baddesley Common SP276979 – dry heathland straddling The Common (road) just south of Baddesley Ensor village, some long-established but other areas more recently formed on restored open cast coal workings since 1950. Owned by the Merevale Estate.
- Priory Fields, Yardley (a Warwickshire Wildlife Trust reserve) – remnant heathland and mire with Heather, Western Gorse, Heath Rush and other acidophilic plants.
- Clowes Wood, near Earlswood SP101743 (a Warwickshire Wildlife Trust reserve) – a small patch of heathland occurs in a clearing just north of the railway line.

- Rough Hill Wood, near Redditch SP052637 (a Warwickshire Wildlife Trust reserve) – a small patch of heathland occurs in a clearing a short distance due north of the reserve car park.

Heathland and mire plant list (excluding casuals)

Shrubs
✔ Bilberry *Vaccinium myrtillus* – acid woodland too
✔ Cowberry *Vaccinium vitis-idaea* – wet heath, rare (only Sutton Park now)
✔ Cranberry *Vaccinium oxycoccus* – wet heath and bog, rare (only Sutton Park now)
✔ Crowberry *Empetrum nigrum* – dry heathland, rare (only Sutton Park)
✔ Western Gorse *Ulex gallii* – dry heath, scarce
✔ Bell Heather *Erica cinerea* – dry heathland, rare
✔ Cross-leaved Heath *Erica tetralix* – wet heath, mire and bog, rare
✔ Heather *Calluna vulgaris* – dry heathland, scarce
✔ Petty Whin *Genista anglica* – wet heath, rare
✘ Heart-leaved Willow *Salix eriocephala* – a neophyte naturalised at Sutton Park

Grasses, sedges and rushes
✔ Floating Club-rush *Eleogiton fluitans* – an emergent of boggy pools, rare (only Packington now)
✔ Common Cotton-grass *Eriophorum angustifolium* – wet heath, mire and bog, rare
✔ Hare's-tail Cotton-grass *Eriophorum vaginatum* – wet heath, mire and bog, rare
✔ Deergrass *Trichophorum cespitosum* – wet heath and bogs, rare (only Sutton Park now)
✔ Wavy Hair-grass *Deschampsia flexuosa* – dry heathland and acid grassland
✔ Heath-grass *Danthonia decumbens* – dry heath, acid grassland too, scarce
✔ Mat-grass *Nardus stricta* – wet heath, rare
✔ Purple Moor-grass *Molinia caerulea* – wet heath, bog and mire, scarce
✔ Heath Rush *Juncus squarrosus* – wet heath and mire, also damp acid grassland, rare
✔ Dioecious Sedge *Carex dioica* – wet heath and poor-fen (only Sutton Park)
✔ Flea Sedge *Carex pulicaris* – wet heath and poor-fen (only Sutton Park now)
✔ Green-ribbed Sedge *Carex binervis* – wet heath, rare
✔ Pill Sedge *Carex pilulifera* – dry heath and acid grassland, rare
✔ Star Sedge *Carex echinata* – mire and wet heath, rare
✔ White Sedge *Carex curta* – bogs, rare
✔ Fine-leaved Sheep's-fescue *Festuca filiformis* – dry heath and acid grassland, rare and declined
✔ Few-flowered Spike-rush *Eleocharis quinqueflora* – mire and boggy watersides are the preferred habitat in Warwickshire, rare (only Sutton Park now)
✔ Lesser Tussock-sedge *Carex diandra* – mire including poor-fen, rare (only Sutton Park now)
✔ Heath Wood-rush *Luzula multiflora* – heathland and acid grassland, rare

Other flowering plants
- ✔ Heath Bedstraw *Galium saxatile* – dry heathland and acid grassland
- ✔ Blinks *Montia fontana* – mostly mire, rare (3 subspecies recorded)
- ✔ Bogbean *Menyanthes trifoliata* – margins of pools, especially in mire, rare
- ✔ Common Butterwort *Pinguicula vulgaris* – bog and mire, rare (only Sutton Park now)
- ✔ Marsh Cinquefoil *Potentilla palustris* – mostly mire, rare
- ✔ Round-leaved Crowfoot *Ranunculus omiophyllus* – water margins and small pools in mire and bog, rare (only Sutton Park)
- ✔ Heath Cudweed *Gnaphalium sylvaticum* – dry heathland and acid grassland, rare
- ✔ Creeping Forget-me-not *Myosotis secunda* – mire and associated watersides, rare
- ✔ Grass-of-Parnassus *Parnassia palustris* – mire, rare (only Sutton Park now)
- ✔ Lousewort *Pedicularis sylvatica* – wet heath, rare
- ✔ Marsh Lousewort *Pedicularis palustris* – mire and bog, rare (only Sutton Park now)
- ✔ Heath Milkwort *Polygala serpyllifolia* – dry heath and acid grassland, scarce
- ✔ Knotted Pearlwort *Sagina nodosa* – mire, rare (only Sutton Park now)
- ✔ Marsh Pennywort *Hydrocotyle vulgaris* – mire, rare
- ✔ Bog Pimpernel *Anagallis tenella* – mire and bog, rare (only Sutton Park)
- ✔ Bog Pondweed *Potamogeton polygonifolius* – an aquatic of boggy pools and other acidic waterbodies, rare
- ✔ Shoreweed *Littorella uniflora* – an aquatic and marginal, mainly of standing acidic water, especially associated with mire in Warwickshire, rare
- ✔ Sneezewort *Achillea ptarmica* – wet heath and damp acid grassland, scarce
- ✔ Heath Speedwell *Veronica officinalis* – also acid grassland
- ✔ Heath Spotted-orchid *Dactylorhiza maculata* – wet heath, also damp acid grassland, scarce
- ✔ Common Sundew *Drosera rotundifolia* – bog and mire, rare (only Sutton Park now)
- ✔ Meadow Thistle *Cirsium dissectum* – mire and wet heath, also damp acid grassland, rare
- ✔ Tormentil *Potentilla erecta* – acid grassland and woodland too
- ✔ Marsh Violet *Viola palustris* – wet heath and bog, rare
- ✔ Six-stamened Waterwort *Elatine hexandra* – boggy water margins, rare (only Coleshill Pool now)
- ✔ Marsh Willowherb *Epilobium palustre* – mire and more acidic wetlands

Ferns
- ✔ Lemon-scented Fern *Oreopteris limbosperma* – wet heath, rare

Chapter 11

Disturbed Ground

*Land that has been subject to catastrophic change that brings about a major
re-colonisation process that in its early stages is dominated by pioneer plant species*

All semi-natural habitats in Warwickshire experience a level of disturbance,
whether grazing pressure and associated trampling, flooding, storm damage,
or even nature conservation management. But for certain sites, a
catastrophic change in circumstances can kick-start the production of some of our
most diverse and interesting wildflower sites. These changes include quarrying and
other forms of excavation, demolition, excessive vehicle disturbance, dumping of
waste, and large scale earth movement. Once disturbance ceases (even for just a
few years) a veritable explosion of floristic diversity can unfold as pioneer plants
battle to gain dominance of the bare ground. The new habitat is termed 'ruderal'
and is initially dominated by short-lived, highly mobile (in terms of seed dispersal)
plants growing within a matrix of bare ground.

Emscote Power Station, Warwick in 1995.

The colonisation process can be complex and unpredictable, being influenced by whatever seeds or living plant bits happen to be in the new ground, what seeds get blown or carried into the site from external sources, and what species are best suited to the soils and substrates present. These substrates can range from highly calcareous (in a limestone quarry for instance) to highly acidic (on a colliery spoilheap). They can be polluted by a wide variety of substances including heavy metals, salts, solvents and organic waste. They can be prone to excessive drying or flooding (in some cases both within a typical year) and are sometimes poor in nitrogen and other key nutrients. This means that some disturbed sites present substantial challenges to plants, and this can result in unusual plant communities featuring rare and unusual species that cannot compete in less harsh environments. Many disturbed sites are also subject to busy vehicle movement, land-filling, fly-tipping and temporary storage of items that may come from many parts of the world. These are all sources of casual wildflowers that can augment the rich flora of native and naturalised species that may already be present. Warwickshire, with its varied industrial history, supports a good deal of disturbed ground, and this includes some of our finest wildflower sites.

Weld, Musk Thistle, Ragwort and Colt's-foot stake a claim to a patch of limestone spoil at Cross Hands Quarry.

The history of Warwickshire's disturbed ground

Large scale quarrying has existed in Warwickshire for nearly two centuries, and at a smaller scale it can be traced back at least as far as Roman times. Excavation and large scale disturbance and earth movement has also been associated with the creation of the local road, railway and canal networks over the past two centuries, and with urban growth and renewal for many centuries before this. Any sizeable settlement is likely to have generated disturbed conditions and dumps that would suit the sorts of pioneer plant species covered by this chapter. The pollen and seeds of disturbance-liking plants such as Mugwort, Redshank, Groundsel, Stinging Nettle, Fat-hen and docks have frequently been encountered by archaeologists studying local Neolithic, Bronze Age and Iron Age settlements. Most of these are native species that would have exploited any disturbed ground within the natural woodland, grassland and coastal habitats that existed in Britain before humans had made much impact on the landscape. But the size of the flora associated with disturbed ground has expanded dramatically over recent centuries as the quantity of suitable habitat has grown and as an increasing number of disturbance-tolerant neophytes from other parts of the world have become established in Britain. This means that a patch of disturbed ground in the twenty-first century has the potential to support many more plant species than an equivalent piece of ground in the Neolithic period.

However, disturbed ground may be a habitat on the wane. The pressure for new housing and employment land in Warwickshire is now so acute that much industrial wasteland (also termed post-industrial land) has recently been developed, and newly neglected sites tend to be developed within a matter of years, as opposed to a matter of decades as often occurred in the past. Examples of floristically diverse sites lost in recent years include Foleshill Gasworks and Keresley Colliery (both in north Coventry), Emscote Power Station in Warwick and Hams Hall Power Station near Coleshill. Previously-used sites such as these are also termed 'brownfield land' by planners and developers, and viewed as a more favourable location for development than 'greenfield land' (essentially agricultural land). But as many naturalists will be aware, perhaps

The Coventry Homefire Plant, Keresley in 1998, prior to development.

especially in areas like Warwickshire and the West Midlands, brownfield land is often far better for biodiversity than agricultural land, and often ideally located to bring people into closer contact with wildflowers and other wildlife.

Excavation features such as quarries and gravel pits have fared better locally than industrial wasteland, being physically more difficult to develop either due to topography or flood-risk. Many flooded gravel pits are now celebrated local wildlife sites with public access e.g. Brandon Marsh and Kingsbury Water Park. But several local quarries have been subject to landfill followed by restoration, and sometimes in a manner that has severely compromised their final value for wildlife. Fortunately, the current mineral planning process for Warwickshire is taking account of biodiversity and, with the prospect of less waste in the future (due to improved recycling), there is a greater chance of current working quarries, plus new quarries of the future, being returned to nature and informal green-space once excavation is completed.

Local types of disturbed ground

Excavations (quarries, gravel workings, sandpits and recent cuttings)

There is a variety of excavation features in Warwickshire, exploiting and exposing a range of rock types. Quarries, gravel workings and sandpits provide a loose categorisation of these, though in reality there is much overlap between their ecological character, and sand and gravel are often excavated from the same area. Excavation features vary greatly in size, depth, age and wetness, and many are now abandoned and in a well advanced stage of succession to secondary woodland. Those that have already reverted to established grassland, wetland, dense scrub or secondary woodland are better covered in the Permanent Grassland, Water Courses and Wetlands, or Woodland chapters of this book.

Quarries in the south and east of the County tend to be calcareous (rich in lime) and exploit various sedimentary deposits laid down in shallow seas during the Triassic and Jurassic periods. The ruderal vegetation that forms on these tends to be very rich and flowery, typically with a high proportion of scarce and unusual species: indeed, they are some of our most exciting wildflower locations. Bishops Bowl, Southam Quarry, Nelsons Quarry and the various quarries in north-west Rugby are deep voids

Bishops Bowl Quarry, Harbury, an old cement quarry with an exceptionally rich calcareous flora (left). Hartshill Quarry, near Nuneaton, exposes ancient quartzites that produce acidic conditions supporting lower floristic diversity than most calcareous quarries (right).

featuring **Blue Lias** mudstone and limestone used in the cement industry. These are especially calcareous sites prone to water-logging, and so often feature wetlands. But they are also drought-prone on any higher spoil-heaps and slopes. **White Lias** quarries are fewer in number and shallower, with Ufton Fields being the finest of the local ones. **Marlstone** (a hard ironstone) has been quarried at a number of sites in the Edge Hill and Avon Dassett area, and these quarries produce the least calcareous conditions of the southern quarries, typically with much rock rubble. Quarries in the very south of the County, for example Cross Hands, feature Middle Jurassic limestones such as **Clypeus Grit** and **Chipping Norton Limestone**. These quarries physically resemble Marlstone ones though are more strongly calcareous with many of the special plants of Blue Lias quarries. Another limestone of note is **Wilmcote Limestone**, a fine-grained pale-grey rock that was quarried from several sites west of Stratford on Avon. It also gives rise to highly calcareous conditions.

The deep quarries in the north of the County typically exploit much harder and older **shales**, **quartzites** and **igneous rocks** of great value for aggregate. They tend to produce acidic ground conditions and many are flooded at the bottom, but often in a steep-sided manner that fails to support interesting wetland habitat. Most of these quarries are located along the Nuneaton-Atherstone Ridge between Nuneaton and Dordon. Outliers include Griff Quarry near Bedworth and Dosthill Brickpit near Kingsbury.

Most of our large gravel workings and sandpits are located within the river valleys of the Tame (e.g. Kingsbury Water Park, Middleton Hall, Whitacre Heath and Ladywalk Bird Reserve), the Avon (Brandon Marsh) and the Arrow (Marsh Farm near Salford Priors). A few occur on higher ground, e.g. Ryton Pools and associated quarries near Bubbenhall, Ling Hall Quarry near Church Lawford, and Cornet's End Quarry near Meriden. A single site will often produce a range of deposits ranging from fine sands through to larger pebbles.

Quarries, gravel workings and sandpits can be physically complex sites with hummocks and hills (including spoilheaps), slopes of various orientations, pits and water bodies of different sizes and highly varied surface substrates that might

Marsh Farm Quarry in 2004, a large sand and gravel extraction site near Salford Priors, still at an early stage of colonisation (left). Ettington by-pass in 2003 – the exposures of Blue Lias have been allowed to regenerate naturally over several decades and have acquired an exceptional flora (right).

include the material being exploited plus piles of unwanted overburden (i.e. the superficial soils, clays and sands that used to overlie the wanted substrate). Imported materials associated with the working infrastructure of the site, such as gravel, sand and hard-core can also be present, producing conditions resembling those of industrial wasteland. Derelict buildings, old walls and surfaced ground can provide a further set of plant habitats that this book deals with in the next chapter. The complicated histories of many excavation features (which often involve phased enlargement and phased abandonment), plus constant vehicle movement and earth movement, can also result in a complex mosaic of successional stages in which some areas are much more recently disturbed and therefore at an earlier stage of the ecological succession process than others.

Cuttings, such as the Ettington and Southam by-passes, where plants have been allowed to regenerate naturally on calcareous Blue Lias, resemble limestone quarries. Ettington by-pass is older than the Southam one, and is turning into limestone grassland. Even older road and railway cuttings at places like the Fosse Way near Darlingscott, the A439 at Binton, or Ashlawn Cutting near Rugby, already support well-established species-rich grassland.

Derelict and disturbed industrial land

Derelict industrial sites are frequent though often short-lived features in our area that arise after the demolition or abandonment of factories, power stations and other buildings. Actively-used sites which have not been substantially landscaped and are subject to piecemeal disturbance (e.g. good yards, storage depots, construction sites and the land often associated with active factories, collieries, power stations and railways) can support similar floras. All such sites typically feature imported aggregate, compacted subsoil lacking humus, spoil and rubble, and other areas surfaced with concrete or tarmac. The ground is often polluted by solvents and heavy metals. Sites associated with former power stations (e.g. Ladywalk Bird Reserve) may feature pulverized fly-ash, whilst those associated with former collieries (e.g. Claybrookes Marsh) can feature much coal waste.

Assorted plants colonise spoil and rubble on an industrial site in north Coventry.

Such sites have much in common with quarries though they tend to be less physically complex with fewer slopes and pits. They may also have been subject to phased activities and piecemeal disturbance that results in a variety of successional stages at a single site. The specialised plants of walls, roofs and other hard surfaces are dealt with in the Built Environment chapter. Here we are concerned with the plants that typically re-colonise new porous ground.

Dumps and landfill sites

These are often located within old excavation features, but scrap-heaps may occur on post-industrial land or farmland. Where inert waste is involved, the conditions resemble those of industrial wasteland. But where organically rich garden or household waste is present, highly fertile, nitrogen-rich ground will be present which strongly influences the flora.

The plants of disturbed ground

Disturbed ground in Warwickshire is a major habitat for some 230 native and naturalised species of wildflower (see plant list at the end of chapter), which is the highest figure for any local habitats category. Given that many 'disturbed' sites can also support patches of established grassland, wetland, scrub, secondary woodland and old or derelict built structures, each with their own suites of plants, some of these sites constitute Warwickshire's richest plant locations.

The number of archaeophytes and neophytes within the 230 species noted above is high (130 species) and as a proportion of the flora this is only exceeded by arable land. Disturbed ground is also the richest habitat for casuals. The other notable feature of this flora is the large number of hybrids present. Some of these arrived in Warwickshire already in the hybrid state, but many have probably hybridised *in situ* as a consequence of two or more very closely-related species coming to grow alongside each other in a manner that could never happen in their native ranges. A particularly good example of this locally can be found in the evening-primroses, with three species freely interbreeding to create hybrid-swarms at a number of sites. These were the subject of a classic study by Warwickshire botanist John Bowra at a ruderal site in Warwick (Bowra, 1999, 2001).

Plant succession at disturbed sites

The plants that tend to dominate the early stages of ruderal habitat are overwhelmingly annuals and biennials, much like the flora of arable land (which shares many species with disturbed ground). This is in striking contrast to permanent grassland or heathland where perennials dominate. Indeed some species, such as Groundsel, are very short-lived and can set seed within a few weeks of germination, allowing them to colonise very temporary sites. Many species devote a large proportion of their annual growth to producing an abundance of seed, making the most of what might be just a few years of favourable conditions. Those seeds typically have excellent powers of dispersal, which can include dispersal by wind (e.g. the fluffy seeds of willowherbs and the many members of the thistle and daisy family), ants (the seeds of plants like fumitories, Gorse and violets), and animal fur (the 'sticky' or hooked seeds of plants like Cleavers, forget-me-nots and burdocks). Butterfly-bush (Buddleia) is unusual in that it is a rapidly colonising woody perennial. It only became naturalised in Britain in the 1930s and owes its success to massive seed production which can amount to several million tiny seeds within a few years of growth. These quickly infiltrate seed banks in the soil, debris and dust of urban and industrial areas and are easily moved around by wind, surface water, vehicle tyres and shoes.

After a few years, in the absence of regular disturbance or heavy rabbit grazing, sites acquire an increasing number of perennials plus less mobile annuals and biennials that take longer to arrive. Any accumulation of plant remains, including wind-blown leaf litter from nearby trees, carrion or faeces, can help to produce a soil, whilst nitrogen-fixing plants such as legumes (clovers, vetches, melilots and their relatives) can improve the soil allowing further plants to colonise. In time, the ruderal community usually gives way to grassland or tall herb, then to brambles, shrubs and young trees, and finally to secondary woodland. The rate at which this occurs, and the species involved, is strongly determined by the type of site, the substrate(s) involved, and factors such as rabbit grazing, disturbance and drainage.

Plants of industrial wasteland and derelict land

The first plants to colonise such sites locally include Shepherd's-purse, Hairy Bitter-cress, melilots, Sticky Mouse-ear, pearlworts, Weld, Common Centaury, Groundsel, Pineappleweed, Scentless Mayweed, Canadian Fleabane and Oxford Ragwort. Grasses can include Yorkshire-fog and Barren Brome. A few perennials can also become established early on, notably Common Bird's-foot-trefoil, Rosebay Willowherb, Common Ragwort, Colt's-foot and Butterfly-bush. If tarmac or concrete is present, species such as Biting Stonecrop may be present (see next chapter). Many species are small or short.

After a few years larger, taller and leafier herbs increase dominance. Rosebay Willowherb can still remain abundant but is joined by St John's-worts, thistles,

Characteristic plants of industrial wasteland

Butterfly Bush

Colt's-foot

Common Bird's-foot-trefoil

Scentless Mayweed

Rosebay Willowherb

Common Centaury

Characteristic plants of industrial wasteland

Yorkshire-fog

Great Mullein

Pineappleweed

Common Knapweed

Tufted Vetch

Mugwort

Mugwort, Tufted Vetch, Common Knapweed, Cat's-ear, mulleins, evening-primroses, buttercups and grasses like False Oat-grass and Cock's-foot. Showy exotics such as Japanese Knotweed, Shasta Daisy, michaelmas-daisies, goldenrods and Cotton Thistle may also be conspicuous. These come from many parts of the northern hemisphere, both Old World and New World. Eventually grasses can increase their dominance and form established grassland resembling neutral permanent grassland (but usually without old grassland indicators). Characteristic plants within such grassland include Common Knapweed, Yarrow and Hogweed. This grassland generally classifies as NVC category *MG1* (False Oat-grass grassland), which is not considered particularly conservation-worthy, but can be surprisingly rich in species. Grassland can eventually give way to scrub as woody species such as Grey Willow, Goat Willow, Butterfly-bush, Hawthorn, Elder, Blackthorn, Silver Birch, roses, brambles and Sycamore move in. The secondary woodland that finally forms after several decades is not infrequently dominated by Sycamore or Silver Birch.

There can be much local variation in the details of the above, but this is a typical scenario on post-industrial sites in Coventry, Birmingham, Solihull, Leamington, Warwick, Rugby and Nuneaton. Where sites are slightly more acidic (e.g. some sites in north Coventry and Nuneaton), calcifuges such as Bracken, Gorse, Broom, Downy Birch, Wood Sage and other species more characteristic of acid grassland may enter the flora. Where sites are associated with limestone, you may start to encounter some of the calcicoles associated with calcareous quarries.

Plants of calcareous quarries

These can harbour many of the species associated with the previous category, but additionally feature numerous calcicoles that require lime-rich soils. These calcicoles can feature in all the successional stages leading up to secondary woodland. Characteristic species of the earliest successional stages or barer areas include Wild Carrot, Kidney Vetch, Oxeye Daisy, Common and Narrow-leaved Bird's-foot-trefoils, Wild Mignonette, Carline Thistle, Salad Burnet, Yellow-wort, Wild Basil, Marjoram, eyebrights and Fern-grass. The tall-herb stage typically features Wild Parsnip, Greater Knapweed, Musk Thistle and Hoary Ragwort. Orchids can include Common spotted, Bee, Greater Butterfly and Common Twayblade, though they are somewhat sporadic and unpredictable in appearance. The very rare Man Orchid hangs on precariously at one site where it needs to be fenced against rabbit grazing.

At Blue Lias sites, where acute drying out of the substrate can occur, dense grassland and scrub may struggle to develop, with weak growth of Tor-grass and roses, accompanied by drought-tolerant species such as Dwarf Thistle and Autumn Gentian, lasting for many years (e.g. on the main spoilheap of Nelson's Quarry, Stockton). Where conditions are less extreme, more fully expressed calcareous grassland may form in 15-20 years (see the Permanent Grassland chapter), and rabbit activity may maintain this for several decades. However, in the absence of management shrubs and trees will eventually gain the upper hand and include many of the same species found on industrial waste ground, though birch, Gorse and Broom are scarce or absent, Ash is common, and Wild Privet and Wayfaring-tree are often present. Open-structured calcareous scrub can harbour considerable interest

Plants characteristic of calcareous quarries

Salad Burnet

Wild Mignonette

Wild Basil

Man Orchid

Musk Thistle

Oxeye Daisy

Plants characteristic of calcareous quarries

Kidney Vetch

Wild Parsnip

Autumn Gentian

Carline Thistle

Greater Knapweed

Wild Carrot

with species such as Common Spotted-orchid, Common Twayblade, Greater Butterfly-orchid, Hawkweed Oxtongue, Hemp-agrimony and Spurge-laurel. Because of the scarcity of old limestone grassland in Warwickshire, calcicolous plants are far more dependent on disturbed sites such as limestone quarries and cuttings than in most chalk and limestone districts of Britain.

Plants of non-calcareous quarries
These quarries tend to be much less species-rich than calcareous ones, with fewer rarities. The flora can resemble that of industrial wasteland but most of the quarries on the Nuneaton ridge have rather acidic soil and feature calcifuges such as Broom, Gorse, Bracken, Wood Sage, Foxglove, Sheep's Sorrel, Sticky Mouse-ear, Downy Birch and occasionally Heather. Most of the old sandstone quarries associated with Coventry, Warwick and Kenilworth have reverted to secondary woodland (where not infilled and built over) and lack a flora of any note.

Plants of sand and gravel workings
The drier parts of sand and gravel workings tend to pass through a succession similar to well-drained industrial wasteland and typically at a fast rate, with dense scrub often developing within 15-20 years. The most abundant species include Common Ragwort, Weld, Spear Thistle, Teasel and melilots. Local gravel workings also tend to feature extensive wetlands and water bodies that soon acquire marsh, swamp and carr (see Chapter 8, Water Courses and Wetland) and such areas typically revert to Alder and willow woodland within a few decades unless managed.

Plants of railway land
The plant communities are again much influenced by underlying geology, with calcifuges such Broom, Gorse, Downy Birch and occasionally patches of heather evident on railway land in northwest Warwickshire, but a rich variety of calcicoles in any cuttings and sidings on the Lias of south and east Warwickshire. The ballast associated with the tracks and the compacted soils beside this are interesting plant habitats, and there is little doubt that many disturbance-loving plants have used railway lines to spread into parts of Britain where they were not originally found, most notably Sea Mouse-ear.

Plants of dumps, landfill sites and farmyards
The organically-rich conditions that can develop where garden or domestic waste is dumped favour highly competitive, fast-growing species such as Stinging Nettle, Fat-hen, Common Orache, goosefoots, Knotgrass, Hogweed, Hemlock, Rosebay Willowherb, Common Ragwort, Pineappleweed, Mugwort, docks, burdocks, thistles, brambles, Elder and Japanese Knotweed. Smaller and less competitive species are usually squeezed out of the flora, unless there are patches of skeletal ground. Farmyards can develop similar floras, though typically with arable weeds and escaped crop species much in evidence (e.g. poppies and Oil-seed Rape). Organic waste from silage and slurry can result in strong growth of nitrogen-tolerant plants such as Good-King-Henry, Fat-hen, Common Orache, Red Goosefoot, Fig-leaved Goosefoot, Stinging Nettle, Hemlock and docks.

Plants of imported sea sand

Sand from the coast has evidently been imported to Warwickshire on a number of occasions, and has resulted in naturalised populations of plants that one would not expect to see in the heart of Britain. These include Sand Cat's-tail, Sand Couch, Small-flowered Evening-primrose, Marram, Sea Rocket, Prickly Saltwort, Sand Sedge, Rough Star-thistle, Sticky Stork's-bill and Creeping Willow (the last mentioned plant also being an extinct former native of wet heath at Sutton Park). Emscote Power Station, Warwick, was the most interesting site for such plants. The sand, which was from a Welsh dune, was used to help extinguish a subterranean coal-dust fire (such fires can burn for several years unless extinguished). Unfortunately, much of this site has now been developed.

Losses and gains

Very few species associated with disturbed ground have shown a demonstrable decrease (some casuals reported from disturbed ground only represented transient populations). This probably reflects the fact that the amount of disturbed land in all categories has tended to increase over the course of the twentieth century and is being constantly colonised. It will be interesting to see how the species in the plant list at the end of this chapter fare in the twenty-first century when the amount of industrial wasteland decreases through development, and many sites finally succeed to dense scrub and secondary woodland. Only four native or naturalised species characteristic of disturbed ground are considered to have become extinct in Warwickshire, and all have declined nationally:

- Narrow-leaved Bittercress *Cardamine impatiens* – last recorded from two diorite quarries south of Atherstone, up to 1963
- Shepherd's Cress *Teesdalia nudicaulis* – last recorded at Flecknoe in 1961
- Stinking Goosefoot *Chenopodium vulvaria* – last recorded at Langley Hall in 1960, its decline nationally possibly due to reduced use of dung as a fertilizer (it likes ruderal areas enriched with animal dung)
- White Horehound *Marrubium vulgare* – last recorded in about 1958, most local records may have represented casuals, though there is archaeological evidence of its presence in Warwickshire

But many species have increased, reflecting a national pattern of expansion as neophytes increase their foothold in this country. However, it is important to distinguish genuine increase from any increase in records resulting from better recording of disturbed land and better recording of casual plants in recent decades.

Local disturbed ground sites you can visit

Inevitably, a high proportion of quarries and old industrial sites lack public access and are deemed hazardous, and that includes some of our finest sites such as Bishops Bowl near Harbury and Nelsons Quarry near Stockton. Gravel pits provide a more favourable situation – several are Warwickshire Wildlife Trust reserves and Warwickshire County Council Country Parks with open access. A number of others are private nature reserves with controlled access.

Imported sea-sand plants

Sand Couch

Sea Rocket

Small-flowered Evening-primrose

Creeping Willow

Prickly Saltwort

Sand Cat's-tail

Calcareous quarries, cuttings and spoilheaps

- Ashlawn Cutting, Rugby SP516732 (a Warwickshire Wildlife Trust reserve) – supports a variety of conditions with some established limestone grassland, small wet features and some ruderal habitat. Newton Cutting NE of Rugby SP530786 (part of the same disused line) has similar conditions.
- Ettington by-pass, Ettington SP263490 – a fairly young road verge and round-about featuring Pyramidal Orchid, Bee Orchid and Dropwort amongst its numerous calcicoles. Other calcareous road cuttings of note include the Fosse Way near Darlingscott SP256422 and the relatively new Southam by-pass SP420626.
- Goldicote Cutting, near Ettington SP247505 (a Warwickshire Wildlife Trust reserve) – calcareous ruderal, grassland and wetlands.
- Harbury Spoilbank, near Harbury SP384598 (a Warwickshire Wildlife Trust reserve) – calcareous grassland, scrub and disturbed ground on a spoilheap resulting from construction of adjacent railway cutting in the 1840s. Many calcicoles present including Carline, Dwarf and Woolly Thistles, Ploughman's-spikenard, Hawkweed Oxtongue, Common Twayblade, Autumn Gentian, Wild Parsnip and Yellow-wort.
- Newbold Quarry, Rugby SP497770 (a Warwickshire Wildlife Trust reserve) – a few species of interest including Wild Strawberry, Common Twayblade and Bee Orchid.
- Stockton Cutting SP437651 (a Warwickshire Wildlife Trust reserve) – an abandoned Blue Lias quarry and associated railway cutting featuring patches of calcareous ruderal habitat with calcicoles such as Dwarf and Woolly Thistles, Yellow-wort, Hairy Violet, Autumn Gentian, Blue Fleabane and Greater Butterfly-orchid.
- Ufton Fields SP378615 (a Warwickshire Wildlife Trust reserve) – features calcareous grassland and scrub on former shallow limestone workings plus some semi-improved neutral grassland that predates this. Many calcicoles, including Man Orchid (at its only surviving site in the County), Autumn Gentian, Wild Basil, Common Twayblade and Greater Butterfly-orchid.

Gravel workings

- Brandon Marsh SP386761 (a Warwickshire Wildlife Trust reserve) – a large site featuring a mosaic of wet and dry habitats that have mostly developed over abandoned gravel workings. Still much ruderal habitat with disturbance-loving plants (much encouraged by the local rabbit population) and a very long plant list for the site as a whole.
- Kingsbury Water Park, near Kingsbury SP205960 (a Warwickshire County Council Country Park) – most disturbed areas have now reverted to grassland, wetland or wet woodland. More disturbed conditions can be found at the adjacent Middleton Lakes area SP193980, which is a Royal Society for the Protection of Birds reserve.
- Ryton Pools, near Bubbenhall SP373726 (a Warwickshire County Council Country Park) – partially landfilled but still with some areas of sparse vegetation, especially within the butterfly reserve between the Country Park and Ryton Police College.

- Whitacre Heath SP209931 (a Warwickshire Wildlife Trust reserve) – now largely wetland and scrub, but with a little ruderal ground featuring species like Blue Fleabane.

Former industrial sites and spoilheaps

- Baddesley Common SP277979 – disturbed land and heathland partly associated with a series of spoilheaps and quarries.
- Claybrookes Marsh, Coventry SP380769 (a Warwickshire Wildlife Trust reserve) – formerly a railhead serving Binley Colliery, now a complex habitat mosaic of ruderal habitat plus scrub and wetland, with disturbance-loving plants such as Weld, Mugwort and Hare's-foot Clover, plus a very strong population of Common Spotted-orchid.
- Pooley Fields and Alvecote Pools SK256037 (a Warwickshire Wildlife Trust reserve and Warwickshire County Council Country Park) – contains areas of acid grassland and disturbed ground that have formed on an old spoilheap and adjacent land.
- Emscote Power Station, Warwick SP300653 – ruderal ground which features sand bought in from a Welsh sand dune, with a number of associated plants (e.g. Marram Grass). Now largely developed, though a small patch remains as open access land, and may still be supporting plants such as Ploughman's Spikenard, Sticky Groundsel, Soapwort, Viper's-bugloss and a hybrid swarm of evening-primroses.
- Harbury Spoilbank, near Harbury SP384598 (a Warwickshire Wildlife Trust reserve) – resembling a limestone quarry in botanical terms, but actually an old spoilheap resulting from an adjacent railway cutting. Ongoing management ensures that ruderal habitat, rich in calcicoles, persists.

Disused railways

- Ashlawn Cutting, Rugby (see above).
- The Crackley-Burton Green Greenway, near Kenilworth SP290739.
- Goldicote Cutting, near Ettington (see above).
- Henley Sidings, near Henley-in-Arden SP147667 (a Warwickshire Wildlife Trust reserve) – features limestone grassland (from imported spoil) with Woolly Thistle, Fairy Flax and Wild Carrot, plus plants of relatively unimproved neutral grassland such as Cowslip and Lady's Bedstraw.
- The Offchurch Greenway, between Radford Semele SP353649 and Bilton, Rugby.
- The Stratford Greenway, running SW from Stratford-upon-Avon SP195539.
- Weddington Nature Walk, Nuneaton SP360940.

Disturbed ground plant list (excluding casuals)

Trees and shrubs

- ✔ Downy Birch *Betula pubescens* – one of the most invasive woody species of the acidic quarries on the Nuneaton ridge
- ✔ Broom *Cytisus scoparius* – in the north, it avoids lime
- ✘ Butterfly-bush *Buddleja davidii* – a neophyte, also on walls and roofs, increasing

✔ Glaucous Dog-rose *Rosa caesia* ssp. *vosagiaca* – this subspecies mainly in limestone quarries, rare
✘ Mock-orange *Philadelphus coronarius* – a neophyte, a popular garden shrub that occasionally naturalises
✘ Garden Privet *Ligustrum ovalifolium* – a neophyte, popular in gardens
✔ Grey Willow *Salix cinerea* – one of the most invasive woody species of disturbed land, especially in damper areas

Grasses and sedges

✘ Foxtail Barley *Hordeum jubatum* – a rare but increasing neophyte
✘ Wall Barley *Hordeum murinum* – an archaeophyte
✘ Black Bent *Agrostis gigantea* – an archaeophyte, also on arable land
✘ Green Bristle-grass *Setaria viridis* – a neophyte, also on arable land (several other bristle-grasses can occur on disturbed ground as casuals from bird-seed)
✘ Barren Brome *Anisantha sterilis* – an archaeophyte, also on arable land
✘ Great Brome *Anisantha diandra* – an increasing neophyte
✘ Canary-grass *Phalaris canariensis* – a neophyte
✘ Rat's-tail Fescue *Vulpia myuros* – an archaeophyte
✔ Squirreltail Fescue *Vulpia bromoides*
✔ Crested Hair-grass *Koeleria macrantha* – calcareous ground, also calcareous grassland, probably declining
✔ Early Hair-grass *Aira praecox* – avoids lime, declining
✔ Silver Hair-grass *Aira caryophyllacea* – declining?
✘ Hare's-tail *Lagurus ovatus* – a neophyte
✔ Annual Meadow-grass *Poa annua*
✔ Flattened Meadow-grass *Poa compressa* – also walls
✔ Sand Sedge *Carex arenaria* – a coastal species that occasionally occurs inland, rare
✔ Soft-brome *Bromus hordeaceus*
✘ Lesser Soft-brome *Bromus* x *pseudothominei* – a hybrid neophyte
✘ Slender Soft-brome *Bromus lepidus* – a neophyte
✘ Wild-oat *Avena fatua* – an archaeophyte, also on arable land

Other flowering plants

✘ Sweet Alison *Lobularia maritima* – a neophyte
✘ Apple-of-Peru *Nicandra physalodes* – a neophyte
✘ Balm *Melissa officinalis* – a neophyte, grown as a garden herb
✔ Red Bartsia *Odontites vernus* – prefers calcareous ground
✘ Yellow Bartsia *Parentucellia viscosa* – a scarce native that has spread inland and is new and increasing in Warwickshire
✔ Wild Basil *Clinopodium vulgare* – calcareous ground, also calcareous grassland
✔ Basil Thyme *Clinopodium acinos* – calcareous ground, also calcareous grassland
✘ Peach-leaved Bellflower *Campanula persicifolia* – a neophyte, rare
✔ Field Bindweed *Convolvulus arvensis*
✔ Bird's-foot *Ornithopus perpusillus* – declining
✔ Narrow-leaved Bird's-foot-trefoil *Lotus glaber* – calcareous ground, also calcareous grassland

✗ Red Bistort *Persicaria amplexicaulis* – a rare neophyte
✔ Hairy Bitter-cress *Cardamine hirsuta*
✗ Bladder-senna *Colutea arborescens* – a neophyte
✗ Borage *Borago officinalis* – a neophyte, also grown as a crop
✔ Salad Burnet *Sanguisorba minor* – on calcareous ground, also calcareous grassland
✔ Greater Butterfly-orchid *Platanthera chlorantha* – calcareous ground, including scrub
✗ Bastard Cabbage *Rapistrum rugosum* – an increasing neophyte
✔ Bladder Campion *Silene vulgaris*
✔ Wild Carrot *Daucus carota* – prefers calcareous ground, also calcareous grassland
✗ Greater Celandine *Chelidonium majus* – a neophyte, also on walls
✔ Common Centaury *Centaurium erythraea*
✔ Charlock *Sinapis arvensis* – an archaeophyte, also on arable land
✗ Sulphur Cinquefoil *Potentilla recta* – a scarce but increasing neophyte
✔ Hare's-foot Clover *Trifolium arvense*
✔ White Clover *Trifolium repens* – also grassland
✔ Colt's-foot *Tussilago farfara*
✗ Russian Comfrey *Symphytum* x *uplandicum* – a neophyte hybrid that is increasing
✗ White Comfrey *Symphytum orientale* – an increasing neophyte
✗ Perennial Cornflower *Centaurea montana* – a neophyte, also grown in gardens
✔ Common Cornsalad *Valerianella locusta*
✗ Keeled-fruited Cornsalad *Valerianella carinata* – also walls and pavements, an increasing archaeophyte
✗ Yellow Corydalis *Pseudofumaria lutea* – a neophyte, also walls and pavements, increasing
✗ Wall Cotoneaster *Cotoneaster horizontalis* – a neophyte, also on walls and pavements
✔ Cowherb *Vaccaria hispanica* – rare
✔ Dove's-foot Crane's-bill *Geranium molle*
✔ Long-stalked Crane's-bill *Geranium columbinum* – calcareous ground, also calcareous grassland
✗ Small-flowered Crane's-bill *Geranium pusillum* – an archaeophyte
✗ Hoary Cress *Lepidium draba* – an increasing neophyte
✔ Thale Cress *Arabidopsis thaliana*
✔ Oxeye Daisy *Leucanthemum vulgare* – mostly calcareous ground, though a frequent species of wildflower seed mixtures applied elsewhere
✗ Shasta Daisy *Leucanthemum* x *superbum* – a neophyte hybrid, also used in wildflower seed mixtures
✗ Dame's-violet *Hesperis matronalis* – a neophyte
✗ Red Dead-nettle *Lamium purpureum* – an archaeophyte, also arable land and other habitats
✗ Spotted Dead-nettle *Lamium maculatum* – a neophyte, also in gardens
✗ Dittander *Lepidium latifolium* – a native of the coast, but not of Warwickshire where occasionally naturalising
✔ Broad-leaved Dock *Rumex obtusifolius*
✗ Common Evening-primrose *Oenothera biennis* – a neophyte (all three evening-primroses listed hybridise with each other in Warwickshire)

✗ Large-flowered Evening-primrose *Oenothera glazioviana* – a neophyte
✗ Small-flowered Evening-primrose *Oenothera cambrica* – a neophyte
✗ Broad-leaved Everlasting-pea *Lathyrus latifolius* – an increasing neophyte
✗ Two-flowered Everlasting-pea *Lathyrus grandiflorus* – a scarce but increasing neophyte
✔ Eyebrights *Euphrasia* sp – on calcareous ground, most populations are probably *E. nemorosa*
✔ Fat-hen *Chenopodium album* – abundant, also on arable land
✗ Fennel *Foeniculum vulgare* – an archaeophyte
✗ Feverfew *Tanacetum parthenium* – an archaeophyte
✗ Flax *Linum usitatissimum* – a neophyte crop and bird seed mixture escape
✔ Pale Flax *Linum bienne* – rare
✔ Blue Fleabane *Erigeron acer* – increasing
✗ Canadian Fleabane *Conyza canadensis* – an increasing neophyte
✗ Mexican Fleabane *Erigeron karvinskianus* – an increasing neophyte
✗ Flixweed *Descurainia sophia* – an archaeophyte
✔ Early Forget-me-not *Myosotis ramosissima* – prefers calcareous ground
✗ Field Forget-me-not *Myosotis arvensis* – an archaeophyte
✗ Common Fumitory *Fumaria officinalis* – an archaeophyte
✗ Gallant-soldier *Galinsoga parviflora* – an increasing neophyte, also on arable land
✔ Autumn Gentian *Gentianella amarella* – calcareous quarries, also calcareous grassland, scarce
✗ Goat's-rue *Galega officinalis* – a neophyte
✗ Canadian Goldenrod *Solidago canadensis* – an increasing neophyte
✗ Early Goldenrod *Solidago gigantea* – an increasing neophyte
✗ Good-King-Henry *Chenopodium bonus-henricus* – an archaeophyte
✗ Fig-leaved Goosefoot *Chenopodium ficifolium* – farmyards and manure heaps, an archaeophyte that is probably increasing
✗ Maple-leaved Goosefoot *Chenopodium hybridum* – an archaeophyte, especially tips, also on arable land
✔ Red Goosefoot *Chenopodium rubrum* – increasing
✔ Groundsel *Senecio vulgaris* – also frequent on arable land
✗ Sticky Groundsel *Senecio viscosus* – an increasing neophyte
✗ Beaked Hawk's-beard *Crepis vesicaria* – an increasing neophyte
✔ Hawkweeds *Hieracium* spp. – a very difficult group, though *H. diaphanum, H. exotericum, H. salticola, H. maculatum* and *H. vagum* seem to favour disturbed sites
✗ Horse-radish *Armoracia rusticana* – an archaeophyte, also along road verges
✔ Hound's-tongue *Cynoglossum officinale* – calcareous ground, scarce
✔ Greater Knapweed *Centaurea scabiosa* – calcareous quarries, also calcareous grassland
✔ Knotgrass *Polygonum aviculare* – also arable land
✗ Equal-leaved Knotgrass *Polygonum arenastrum* – an archaeophyte, increasing?
✗ Himalayan Knotweed *Persicaria wallichii* – a rare neophyte, mostly at urban sites
✗ Giant Knotweed *Fallopia sachalinensis* – a rare but increasing neophyte
✗ Japanese Knotweed *Fallopia japonica* – an increasing neophyte, also on grassy road verges

✘ Laburnum *Laburnum anagyroides* – a neophyte garden escape
✘ A lady's-mantle *Alchemilla mollis* – an increasing neophyte
✔ Great Lettuce *Lactuca virosa* – increasing
✘ Prickly Lettuce *Lactuca serriola* – an increasing archaeophyte
✘ Garden Lobelia *Lobelia erinus* – a neophyte
✘ Lucerne *Medicago sativa* – a neophyte (escaped fodder crop)
✘ Garden Lupin *Lupinus polyphyllus* – a neophyte (garden escape), wild populations include hybrids with the next species (called Russell Lupin)
✘ Tree Lupin *Lupinus arboreus* – a neophyte (a garden escape)
✘ Common Mallow *Malva sylvestris* – an archaeophyte
✘ Dwarf Mallow *Malva neglecta* – an archaeophyte
✘ Pot Marigold *Calendula officinalis* – a neophyte, also grown in gardens
✔ Marjoram *Origanum vulgare* – calcareous quarries and cuttings, also grassland
✘ Scentless Mayweed *Tripleurospermum inodorum* – an archaeophyte, also on arable land
✔ Black Medick *Medicago lupulina* – also grasslands
✘ White Melilot *Melilotus albus* – a neophyte
✘ Ribbed Melilot *Melilotus officinalis* – a neophyte
✘ Small Melilot *Melilotus indicus* – a scarce neophyte
✘ Tall Melilot *Melilotus altissimus* – a neophyte
✘ Annual Mercury *Mercurialis annua* – an increasing archaeophyte
✘ Confused Michaelmas-daisy *Aster novi-belgii* – a neophyte, also on grassy road verges
✘ Narrow-leaved Michaelmas-daisy *Aster lanceolatus* – an increasing neophyte
✘ White Mignonette *Reseda alba* – a rare neophyte
✔ Wild Mignonette *Reseda lutea* – usually on calcareous ground
✘ Spear Mint *Mentha spicata* – an archaeophyte
✘ Montbretia *Crocosmia* x *crocosmiiflora* – a neophyte hybrid, garden escape
✔ Sea Mouse-ear *Cerastium diffusum* – increasing along railways
✘ Mugwort *Artemisia vulgaris* – an archaeophyte, also along road verges
✔ Dark Mullein *Verbascum nigrum* – prefers calcareous ground, also in gardens
✔ Great Mullein *Verbascum thapsus* – a native but frequent garden escape
✘ Orange Mullein *Verbascum phlomoides* – a scarce but increasing neophyte
✘ Twiggy Mullein *Verbascum virgatum* – a rare neophyte
✔ Black Mustard *Brassica nigra* – also roadsides and arable land
✘ Hoary Mustard *Hirschfeldia incana* – a rare but increasing neophyte
✔ Deadly Nightshade *Atropa belladonna* – scarce
✔ Common Orache *Atriplex patula* – also on arable land and saline ground
✘ Garden Orache *Atriplex hortensis* – a neophyte that is possibly increasing
✔ Spear-leaved Orache *Atriplex prostrata* – increasing, also along salt-treated roads
✔ Bee Orchid *Ophrys apifera* – also permanent grassland to a smaller extent
✔ Man Orchid *Acera anthropophorum* – calcareous ground, rare (just Ufton Fields now), calcareous grassland elsewhere in Britain
✔ Pyramidal Orchid *Anacamptis pyramidalis* – calcareous ground, more typical of calcareous grassland elsewhere in Britain
✔ Bristly Oxtongue *Picris echioides* – mainly on calcareous ground, increasing

✔ Hawkweed Oxtongue *Picris hieracioides* – calcareous ground, also limestone grassland

✔ Wild Parsnip *Pastinaca sativa* – usually on calcareous ground, also calcareous grassland

✔ Annual Pearlwort *Sagina apetala*

✔ Procumbent Pearlwort *Sagina procumbens*

✘ Pearly Everlasting *Anaphalis margaritacea* – a scarce neophyte

✘ Narrow-leaved Pepperwort *Lepidium ruderale* – an archaeophyte

✔ Smith's Pepperwort *Lepidium heterophyllum* – avoiding lime, rare

✔ Pale Persicaria *Persicaria lapathifolia* – also on arable land

✘ White Pigweed *Amaranthus albus* – a scarce neophyte

✘ Pineappleweed *Matricaria discoidea* – a neophyte

✔ Deptford Pink *Dianthus armeria* – rare and declined

✔ Greater Plantain *Plantago major*

✔ Ploughman's-spikenard *Inula conyza* – especially on calcareous ground

✘ Common Poppy *Papaver rhoeas* – an archaeophyte, also on arable land

✘ Long-headed Poppy *Papaver dubium* – an archaeophyte, also on arable land, ssp. *lecoquii* (Babington's Poppy) prefers calcareous soils in S Warwickshire

✘ Opium Poppy *Papaver somniferum* – an archaeophyte, also grown in gardens

✘ Welsh Poppy *Meconopsis cambrica* – a native of west Britain but not Warwickshire, also grown in gardens

✔ Common Ragwort *Senecio jacobaea* – also in grasslands

✔ Hoary Ragwort *Senecio erucifolius* – calcareous sites, also calcareous grassland

✘ Oxford Ragwort *Senecio squalidus* – an increasing neophyte, also on walls

✔ Redshank *Persicaria maculosa* – also on arable land

✘ Eastern Rocket *Sisymbrium orientale* – a neophyte

✘ Tall Rocket *Sisymbrium altissimum* – a neophyte

✔ Sainfoin *Onobrychis viciifolia* – on calcareous ground

✔ Fine-leaved Sandwort *Minuartia hybrida* – scarce

✔ Thyme-leaved Sandwort *Arenaria serpyllifolia* – also walls

✘ Shaggy-soldier *Galinsoga quadriradiata* – an increasing neophyte

✘ Shepherd's-purse *Capsella bursa-pastoris* – an archaeophyte, also on arable land

✘ Snapdragon *Antirrhinum majus* – an increasing neophyte, also on walls

✘ Snow-in-summer *Cerastium tomentosum* – an increasing neophyte

✘ Soapwort *Saponaria officinalis* – an archaeophyte

✔ Prickly Sow-thistle *Sonchus asper*

✔ Smooth Sow-thistle *Sonchus oleraceus*

✔ Wall Speedwell *Veronica arvensis* – also walls and pavements

✘ Caper Spurge *Euphorbia lathyris* – an increasing archaeophyte

✔ Sand Spurrey *Spergularia rubra* – declining

✔ Imperforate St John's-wort *Hypericum maculatum*

✘ Reflexed Stonecrop *Sedum rupestre* – a neophyte, also on walls

✔ Common Stork's-bill *Erodium cicutarium*

✘ Garden Strawberry *Fragaria* x *ananassa* – a neophyte, often naturalising from garden escapes

✘ Swine-cress *Coronopus squamatus* – an archaeophyte that is possibly increasing

✘ Lesser Swine-cress *Coronopus didymus* – a neophyte
✔ Tansy *Tanacetum vulgare* – also grown in gardens
✔ Hairy Tare *Vicia hirsuta*
✔ Smooth Tare *Vicia tetrasperma* – also on arable land
✔ Carline Thistle *Carlina vulgaris* – calcareous quarries, also calcareous grassland
✘ Cotton Thistle *Onopordum acanthium* – an archaeophyte, also grown in gardens
✔ Dwarf Thistle *Cirsium acaule* – calcareous ground, also calcareous grassland
✘ Thorn-apple *Datura stramonium* – a neophyte
✔ Common Toadflax *Linaria vulgaris*
✘ Pale Toadflax *Linaria repens* – an archaeophyte
✘ Purple Toadflax *Linaria purpurea* – a neophyte
✘ Small Toadflax *Chaenorhinum minus* – an archaeophyte
✘ Spreading Treacle-mustard *Erysimum cheiranthoides* – an archaeophyte
✔ Hop Trefoil *Trifolium campestre* – also grassland
✔ Lesser Trefoil *Trifolium dubium* – also grassland
✔ Common Twayblade *Listera ovata* – especially in open scrub of calcareous quarries
✔ Red Valerian *Centranthus ruber* – a neophyte, also walls and buildings, increasing
✘ Vervain *Verbena officinalis* – a rare archaeophyte
✔ Common Vetch *Vicia sativa* – also in grassland
✘ Crown Vetch *Securigera varia* – a rare neophyte
✘ Fine-leaved Vetch *Vicia tenuifolia* – a rare neophyte
✔ Kidney Vetch *Anthyllis vulneraria* – calcareous ground, also limestone grassland, declining
✘ Yellow Vetchling *Lathyrus aphaca* – a native, but probably not of Warwickshire where rare
✔ Viper's-bugloss *Echium vulgare*
✘ Annual Wall-rocket *Diplotaxis muralis* – a neophyte
✘ Perennial Wall-rocket *Diplotaxis tenuifolia* – a rare archaeophyte
✘ Weld *Reseda luteola* – an archaeophyte
✔ Common Whitlowgrass *Erophila verna* – also pavement cracks and walls
✔ Glabrous Whitlowgrass *Erophila glabresens* – as per Common Whitlowgrass, from which it was only distinguished in 1987
✔ Hairy Whitlowgrass *Erophila majuscula* – as per Common Whitlowgrass, from which it was only distinguished in 1987, the rarest of the three
✘ American Willowherb *Epilobium ciliatum* – an increasing neophyte, also on walls, pavements
✔ Broad-leaved Willowherb *Epilobium montanum*
✘ Rosebay Willowherb *Chamerion angustifolium* – probably not native to Warwickshire (first recorded here in 1830, late for such a conspicuous plant)
✔ Spear-leaved Willowherb *Epilobium lanceolatum* – scarce
✔ Square-stalked Willowherb *Epilobium tetragonum*
✘ Wormwood *Artemisia absinthium* – an archaeophyte
✔ Yellow-wort *Blackstonia perfoliata* – mainly calcareous ground, also calcareous grassland

Chapter 12

The Built Environment

Built structures, including walls, buildings, bridges, pavements and roads

Garden flowers and the planted flowers of landscaped business parks, urban flower beds, shrubberies or roof gardens, do not fall within the scope of this book. But naturalised wild plants and a plethora of casual species still manage to colonise and exploit some of our most artificial environments, including walls, roofs, pavements, bridges and surfaced roads. For some species, these are their favoured habitats in Warwickshire, and the challenging conditions associated with such locations means that they experience relatively little competition from other plants.

Maidenhair Spleenwort and Reflexed Stonecrop on a Harbury wall.

Solid built structures such as stone buildings and stone walls have existed in Warwickshire since at least Romano-British times and will almost certainly have supported certain native species such as some of the ferns listed below. However, the quantity and variety of built structures increased dramatically following the start of the industrial revolution in the late eighteenth century through the construction of factories, mills, canals and eventually railway, road and river channel infrastructures, tiled roofs (in preference to thatched ones) and pavements. Today, many of these features may be derelict and have even greater potential for wild plants, including many of the species typically associated with disturbed ground. However, it is the specialists of built structures that this chapter is most concerned with.

The types of built structures used by plants

The habitats considered in this chapter are typically characterised by a hard and impervious surface, an absence or minimum of soil, and a need by plants to root directly into rock, mortar, brick or concrete. Such conditions are similar to those that occur on natural cliffs and gullies, and about twenty of the species listed in the plant list at the end of this chapter are British natives that have spread from those natural habitats. Where such habitats occur within highly urbanised or industrial settings a variety of pollutants can influence the plants that grow there, and include pollutants that are waterborne, atmospheric or leaching out of the substrate upon which the plants are growing.

Walls

Walls, especially old ones, are an important type of built structure for plants (see Gilbert, 1992) and there is a good deal of variation in the conditions they afford. This can be related to the type of wall involved (e.g. whether it is a dividing wall or a retaining one), from what materials it is constructed, what mortar is used (if any), whether the wall is shaded or wet, which part of the wall is being considered, its age (including both the stone/brick plus the mortar, which may have been retouched since the wall was built), and the other habitats that surround it. The walls of buildings can be constructed of brick, stone, plaster, concrete, metal or wood. Old limestone walls are particularly frequent in the south of the county, with old sandstone and brick ones predominating in the centre, north and west. Walls constructed of limestone or with lime-based mortar will be calcareous. Sandstone and granite walls are generally acidic. The walls of well-maintained and modern buildings typically have negligible value for plants.

Red Valerian growing on a dry stone wall in Ilmington.

Surfaced ground

The modern urban and industrial landscapes of Warwickshire are characterised by much surfaced land, in which tarmac and concrete mask the underlying soil. Such ground is usually kept free of significant vegetation by usage, herbicides, pollutants or simply the harshness of the conditions. Gaining water and nutrients can be very difficult on such surfaces. But where such ground falls into neglect, weathering can produce cracks in it that ameliorate the harshness, and a simple soil can form from accumulated leaf litter, faeces and dust. Weathered concrete produces calcareous conditions.

Weathering concrete at Cross Hands Quarry featuring patches of Biting Stonecrop.

Salty (saline) road verges

Most of our busier roads are now treated with salt in cold winter spells. Much of that salt becomes diluted by melt water and drains away, but a proportion gets sprayed onto the kerb or any central reservation. The special plants of saline road verges are also considered in this chapter.

Danish Scurvy-grass flowers produce a spring 'frosting' of a salty road verge in south Coventry, an increasingly common sight throughout Warwickshire in April.

The plants of built structures

About fifty native or naturalised plant species rely heavily or entirely upon built structures for their existence in Warwickshire, or are extremely frequent at such locations (see plant list at end of chapter). Most of these are neophytes, though a high proportion of the ferns are native and can be found growing in natural locations such as damp rock faces beside wooded streams, especially in north and west Britain. There is also a good number of short-lived casuals, garden escapes and strays from other habitats that have been reported exploiting cracks in paving stones, rockeries and garden walls in Warwickshire. Neglected walls and crumbling buildings away from gardens can support many of the species more typically associated with disturbed ground, as a train journey between Coventry and Birmingham, or a walk around a derelict factory will soon reveal.

The true specialists of built structures are for the most part slow-growing, stress-tolerant perennials, with low competitiveness in any other habitat. Many have wind-dispersed seeds or (in the case of ferns) spores, though a proportion, including Snapdragon, Wallflower, Greater Celandine, Yellow Corydalis, Ivy-leaved Toadflax and Pellitory-of-the-wall, use ants and have an oily coating to their seed or an oily structure known as an 'elaisome' to make the seeds more attractive to these insects. Elder has berries attractive to birds such as Starlings, which frequently roost on walls and bridges. This may account for the frequency of this shrub on walls. Yew, Hawthorn and Gooseberry on walls probably have similar origins.

Plants of walls

Gilbert (1992) classifies the plants of walls into three categories. ***Selective species*** are those for which walls are their main habitat in Britain, and he lists twenty such plants, most of which are recorded from Warwickshire (though not all are quite as restricted to walls here as Gilbert suggests). These are highlighted in the plant list below with an asterix. ***Companion species*** are those that frequently colonise walls but have no special preference for this habitat (plants like Oxford Ragwort, Butterfly-bush, Rosebay Willowherb, Hairy Bitter-cress, Wild Strawberry, Procumbent Pearlwort, Thyme-leaved Sandwort, Wall Barley, Barren Brome and Male-fern). ***Accidental species*** are those that have strayed onto walls from surrounding habitats, and there are dozens of these. The plant list includes all the selective species plus the companion species that have a significant proportion of their Warwickshire populations on walls.

Dividing walls are those exposed on both sides, and characterise property boundaries. Most have mortar between bricks or stones, but dry-stone walls lack mortar. Older, thicker dividing walls tend to be the better ones for wildflowers. It can take several decades for a cement-mortared wall to weather sufficiently to start supporting higher plants (mosses and lichens can appear more quickly). Dry-stone walls are particularly frequent in the south of Warwickshire, both as field boundaries (as an alternative to a hedge) and in property boundaries in villages such as Ilmington and Whichford. Such walls seem to suit certain species such as Intermediate Polypody, Shining Crane's-bill and Biting Stonecrop, but not others such as Wall-rue. Dry-stone walls have been the subject of detailed studies in a number of English counties. In the Chew Valley of North Somerset and Avon, 291 species of plant were recorded from such walls; in SE Essex 286; in Middlesex 204; in Cambridgeshire 186; and in Durham 168. These studies reveal that the flora on them (and therefore the habits of certain individual species) can vary significantly between different parts of Britain. Warwickshire's walls have yet to be studied in this level of detail, but this would be a worthy project for anybody who has the time. Retaining walls have earth on one side and therefore hold more moisture and provide easier access to soil and nutrients. This makes them a less challenging environment for plants, especially where the mortar has weathered or cracks are present.

North-facing walls and those shaded by trees or shrubs are cooler and damper, which can favour ferns such as Polypody, Maidenhair Fern and Maidenhair Spleenwort. Shaded wet walls affected by overflowing gutters or drains can be especially good for ferns. Wall-rue and stonecrops by contrast dislike shade. Calcareous walls are favoured by Rustyback, Intermediate Polypody, Wallflower, Biting Stonecrop, Rue-leaved Saxifrage, Fern-grass, Wild Strawberry, Red Valerian, Shining Crane's-bill and Early Forget-me-not. Acidic walls are necessary for Navelwort and English Stonecrop (the latter is a rare casual here). Garden walls can be very rich in plant species but generally have a higher proportion of short-

Plants that characteristically grow on wall surfaces

Wallflower

Pellitory-of-the-wall

Navelwort

Ivy-leaved Toadflax

Yellow Corydalis

Mind-your-own-Business

Plants that characteristically grow on wall surfaces

Maidenhair Spleenwort

Fairy Foxglove

Maidenhair Fern

Rustyback

Wall-rue

Ribbon Fern

Plants frequently growing from the base of a wall

Shining Crane's-bill

Ivy

Herb-Robert

Greater Celandine

Feverfew

Nipplewort

Characteristic plants of surfaced ground

Fern-grass

Butterfly-bush

Common Whitlowgrass

Red Dead-nettle

Biting Stonecrop

Caucasian-stonecrop

Roadside halophytes

Buck's-horn Plantain

Grass-leaved Orache

Lesser Sea Spurrey

Danish Scurvy-grass

lived casuals, typically garden escapes. Ivy-leaved Toadflax seems to cope with walls of many sorts and is the most frequent wall specialist in Warwickshire.

In addition to those plants growing solely on the face of a wall, species such as Pellitory-of-the-wall, Ivy, Stinging Nettle, brambles, bindweeds, dandelions, Wall Lettuce, Herb-Robert, Wild Strawberry, Feverfew, Cleavers and Russian-vine can frequently grow from the foot of a wall, and Ivy will typically send further anchoring roots into the wall itself and entirely smother the wall if not controlled. If the wall has a fairly wide and flat top, or develops even a moderate lean, various grasses plus many of the flowers characteristic of disturbed ground (e.g. American Willowherb, Mouse-ear-hawkweed and Foxglove), even shrubs such as Elder, Hawthorn and Yew, can be present. As stated earlier, old walls (Victorian or older) tend to have the most interesting floras and with this in mind it is always worth checking old buildings and alleyways, eighteenth and nineteenth century bridges, old churches, local castles and canal walls.

Plants of surfaced ground

The other major habitat category of the built environment is flatter ground surfaced by concrete, tarmac or other impervious coverings. Examples include pavements, road kerbs and associated stonework, the foundations of demolished buildings, flat roofs, abandoned car parks or access roads, concreted farm tracks and old railway platforms. Biting Stonecrop, Oxford Ragwort, Fern-grass, Butterfly-bush, Wall Cotoneaster, Red Dead-nettle, Mind-your-own-business and whitlowgrasses are some of the more characteristic species of these situations, though generalist species such as dandelions, Smooth Sow-thistle and various common grasses may also be present, especially if cracks in the surface are present that allow some access to soil. In time soil will start to accumulate on these artificial surfaces and weathering will break them up, allowing the plant list to rise and giving way to a more typical ruderal flora (see Disturbed Ground chapter).

Salt-tolerant plants (halophytes)

Warwickshire has a small but growing number of halophytes associated with road verges. They include Danish Scurvy-grass, Buck's-horn Plantain, Reflexed Saltmarsh-grass, Lesser Sea-spurrey and Grass-leaved Orache. All of these can be found growing between cracks in pavement and kerbstones, though they will grow on roadside soil too. The Orache was only discovered locally in 2006 (Birmingham) and is still considered a rare casual here. Alexanders is also a predominantly coastal salt-tolerant plant starting to spread along grassy road verges in Warwickshire.

Losses and gains

There are relatively few declining species associated with the built environment as many of the habitat features involved e.g. bridges, historic buildings and old stone walls (at least the well constructed ones) are fairly permanent features. There is also a constant turnover of temporarily abandoned tarmac or concreted land, with new areas appearing as others disappear. However, planning policies favouring the development of brownfield sites over greenfield ones, are starting to reduce the quantity and longevity of such land. Two species considered extinct in Warwickshire are known to grow on walls: Hairy Rock-cress *Arabis hirsuta* which was last recorded at Little Compton in 1963 and Tasteless Stonecrop *Sedum sexangulare* was last recorded in 1848. Neither of these species is restricted to walls, and it is unclear whether they were ever more than casuals here. Species such as Polypody, Flattened Meadow-grass, House-leek and Navelwort may be declining, on the basis of Flora 2000 data.

More intensive recording of artificial environments and of casual plants in recent decades will be partly responsible for the increase in records for many species since *A Computer-Mapped Flora* was published in 1971. Nevertheless, certain species do seem to have increased substantially, most notably Butterfly-bush, the three whitlowgrasses, Wall Cotoneaster, Caucasian-stonecrop, Mind-your-own-business, Keeled-fruited Cornsalad and all the halophytes except Buck's-horn Plantain. Ribbon Fern was discovered in Leamington Spa in 2001 and Grass-leaved Orache and Fairy Foxglove were discovered in Birmingham in 2006 and 2007 respectively, all as part of well-documented national expansions. One species that attracted special attention in 2005 was the nettle *Urtica membranacea*, a casual that turned up beside a wall in the centre of Warwick, the first record of this species from the British Isles (Boucher & Partridge, 2006).

Local sites you can visit
Many fine old walls exist in Birmingham, Coventry, Warwick, Stratford-upon-Avon, Rugby and Coventry. The castles of Kenilworth and Warwick have some quite good shaded wall sections. Rural villages with many old walls include Ilmington, Little Compton and Whichford. Canal bridges and lock areas can be checked easily from towpaths. For halophytes, cautiously check the road verges of busier roads, such as the A45 through Coventry and Birmingham.

Built environment plant list (excluding casuals)
An asterix * denotes a wall specialist (in the sense used by Gilbert, 1992)

Shrubs
✗ Butterfly-bush *Buddleja davidii* – a neophyte, walls and roofs (also disturbed ground), increasing
✗ Wall Cotoneaster *Cotoneaster horizontalis* – a neophyte, pavements and walls (also disturbed ground), increasing

Grasses
✔ Fern-grass *Catapodium rigidum* – walls and pavements
✔ *Flattened-Meadow-grass *Poa compressa* – mainly on walls
✗ Reflexed Saltmarsh-grass *Puccinellia distans* – a native halophyte of the coast that has spread inland along salted roads and is increasing

Other flowering plants
✗ *Adria Bellflower *Campanula portenschlagiana* – a neophyte garden escape of walls (as a wild species it is restricted to the former Yugoslavia where it now endangered)

✘ Aubretia *Aubrieta deltoidea* – a neophyte, especially walls and paths

✘ Trailing Bellflower *Campanula poscharskyana* – a neophyte garden escape of walls and pavements

✘ Caucasian-stonecrop *Sedum spurium* – walls and concrete tracks (also disturbed ground), an increasing neophyte

✘ Greater Celandine *Chelidonium majus* – walls (also disturbed ground), a neophyte

✘ Keeled-fruited Cornsalad *Valerianella carinata* – walls and pavements, also disturbed ground, an increasing archaeophyte

✘ Pale Corydalis *Pseudofumaria alba* – a neophyte, walls, rare

✘ *Yellow Corydalis *Pseudofumaria lutea* – walls and pavements (also disturbed ground), an increasing neophyte

✘ Wall Cotoneaster *Cotoneaster horizontalis* –walls and pavements (also disturbed ground), a neophyte

✔ Shining Crane's-bill *Geranium lucidum* – walls and disturbed ground

✘ *Fairy Foxglove *Erinus alpinus* – a neophyte discovered at Birmingham's Winterbourne Botanic Gardens in 2007

✘ House-leek *Sempervirum tectorum* – walls and old roofs, a scarce and possibly declining neophyte

✘ *Mind-your-own-business *Soleirolia soleirolii* – walls, an increasing neophyte

✔ *Navelwort *Umbilicus rupestris* – a wall specialist (Maxstoke Priory only)

✔ *Pellitory-of-the-wall *Parietaria judaica* – a wall specialist, especially at the base

✘ Buck's-horn Plantain *Plantago coronopus* – a native halophyte of the coast that has spread inland along salted roads

✘ Oxford Ragwort *Senecio squalidus* – walls and cracks in pavement, concrete etc. (also disturbed ground), an increasing neophyte

✔ Thyme-leaved Sandwort *Arenaria serpyllifolia* – walls, also disturbed ground

✔ Rue-leaved Saxifrage *Saxifraga tridactylites* – limestone or lime-mortared walls and pavements, possibly declining

✘ Danish Scurvygrass *Cochlearia danica* – a native halophyte of the coast that has spread inland along salted roads and is increasing

✘ Lesser Sea-spurrey *Spergularia marina* – a native halophyte of the coast that has spread inland along salted roads and is increasing

✘ Snapdragon *Antirrhinum majus* – walls and disturbed ground, an increasing neophyte

✔ Biting Stonecrop *Sedum acre* – walls, roofs, concrete and tarmac (also disturbed ground)

✘ Reflexed Stonecrop *Sedum rupestre* – walls and roofs (also disturbed ground), a neophyte

✘ White Stonecrop *Sedum album* – habitats as per Biting Stonecrop, an increasing archaeophyte

✘ *Ivy-leaved Toadflax *Cymbalaria muralis* – walls, an increasing neophyte

✘ Red Valerian *Centranthus ruber* – walls and pavement cracks, also disturbed ground, an increasing neophyte

✘ *Wallflower *Erysimum cheiri* – walls, an archaeophyte

✔ Common Whitlowgrass *Erophila verna* – pavement cracks and walls (also on disturbed ground)

✔ Glabrous Whitlowgrass *Erophila glabresens* – as per Common Whitlowgrass
✔ Hairy Whitlowgrass *Erophila majuscula* – as per Common Whitlowgrass
✘ American Willowherb *Epilobium ciliatum* – walls and pavements (also disturbed ground), an increasing neophyte

Ferns

✔ *Brittle Bladder-fern *Cystopteris fragilis* – damp walls, scarce
✘ Limestone Fern *Gymnocarpium robertianum* – walls, culverts, a native, but not of Warwickshire where rare (last recorded Tanworth-in-Arden in 1979)
✘ *Maidenhair Fern *Adiantum capillus-veneris* – a native of a few coastal areas, also grown indoors, from which it has escaped to become a scarce damp-wall specialist
✘ Ribbon Fern *Pteris cretica* – has recently colonised a wall in Leamington Spa, a neophyte
✔ Hart's-tongue *Phyllitis scolopendrium* – walls, bridges (also shaded woods and watersides)
✔ Polypody *Polypodium vulgare* – walls (also hedges and woods)
✔ Intermediate Polypody *Polypodium interjectum* – calcareous walls
✔ *Rustyback *Ceterach officinarum* – a wall specialist
✔ *Black Spleenwort *Asplenium adiantum-nigrum* – a wall specialist in Warwickshire (the less so than the other two aspleniums when considered nationally)
✔ *Maidenhair Spleenwort *Asplenium trichomanes* – a wall specialist (typically the subspecies *quadrivalens*)
✔ *Wall-rue *Asplenium ruta-muraria* – a wall specialist

Chapter 13

Conserving Warwickshire's Flora

A s a discipline, nature conservation has become increasingly sophisticated and broad. This chapter provides a summary of some of the main activities that help to conserve plants and plant habitats in Vice-county Warwickshire at the start of the twenty-first century. By having a basic understanding of these you will be better placed to make your own contribution, and to support the work of others such as local authority ecologists and wildlife trust staff.

Site evaluation and designation

Sites of Special Scientific Interest and National Nature Reserves
Sites of high nature conservation value can be afforded a variety of designations that provide them with a degree of protection from development or other damaging activities. For many years, the statutory organisation covering England that has been variously titled the Nature Conservancy, the Nature Conservancy Council, English Nature and now Natural England has been designating good examples of nationally important sites as either **Sites of Special Scientific Interest** (**SSSIs**) or **National**

Sutton Park, Vice-county Warwickshire's only National Nature Reserve.

Nature Reserves (*NNRs*). The Vice-county of Warwickshire has seventy-two SSSIs plus one NNR (Sutton Park).

Vegetation quality and the presence of scarce plants are major considerations in the designation of such sites, and most Warwickshire SSSIs are species-rich grasslands or semi-natural ancient woodlands. SSSIs and NNRs are known as 'statutory' wildlife sites and receive a level of protection that makes development of them in whole or part especially difficult, though not impossible (the mantra *"there is no such thing as absolute protection"* is well known within professional planning and ecology circles). Statutory wildlife sites are also protected against a range of other damaging activities such as ploughing or fertilising of species-rich grassland or unofficial felling of woodland trees. Offenders can be subject to prosecution.

Second-tier wildlife sites

Local authorities have a duty to identify wildlife sites of county or local importance so that they can account for them in their strategic planning and planning control work (see strategic planning section below for definitions of these activities). These sites are typically of lower ecological quality than SSSIs and NNRs (but not always) and they receive less protection. Various names are given to such sites. In the parts of Vice-county Warwickshire falling within the modern county of the West Midlands (Coventry, Solihull, Sutton Coldfield and Birmingham) they are termed *Sites of Importance for Nature Conservation* (*SINCs*). Warwickshire County Council and Warwickshire Wildlife Trust currently term sites falling into modern Warwickshire *County Wildlife Sites*. But the local authority policies covering them are similar whatever their names, and generally state that proposals which could damage or destroy such sites will not normally be permitted unless there are overriding reasons of public interest. However, post-industrial SINCs have not fared especially well locally because 'Brownfield land' policies have usually been given priority over nature conservation ones. Unlike SSSIs, second-tier wildlife sites are afforded little protection against damaging activities such as bulldozing the vegetation away or spraying a site with herbicide.

Tocil Meadow, a Site of Importance for Nature Conservation for Nature within the University of Warwick's complex.

Other designations

Local Nature Reserves (*LNRs*) – these are sites for both people and wildlife, declared principally by local authorities under the National Parks and Access to the Countryside Act of 1949. They offer people special opportunities to study or learn about nature or simply to enjoy it. LNRs do not need to be outstanding wildlife sites, though most have SINC value, and a few are also SSSIs (e.g. Claybrookes Marsh, Coventry and Ufton Fields). Most Warwickshire LNRs have some botanical interest, and that of Ufton Fields is exceptional. Forty-six LNRs occur in the Vice-County of Warwickshire at the time of writing, the number rising steadily in recent years.

Areas of Outstanding Natural Beauty (*AONBs*) – these are precious landscapes whose distinctive character and natural beauty are so outstanding that it is in the nation's interest to safeguard them. Like LNRs, they are also created through the National Parks and Access to the Countryside Act of 1949 and forty of them occur in England and Wales. Each one is subject to a management plan that includes habitats and rare species within its remit. The southern part of Warwickshire from Ebrington Hill to the northern end of the Edge Hill escarpment falls within the Cotswolds AONB and a number of important botanical sites occur within this area (though extensive areas are botanically poor).

Country Parks – these are typically large areas of informal greenspace, often in the countryside but sometimes in more urban settings. Their nature conservation value is variable, but they can be SSSIs or County Wildlife Sites, at least in part, and hold considerable botanical interest. Country Parks are typically owned and managed by local authorities. Those in Warwickshire are the Burton Dassett Hills, Coombe Country Park, Kingsbury Water Park, Hartshill Hayes, Pooley Fields, Ryton Pools and Stratford Greenway.

Strategic planning

The Vice-county of Warwickshire comprises land controlled by a number of local planning authorities. The main ones are Warwickshire County Council, Solihull Metropolitan Borough Council, Coventry City Council, Birmingham City Council, Stratford-on-Avon District Council, Warwick District Council, North Warwickshire Borough Council, Rugby Borough Council, Nuneaton and Bedworth Borough Council and Tamworth Borough Council. All these local authorities have to prepare *local development plans* to last a period of 10 years. These contain policies and proposals of many kinds that provide a framework for land-use decisions, including those for new housing, new industry, new employment land, new roads, protected greenspace and other conservation areas. The development plan acts both as a forward plan that shapes long-term development of an area, plus a tool by which planning officers and planning committees handle planning applications on a day-to-day basis. Given that conflict is inevitable with so many competing interests fighting for a finite amount of land, development plans try to determine which of those interests ought to have priority, and help to determine the shape of any decisions or compromises.

Local development plans are critically important in plant conservation. Designated wildlife sites such as SSSIs, SINCs and LNRs will be listed in the plan and usually highlighted on an associated *proposals map.* Policies within the plan will generally state that proposals that could destroy or damage a designated wildlife site will not normally be permitted. Occasionally permission is given to develop and destroy a designated wildlife site, but the greatest scrutiny will normally be afforded to all arguments, and the final decision may be referred to the Planning Inspectorate and subject to a *Planning Inquiry* (a type of Public Inquiry) overseen by a *Planning Inspector*. Unavoidable loss of a wildlife site can

A bird's-foot-trefoil bloom at Bishops Hill, Bishops Itchington - quarries and associated spoilheaps support some of Warwickshire's finest wildflower sites and will continue to do so for the foreseeable future.

result in **planning compensation** whereby new habitat is created or funding is made available to improve existing wildlife sites nearby.

Warwickshire County Council, Coventry City Council and Solihull Metropolitan Borough Council also need to produce a second type of development plan called a **Minerals and Waste Plan**. These have a considerable influence on what happens to quarries and gravel pits once they are worked out, and increasingly on how they are managed during their operational phase. As such, they can influence the creation of large new nature reserves and country parks. Given that most quarries and gravel workings acquire high botanical value quite rapidly, these are very important documents indeed. At the time of writing, Warwickshire County Council has been preparing a new Plan, and nature conservation (especially biodiversity action planning) has been a major consideration.

All development plans are prepared in accordance with a set of government guidelines called **Planning Policy Statements** (**PPSs**), and as a consequence the plans generally say more or less the same things, but are tailored towards local needs and circumstances. Public consultation is a strict prerequisite, and all draft plans are scrutinised by the government prior to being adopted. If policies for nature conservation are deemed too weak by PPS standards, or some are missing, the plan may need to be revised.

Planning control

Local planning authorities receive thousands of planning applications each year. Some have no impact on nature conservation, but others can be totally at odds with the nature conservation policies of a local authority. The process by which planning applications are handled is called ***development control***. Typically a professional ecologist or specialised planning officer will screen all applications to identify which ones might impact on wildlife sites or protected or important species. They will then inform a planning officer of any conflict. Members of the public can also object. Where an application is controversial, dialogue may take place with the applicant, sometimes leading to a withdrawal of the application or modification of it to reduce impact. The application is usually determined by the ***Planning Committee*** which is a panel of Elected Members (i.e. Councillors) guided by a Senior Planning Officer. If their decision is contested by either the applicant or objectors, it can be subject to a ***Planning Appeal***, some of which take the form of a Public Enquiry. This provides an opportunity for all parties to explain their concerns directly to a Planning Inspector. Many important botanical sites have been threatened by development in recent years, and a number have been saved by objectors providing a solid argument at a public enquiry.

Site management and acquisition

Designation alone cannot protect important botanical sites. Nearly all sites require an input of management to sustain their interest and safeguard the more important plant populations. This management might entail a summer cut of a hay meadow, grazing of pasture, coppicing of woodland, occasional pond clearance, and removal of scrub. Neglect is one of the greatest threats to wildflowers, particularly those of early successional stages and open habitats.

Warwickshire Wildlife Trust is the organisation most actively involved in the acquisition and management of wildlife sites in Warwickshire, and most of their 55 reserves have moderate to high botanical interest. Each site is subject to a management plan, and the management work is carried out by volunteers and contractors (the latter for bigger operations involving machinery). Other volunteers and local wildlife groups such as Butterfly Conservation Warwickshire help to monitor the reserves to gauge how scarcer species are reacting to ongoing management.

The fate of several rare plants in Warwickshire is now totally dependent upon the work of Warwickshire Wildlife Trust, including Man Orchid at Ufton Fields and Moonwort at Draycote Meadow. The Wildlife Trust also owns and manages our

Ryton Wood, one of Warwickshire Wildlife Trust's most popular reserves (left). Wildlife Trust volunteers play a crucial role in maintaining key wildlife sites (right).

finest meadow (Draycote Meadow), one of our finest ancient woods (Ryton Wood) and one of our finest wetlands (Brandon Marsh).

Other key players include local authorities, who own and manage most Local Nature Reserves and Country Parks. Some of these are managed in partnership with Warwickshire Wildlife Trust, e.g. Ufton Fields, Crackley Wood, Kenilworth Common, Stoke Floods and Stonebridge Meadows. The Forestry Commission own and manage several interesting woods (notably Oversley Wood near Alcester). Several private landowners and estates control important areas, including the Packington Estate (large landholdings in the Blythe Valley near Meriden and Packington), the Compton Scorpion Estate (much farmland in the south of the County), and the Merevale Estate (much of the land north of Atherstone including the important heathland at Baddesley Common).

Agri-environment schemes (Environmental Stewardship)

The conservation of our flora cannot simply take place within nature reserves. Many scarce species occur on working farms, perhaps within arable land, in relatively unimproved pasture and hay meadow, or along ditches, hedgerows or riverbanks. In recognition of this, the government's Department for Environment Food and Rural Affairs (DEFRA) channels funding to landowners and tenant farmers through its agri-environment funding, administered by Natural England.

Environmental Stewardship currently gives applicants a choice of three levels of funding. ***Entry Level Stewardship*** funds simple but effective management techniques, with over fifty options to chose from, including hedgerow management, sensitive grassland management (where the use of fertilisers or pesticides is minimised), and the creation of buffer strips at the edges of field where wildflowers can flourish. ***Organic Entry Level Stewardship*** is similar, but restricted to registered organic farms where the use of herbicides, pesticides and artificial fertilisers is avoided. ***Higher Level Stewardship*** is targeted at sites that already have a high level of wildlife interest or fall within key target areas. It funds more complex management, and involves higher payments.

Advice and training for farmers and landowners is a vital part of Environmental Stewardship, and much of this is delivered by Natural England or organised by the Farming and Wildlife Advisory Group (FWAG), an independent charity that works closely with Natural England and a variety of other organisations to deliver on-farm advice.

Agri-environment funding for maintaining buffer strips around fields results in valuable wildflower habitat within intensively farmed settings.

In Warwickshire, Environmental Stewardship has helped to create and restore wetlands, floodplain meadows, fen and reedbed, as well as a diverse range of key habitats on arable land. Further information can be obtained from the websites of DEFRA (www.defra.gov.uk/erdp/schemes/es), Natural England (www.naturalengland.org.uk) or FWAG (www.fwag.org.uk).

Recording and research

The serious recording of plants in Warwickshire has a history that extends back to the time of John Ray in the seventeenth century. His efforts, and those of the eighteenth and nineteenth century botanists who followed him, provide an invaluable insight into the historic changes in Warwickshire's flora, especially the local loss of key habitats and many native species. The pressure on land and wildlife now is greater than ever, and is likely to become even more intense in the future. It is vital that botanists continue to carry out surveys, plus more structured monitoring and research of key sites and species. This will help us to prioritise our conservation efforts, and could strongly influence future site designation, planning control and environmental stewardship. Many recent surveys in Warwickshire have been linked to national BSBI initiatives, and no doubt this pattern will continue in the future. Plantlife has also launched a number of national surveys in recent years.

Monitoring of sites can involve recording change of the flora in response to structured habitat management, or in the face of mismanagement or neglect. It can involve the use of fixed-point photography to record how the appearance of a site changes from year-to-year (e.g. any encroachment of scrub, or changes in the 'floweriness' of a site). Another method is the use of 1 metre square quadrats. This involves recording the abundance of different plant species within a series of quadrat samples and checking how the relative abundance of these plants changes over time. Care is needed when interpreting results because not all change is linked to management. Drought or wet summers can profoundly affect the appearance of a site and the relative abundance of plants, as will longer-term climate change. Some plants such as orchids are also notorious for having good flowering years and bad flowering years, even in the most stable and well-managed of sites.

The Habitat Biodiversity Audit (HBA)

Monitoring the overall status of plant habitats is just as important as monitoring the plants that grow in them. In the modern administrative areas of Warwickshire, Coventry and Solihull, an ongoing project exists which keeps a reasonably up-to-date computerised map of all the wildlife habitat of this area. The project is called the **Warwickshire, Coventry and Solihull Habitat Biodiversity Audit** (**HBA**) and is co-funded by all the local authorities in the area plus Natural England. The HBA map colour codes different habitats (e.g. orange

Botanical surveyors assessing the quality of a grassland site (Draycote Meadow).

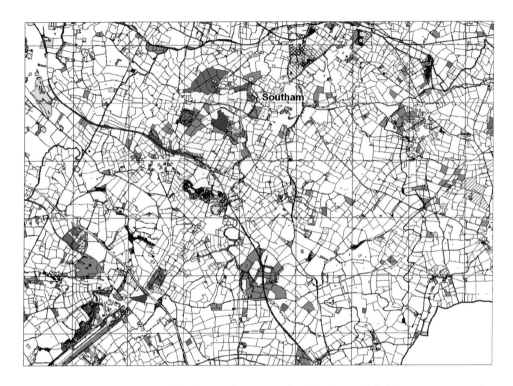

The HBA project has digitised habitat information for all of Warwickshire, Coventry and Solihull and is a vital tool for nature conservation and development control.

for species-rich grasslands, solid green for semi-natural woodland and solid blue for open water). Being computerised, using what is known as GIS software, it is possible to accurately measure all the different habitats, to produce maps of different scales, and to overlay and attach vast amounts of additional information. This can include target notes for important features (e.g. a species list for a meadow, or the presence of a Black-poplar), development proposals, aerial photographs, even archaeological data. Such information is invaluable for local authority ecologists, planning departments, commercial consultants and local biodiversity action planning (which involves monitoring habitat loss and gain).

The Wildlife Sites Project

This project is closely linked to the HBA and helps to bring about the designation of the second-tier wildlife sites (SINCs and County Wildlife Sites). A surveyor (often in consultation with local wildlife experts) gathers information on areas of habitat shown on the HBA map that might attain SINC or County Wildlife Site quality. This information is scrutinised by a panel of experts using a series of criteria. The relevant local planning authority is informed of the panel's decisions, and once the sites are ratified by that authority's planning committee they can become official SINCs or County Wildlife Sites and be highlighted in any new local development plans.

Local biological record centres (LRCs)

These are the official repositories for information on wildlife sites and wildlife species. The main one for Vice-county Warwickshire is the **Warwickshire Biological Records Centre** based at Warwickshire Museum, Warwick. It holds information on several thousand wildlife sites in modern Warwickshire, Coventry and Solihull. **EcoRecord** (a wing of the Wildlife Trust for Birmingham and the Black Country) performs the same role for the Birmingham and Sutton Coldfield part of Vice-county Warwickshire. LRCs are heavily dependent upon data gathered by local amateur wildlife recorders to keep their site files up-to-date. Local authority ecologists and consultants use the information in the site files when preparing reports such as impact assessments and planning responses. Members of the public can view all non-sensitive information in a LRC by appointment and for free (though developers and commercial consultants are charged).

Local Biodiversity Action Planning

Local Biodiversity Action Plans (**LBAPs**) act as the glue that helps to hold all of the above processes together. LBAPs are local initiatives (usually county-based) that bring many organisations and individuals together to agree realistic targets for the conservation of high priority habitats and species. Some of those targets are local responses to national targets in the UK Biodiversity Action Plan (which has targets for a large number of habitats and species), but others are for local species and habitats not covered by the UK Plan. By having agreed targets, delivery mechanisms and responsible parties for different actions, available resources can be targeted more efficiently and monitoring of progress is made much easier.

The Warwickshire, Coventry and Solihull Biodiversity Action Plan is the main one for Vice-county Warwickshire, with that for Birmingham and the Black Country covering Sutton Park and a few other key sites. The Warwickshire Plan, for example, includes targets for Black-poplar and Scarce Arable Weeds (the latter focusing on 15 species). Both plans cover a full range of local wildlife habitats. To find out more, visit the biodiversity websites:
* UK Biodiversity Action Plan (www.ukbap.org.uk)
* Warwickshire, Coventry and Solihull Local Biodiversity Action Plan (www.warwickshire.gov.uk/biodiversity)
* Biodiversity Action Plan for Birmingham and the Black Country (www.wildlifetrust.org.uk/urbanwt/ecorecord/bap)

How you can help to conserve plants

There are a variety of options open to local amateur botanists and wildlife enthusiasts:
* Join a local natural history society that carries out plant recording, e.g. Warwick Natural History Society, Birmingham Natural History Society, Coventry and District Natural History and Scientific Society, Sutton Coldfield Natural History Society and Rugby Natural History Society
* Join Warwickshire Wildlife Trust or the Wildlife Trust for Birmingham and the Black Country and become involved in the monitoring and management of their reserves
* Join Plantlife and the Botanical Society of Britain and Ireland

- Carry out plant surveys for sites in the area where you live, and present the data to your local biological records centre
- Encourage wildflowers on any land that you own or manage, such as your garden
- Create new wildflower habitat where circumstances allow you to do so
- Offer assistance to the Habitat Biodiversity Audit and Wildlife Sites Project as a volunteer surveyor
- Consider objecting to any planning applications or planning proposals that you feel will damage an important wildlife site
- Help your local biological record centre to manage its plant records
- If you are sufficiently experienced, help others to become knowledgeable about plants

Other useful websites
Birmingham Natural History Society (http://freespace.virgin.net/clare.h/bnhs.htm)
Coventry and District Natural History and Scientific Society (www.cdnhss.org.uk)
Sutton Coldfield Natural History Society (www.scnhs.org.uk)
Warwick Natural History Society (http://warkcom.net/live/cme1302.htm)
Warwickshire Museum (www.warwickshire.gov.uk/museum)
Warwickshire Wildlife Trust (www.warwickshire-wildlife-trust.org.uk)
Wildlife Trust for Birmingham and the Black Country (www.bbcwildlife.org.uk)

Contact details can change with time. Warwickshire Museum currently produces a newsletter ('*Wildlife News in Warwickshire, Coventry & Solihull*') three times a year which provides up-to-date contact details for all local natural history groups, plus lists of the events they are organising. The newsletter can be downloaded from the web: www.warwickshire.gov.uk/rings.

Chapter 14

A Summary of Change in Warwickshire's Flora

When the total numbers of different plants in an area are assessed over time, dilemmas arise. Surveys may not include some of the problem plants or casuals mentioned earlier, and some species may no longer be recognised as distinct. More importantly, new plants are regularly arriving in our county and may or may not persist; old ones may become extinct. The main Checklist in this book will itself quickly become history since it is only a snapshot summary of Warwickshire's plantlife up until the time we compiled it.

Bagnall, 1891

Bagnall arranged the Warwickshire Flora using his own terminology, and listed 1,309 separate plants; 254 were 'varieties and ambiguities' (including today's subspecies). There were only three identified hybrids, and he rarely considered that plants were extinct. He included very few garden escapes: "*mere waifs and outcasts*" with "*no claim to be considered part of the flora of this county*". Some people today would agree with him. Using the current classification system, his Flora contains:

Native plants	817 (including 7 extinctions)
Established aliens	130
Casuals	108
Varieties	254
Total	**1309**

A Computer-Mapped Flora, 1971

There is, unfortunately, no analysis of the composition of the 1157 plants listed, and the authors did not consistently identify whether they considered a particular plant native, casual or established. A provisional estimation of the composition of this Flora is:

Native plants	813 (includes 59 extinctions)
Established aliens	209
Casuals	135
Total	**1157**

Present Checklist, 2008

Native plants	991 (includes 78 extinctions)
Established aliens	560
Casuals	227
Total	**1778**

As would be expected, each time an assessment is made of all the wild plants that have ever been found in our county the totals increase because they will include all the previous records in addition to the new discoveries. *A Computer-Mapped Flora* included more naturalised aliens and recognised more hybrids than Bagnall's *Flora*. It reflected the increasing numbers of plants spontaneously arriving in Warwickshire due to the growth of urban areas, international travel, commerce and other changes.

Our Checklist demonstrates further increases in all the categories of plant life (as used above) for the same reasons, but also because of a readiness to include casual finds and garden escapes. Very many more hybrid species are now recognised, and the lists of microspecies (brambles, dandelions) grow almost as fast, it seems, as the plants themselves.

Of the 1,778 plants which have ever been discovered within the County, 239 plants have not been re-found since 1969. Many of these were casual arrivals or garden escapes which never became established. However, about a third of them were long-established members of our flora.

Extinctions of native and archaeophyte plants

We define as **extinct** plants that have not been recorded in a wild/naturalised state since 1969. Some 78 native and archaeophyte plants fall into this category, plus dozens of further neophytes and casuals (see Appendix 1), some of which were relatively well-established as naturalised plants, whilst others perhaps only ever had a tenuous grip in the County. Other species appear to have disappeared since 1969, but are not yet officially extinct and are afforded 'Warwickshire Very Rare' statuses until the 1969 date threshold is revised. The figure of 78 does not include microspecies of plants such as dandelions and brambles which have not been recorded since 1969, simply because there is insufficient data to make an informed judgement. It has also been decided that recent casual records of 'extinct' species that arise from sources such as wildflower seed mixes, bird-seed or cultivation, will not be used to remove a former native or naturalised species from the extinct list because the new casual populations are often short-lived and often have a different ecology to the previous populations.

The 78 lost plants disappeared for several reasons. Some were on the edge of their distribution range in Britain, occupying habitats that were barely tolerable for their climatic needs. Others were in tiny populations, vulnerable to the slightest change. For most it was the loss and deterioration of suitable habitats, such as unpolluted water, undrained wetland, unimproved grassland, and ancient and traditionally managed woodland. These reasons for loss were already beginning in mid-Victorian times when Bagnall wrote his *Flora*.

Number of Extinctions

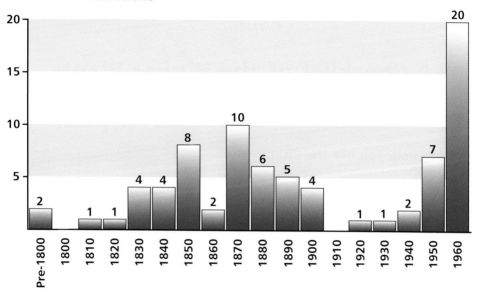

Graph: Last recorded decade for 78 Warwickshire extinct native plants, 1670-1960.

As the graph above shows, there was a second even more dramatic decline in native plant numbers when Dorothy Cadbury and her colleagues were plant-hunting between 1950 and 1969. This corresponded to changes in agricultural practice, with the development of potent herbicides, insecticides and fertilisers, highly efficient mechanised equipment, and the uprooting of hedges and drainage of ponds. Warwickshire continues to lose valuable habitats and is experiencing unprecedented levels of pressure on land for development, especially housing. It seems almost inevitable that some further losses will be incurred despite the best efforts of conservationists.

Chapter 15

A Checklist of the Higher Plants of Vice-County Warwickshire

Notes to help you use the Checklist

The Checklist takes the form of a table, with columns for:
- scientific name, taken from Stace (2003)
- popular name, mostly taken from the same source
- category i.e. whether native, archaeophyte, neophyte, casual or extinct
- notes, giving an indication of frequency (including whether rare or very rare in Warwickshire), main habitat(s), localities for some of the rarities, whether the plants are annuals, biennial or perennial)
- rarity class i.e. whether a National Rarity, Warwickshire Rarity or Warwickshire Notable

The sequence of the checklist is alphabetical by scientific name. Most of the terms used (e.g. archaeophyte, neophyte and hybrid) are explained in the introduction and the glossary, but two sets of terms used in the Checklist (Life expectancy and Frequency) are briefly explained here.

Life expectancy

An **annual** is a plant that lives for a maximum of one year; a **biennial** lives for two years (typically flowering in its second year), and a **perennial** lives for several or many years.

Frequency

The terms **scarce, occasional, frequent**, and **abundant** indicate increasing degrees of abundance. A **local** species is one that is very restricted in geographical terms, though it might be quite frequent where it occurs. An **endemic** is a species that only occurs in a particular place and nowhere else in the world: a hybrid water crowfoot and extinct hybrid pondweed have so far only been found in Warwickshire (so may be endemic to the County).

The checklist is based upon Copson, Partridge & Roberts, 2008, and largely relies upon this work for decisions relating to a plant's category (e.g. neophyte versus casual), and the number of recent sites. The raw data underpinning each species entry can be viewed by appointment at Warwickshire Museum.

Symbols, abbreviations and colours used in the Checklist

Within the Checklist a variety of symbols and abbreviations are used to save space as follows:

'-' after a date, e.g. '1970-', means '1970 and after'

'-' between dates, e.g. '1984-7', means recorded in 1984, 1987 and between those dates

10 km – means a ten kilometre square of Ordnance Survey maps, an area used in biological recording

agg. – aggregate (a collection of very similar species)

Arch – an archaeophyte

B/m – Birmingham

calc. – calcareous, lime-containing, e.g. calcareous grassland, calcareous scrub

Cas – a casual

CMF – the 1971 *A Computer-Mapped Flora of Warwickshire*

Cov – Coventry

DED – Dutch elm disease

escape – a cultivated plant found outside cultivation (garden escapes etc.)

esp. – especially

GB – Great Britain

K/worth – Kenilworth

km – kilometre, 1 km square is an area used in biological recording

L/Spa – Leamington Spa

NC (NC) – Nationally Critically Endangered, (NC) not native to Warwickshire

NE (NE) – Nationally Endangered, (NE) not native to Warwickshire

Neo – a neophyte (see Introduction)

NNT (NNT) – Nationally Near-threatened, (NNT) not native to Warwickshire

NR (NR) – Nationally Rare, (NR) not native to Warwickshire

NS (NS) – Nationally Scarce, (NS) not native to Warwickshire

NT (NT) Nationally Threatened, (NT) not native to Warwickshire

NV (NV) – Nationally Vulnerable, (NV) not native to Warwickshire

R. – river

S/Avon – Stratford-upon-Avon

sp./spp. – species (singular/plural)

ssp. – sub-species

var. – variety

v. – very

VCCC – the BSBI Vice-County Census Catalogue (2003)

WN – a Warwickshire Notable, i.e. scarce or indicative of particularly fine habitat

WR – a Warwickshire Rarity (Rare or Very Rare)

Warks – Warwickshire, Vice County 38 (see Introduction), N(orth), W(est), NW etc.

X or x – indicates a hybrid

☐ extinct

☐ Warwickshire Notable

☐ National and county Rarity

☐ all others

Scientific Name	Popular Name	Cat.	Notes	Rarity
Abutilon theophrasti	Velvetleaf	Cas	Bird-seed annual, casual, Offchurch footpath 2004	
Acaena ovalifolia	Two-spined Acaena	Neo	Escape perennial, Edgbaston Golf Course 2007	
Acaena inermis x A. anserinifolia	A hybrid pirri-pirri-bur	Neo	Escape perennial hybrid, L/Spa allotment 2005-7	
Acer campestre	Field Maple	Native	Widespread native tree, woods and hedges, also planted	
Acer platanoides	Norway Maple	Neo	Widely planted tree, self-sowing, esp. in urban areas, increasing	
Acer pseudoplatanus	Sycamore	Neo	Widely planted tree, but naturalised and invasive in many woods and hedgerows, increasing	
Aceras anthropophorum	Man Orchid	Neo	V. rare perennial, just Ufton Fields 1968-2004	(NE)
Achillea millefolium	Yarrow	Native	Widespread & frequent perennial, esp. in grassland	
Achillea ptarmica	Sneezewort	Native	Local perennial, esp. NW Warks, acid grassland, wetlands	WN
Aconitum napellus	Monk's-hood	Native?	V. rare perennial, possibly native, waterside, Cherington 1835-2000 (ssp. napellus)	WR
Aconitum x cammarum	Hybrid Monk's-hood	Neo	Garden escape, perennial, scarce, 1993-2003 (A. napellus x A. variegatum)	
Acorus calamus	Sweet-flag	Neo	Widespread perennial of watersides, increasing	
Actaea spicata	Baneberry	Ext Cas	Extinct casual perennial, Harborough Magna 1872	NS
Adiantum capillus-veneris	Maidenhair Fern	Neo	Perennial fern, railway walls, K/worth 1959, L/Spa 1990-2007	(NS)
Adonis annua	Pheasant's-eye	Ext Arch	Extinct arable annual, Wilmcote 1920	NE
Adoxa moschatellina	Moschatel	Native	Scattered records mainly in woods, perennial	WN
Aegopodium podagraria	Ground-elder	Arch	Widespread perennial, gardens, allotments, roadsides etc	
Aesculus hippocastanum	Horse-chestnut	Neo	Widely planted tree, possibly self-sown in some woods	
Aethusa cynapium ssp. agrestis	Fool's Parsley ssp.	Arch	This ssp. is a v. rare arable annual, only record Snitterfield 1988, perhaps overlooked, see below	WR
Aethusa cynapium ssp. cynapium	Fool's Parsley ssp.	Native	Widespread annual, cultivated soil, tips, etc., urban & rural, this is the much commoner ssp. (but ssp. often not quoted with a record)	
Agrimonia eupatoria	Agrimony	Native	Widespread but local perennial, grassland & hedges, declining	

Scientific Name	Popular Name	Cat.	Notes	Rarity
Agrimonia procera	Fragrant Agrimony	Native	Rare perennial, scrub, W Warks, 4 current sites 1984-2001	WR
Agrostemma githago	Corncockle	Ext Arch & Cas Neo	Extinct arable annual, last record as such Brailes 1955, now a casual of bird-seed, 'wild flower mix' etc.	
Agrostis avenacea	Blown-grass	Ext Neo	Extinct perennial, Bedworth Colliery dump 1964	
Agrostis canina	Velvet Bent	Native	Perennial, acid grassland, NW Warks, declining	WN
Agrostis capillaris	Common Bent	Native	Widespread perennial, grassland, roadsides etc	
Agrostis castellana	Highland Bent	Neo	Perennial, sown grass-seed constituent, scarce, 1996-	
Agrostis gigantea	Black Bent	Arch	Widespread perennial, cultivated land, tips etc	
Agrostis gigantea x A. stolonifera	A hybrid bent	Ext	Extinct hybrid perennial, Darlingscott meadow 1962	
Agrostis stolonifera	Creeping Bent	Native	Widespread perennial, grassland, wet places	
Agrostis vinealis	Brown Bent	Native	Scarce perennial, acid grassland, N Warks	WN
Ailanthus altissima	Tree-of-heaven	Neo	Widely planted tree, occasionally self-sowing, L/Spa 2005, B/m 2007	
Aira caryophyllea	Silver Hair-grass	Native	Annual, declining, local, railways, roads, heaths	WN
Aira praecox	Early Hair-grass	Native	As for A. caryophyllea	WN
Ajuga reptans	Bugle	Native	Widespread but local perennial of old woodland, hedgebanks etc.	
Alchemilla filicaulis	Lady's-mantle	Native	Local, scarce perennial, old meadows (ssp. vestita)	WN
Alchemilla mollis	A lady's-mantle	Neo	Infrequent garden escape, perennial	
Alchemilla venosa	A lady's-mantle	Ext Neo	Extinct perennial, Hampton-in-Arden 1963	
Alchemilla xanthochlora	A lady's-mantle	Ext Nat	Extinct perennial, Dunchurch 1946-1961	
Alisma lanceolatum	Narrow-leaved Water-plantain	Native	Rare waterside perennial, N Warks wetlands & B/m canals, 5 recent sites, 1981-2007	WR
Alisma plantago-aquatica	Water-plantain	Native	Widespread waterside perennial	
Alliaria petiolata	Garlic Mustard	Native	Widespread biennial of hedges, waste-places etc	
Allium neopolitanum	Neopolitan Garlic	Cas Neo	Garden escape perennial, L/Spa hedge 2006-	
Allium oleraceum	Field Garlic	Native	V. rare perennial, roadsides, Ettington 1996, Bearley 2003-	NV
Allium paradoxicum	Few-flowered Garlic	Neo	Garden escape perennial, L/Spa grassland 2005-	

Scientific Name	Popular Name	Cat.	Notes	Rarity
Allium roseum	Rosy Garlic	Neo	Garden escape perennial escape, Cov 1990, B/m 2006	
Allium schoenoprasum	Chives	Cas	Garden escape perennial, King's Newnham 1989 (also a scarce British native, but not in Warks)	(NS)
Allium sphaerocephalon	Round-headed Leek	Neo	Garden escape perennial, Warwick 1983, Wilmcote 1994 (also a rare British native, but not in Warks)	(NV)
Allium triquetrum	Three-cornered Garlic	Neo	Garden escape perennial, L/Spa roads 2005-	
Allium ursinum	Ramsons	Native	Widespread but local perennial, large colonies in hedges, woods	
Allium vineale	Wild Onion	Native	Widespread local perennial, grassland, gardens, tips etc.	
Alnus glutinosa	Alder	Native	Widespread & frequent waterside tree, sometimes planted	
Alnus incana	Grey Alder	Neo	Widely planted tree, naturalised from 1973, mainly by suckering	
Alopecurus aequalis	Orange Foxtail	Native	Rare perennial, pond-margins etc., 6 recent sites 1985-2004	WR
Alopecurus geniculatus	Marsh Foxtail	Native	Widespread perennial, wet places	
Alopecurus myosuroides	Black-grass	Arch	Annual arable, once pernicious, declining but still common	
Alopecurus pratensis	Meadow Foxtail	Native	Widespread & abundant perennial meadow grass	
Alopecurus x brachylus	A hybrid foxtail	Native	Perennial meadow grass, scarce, Mid Warks 1977- (A. pratensis x A. geniculatus)	
Althaea hirsuta	Rough Marsh-mallow	Neo	Annual arable, only recent record Kineton area 1996-2004, also known as a casual B/m 1957	
Alyssum alyssoides	Small Alison	Ext Neo	Extinct annual, Myton 1891	
Amaranthus albus	White Pigweed	Cas	Transient bird-seed annual, 3 recent sites	
Amaranthus blitoides	Prostrate Pigweed	Cas	Transient bird-seed annual 2005	
Amaranthus blitum	Guernsey Pigweed	Neo	Self-sowing bird-seed annual, Warwick 1983-	
Amaranthus caudatus	Love-lies-bleeding	Cas	Escape annual, Elmdon 2007	
Amaranthus cruentus	Purple Amaranth	Cas	Transient bird-seed annual, 1993 only	
Amaranthus deflexus	Perennial Pigweed	Ext Neo	Extinct perennial, K/worth 1874	
Amaranthus hybridus	Green Amaranth	Cas	Bird-seed annual, 4 sites 1986-2004	
Amaranthus retroflexus	Common Amaranth	Neo	Scarce annual, bird-seed & crop, allotments etc.	
Ambrosia artemisiifolia	Ragweed	Cas	Scarce annual, bird-seed 2004-	
Ammi majus	Bullwort	Cas	Scarce bird-seed annual	
Ammi visnaga	Toothpick-plant	Cas	3 sites, transient, bird-seed annual	

Scientific Name	Popular Name	Cat.	Notes	Rarity
Ammophila arenaria	Marram	Neo	A coastal dune perennial, introduced with imported sea sand, 3 sites 1956-1997	
Amsinckia micrantha	Common Fiddleneck	Neo	A recently arrived annual, scattered records 1999-	
Anacamptis pyramidalis	Pyramidal Orchid	Native	V. local perennial of calc. grassland in S Warks, 16 recent sites 1975-2005	WN
Anagallis arvensis ssp. arvensis	Scarlet Pimpernel	Native	Widespread & frequent on sparsely-vegetated ground, flowers typically red, but sometimes pink and blue	
Anagallis arvensis ssp. foemina	Blue Pimpernel	Native	Rare annual arable weed, calc. soil, S Warks, 9 sites 1984-2007, differs from blue forms of previous ssp. in type of glandular hairs on petals	NS
Anagallis x doerfleri	A hybrid pimpernel	Ext Native	Ext. annual hybrid, 2 arable sites S Warks 1950, possibly the only reliable British records (A. arvensis ssp. arvensis x ssp. foemina)	
Anagallis minima	Chaffweed	Ext Native	Extinct annual, Oversley Wood 1878-1961	NT
Anagallis tenella	Bog Pimpernel	Native	V. rare perennial of bogs, Sutton Park 1809-2007-	WR
Anaphalis margaritacea	Pearly Everlasting	Neo	Perennial, garden escape, 3 sites	
Anchusa arvensis	Bugloss	Arch	Annual arable weed, mainly C & S Warks	WN
Anchusa azurea	Garden Anchusa	Neo	Garden escape perennial, naturalised in S Warks	
Anemanthele lessoniana	An ornamental grass	Neo	Garden escape perennial, grassland, roadsides, L/Spa 2005-, B/m 2007	
Anemone apennina	Blue Anemone	Neo	Perennial, naturalised, Loxley Church 1970-	
Anemone nemorosa	Wood Anemone	Native	Widespread perennial esp. of ancient woods and old hedges	
Anethum graveolens	Dill	Cas	Bird-seed annual, B/m 1983	
Angelica archangelica	Garden Angelica	Cas	Uncommon garden escape biennial 1989, 1998	
Angelica sylvestris	Wild Angelica	Native	Widespread perennial, marshes, damp woods etc.	
Anisantha diandra	Great Brome	Neo	Annual, arable land, roadsides etc., S Warks 1993	
Anisantha rigida	Ripgut Brome	Ext Neo	Extinct annual, K/worth 1886	
Anisantha sterilis	Barren Brome	Arch	Widespread & abundant annual, grassland, roadsides etc.	
Anthemis arvensis	Corn Chamomile	Arch	Rare arable annual weed, almost extinct, 4 recent sites 1978-97	EN
Anthemis cotula	Stinking Chamomile	Arch	Widespread but declining arable annual weed	NV

Scientific Name	Popular Name	Cat.	Notes	Rarity
Anthemis tinctoria	Yellow Chamomile	Cas Neo	Perennial, garden escape, scarce, transient	
Anthoxanthum aristatum	Annual Vernal-grass	Ext Neo	Extinct annual, L/Spa 1891	
Anthoxanthum odoratum	Sweet Vernal-grass	Native	Widespread perennial, relatively unimproved grassland	
Anthriscus caucalis	Bur Chervil	Native	Rare annual, thought extinct c.1891, re-found at Priors Marston 1996 possibly as a casual	WR
Anthriscus cerefolium	Garden Chervil	Ext Cas.	Extinct annual, L/Spa 1849	
Anthriscus sylvestris	Cow Parsley	Native	Widespread & common perennial of roadsides, hedges, woods, etc.	
Anthyllis vulneraria	Kidney Vetch	Native	A scarce & declining perennial of calc. ground in S Warks; Var. langei: 1 casual record 1993 (ssp. vulneraria)	WN
Antirrhinum majus	Snapdragon	Neo	Frequent naturalised escape, roadsides, walls etc.	
Apera spica-venti	Loose Silky-bent	Cas	A rare casual here, but an archaeophyte in other parts of Britain	(NT)
Aphanes arvensis	Parsley-piert	Native	Widespread arable annual	
Aphanes australis	Slender Parsley-piert	Native	Infrequent scattered annual, poor sandy soil	
Apium graveolens	Wild Celery	Native	V. rare waterside perennial, Cov, Fenny Compton, last record 1997	WR
Apium inundatum	Lesser Marshwort	Native	V. rare wetland perennial, Seeswood Pool 1984	WR
Apium nodiflorum	Fool's-water-cress	Native	Widespread waterside perennial	
Apium x moorei	A hybrid marshwort	Ext Native	Extinct hybrid perennial, Flecknoe 1964 (A. inundatum x A. nodiflorum)	
Aponogeton distachyos	Cape-pondweed	Cas Neo	Aquatic escape, seemingly transient, canal, Knowle 1997	
Aquilegia vulgaris	Columbine	Native?	Scattered roadside perennial, doubtful native	
Arabidopsis thaliana	Thale Cress	Native	Widespread annual, waste places, esp. urban	
Arabis glabra	Tower Mustard	Ext Neo	Extinct biennial, Marston Green 1868	(NE)
Arabis hirsuta	Hairy Rock-cress	Ext Native	Extinct biennial/perennial, quarry, Little Compton 1963	
Arctium lappa	Greater Burdock	Arch	Widespread & frequent perennial of roadsides, hedges, waste places etc.	
Arctium minus	Burdock	Native	As for A. lappa	
Arctium nemorosum	Wood Burdock	Ext Native	Extinct perennial, last record Hatton c.1884	

Scientific Name	Popular Name	Cat.	Notes	Rarity
Arenaria balearica	Mossy Sandwort	Ext Neo	Extinct garden escape, Copston Magna 1963	
Arenaria serpyllifolia ssp. leptoclados	Thyme-leaved Sandwort ssp.	Native	Widespread annual of ruderal and waste places	
Arenaria serpyllifolia ssp. serpyllifolia	Thyme-leaved Sandwort ssp.	Native	Same habitats as above, but more frequent	
Arisarum proboscideum	Mousetailplant	Cas	Escape perennial, Salford Priors c.1970	
Armeria maritima	Thrift	Neo	Native perennial of coast, an escape here, Packington 1985, Churchover 1991	
Armoracia rusticana	Horse-radish	Arch	Widespread perennial, roadsides, dumps etc.	
Arrhenatherum elatius	False Oat-grass	Native	Widespread & common perennial of grassland, roadsides, waste places	
Artemisia absinthium	Wormwood	Arch	Scattered perennial of disturbed ground, roadsides & dumps, esp. in urban areas, increasing	
Artemisia vulgaris	Mugwort	Arch	Widespread & frequent perennial, esp. roadsides & disturbed ground	
Artemisia x wurzellii	'Wurzell's Mugwort'	Neo	Local perennial, roadside B/m 2006 (A. vulgaris x A. verlotiorum)	
Arum italicum	Italian Lords-and-Ladies	Neo	Scattered perennial garden escape (ssp. italicum)	
Arum maculatum	Lords-and-Ladies	Native	Widespread & frequent perennial of hedgerow & woods, many popular names e.g. Cuckoo-pint	
Asparagus officinalis	Asparagus	Neo	Perennial crop relic, rarely bird-sown, occasional on roadsides, hedgerows, grassland etc.	
Asperula arvensis	Blue Woodruff	Neo	Uncommon annual from bird-seed	
Asperula cynanchica	Squinancywort	Native	V. rare perennial of calc. grassland, Whichford 1973, Little Compton 1992 (ssp. cynanchica)	WR
Asplenium adiantum-nigrum	Black Spleenwort	Native	Scattered perennial fern, walls, possibly increasing	
Asplenium ruta-muraria	Wall-rue	Native	Widespread perennial fern, walls, increasing	
Asplenium trichomanes	Maidenhair Spleenwort	Native	Scattered perennial fern, walls, increasing (ssp. quadrivalens)	
Asplenium viride	Green Spleenwort	Ext Native	Extinct perennial fern, Lighthorne 1893	
Aster species	Michaelmas-daisies		A difficult group of garden escape perennials, long-established in dumps, roadsides, railway sidings etc.	
Aster lanceolatus	Narrow-leaved Michaelmas-daisy	Neo	Occasional	

Scientific Name	Popular Name	Cat.	Notes	Rarity
Aster novae-angliae	Hairy Michaelmas-daisy	Neo	The least commonly recorded Michaelmas-daisy in Warks	
Aster novi-belgii	Confused Michaelmas-daisy	Neo	The most frequently recorded Michaelmas-daisy in Warks, esp. railways & roadsides	
Aster x salignus	Common Michaelmas-daisy	Neo	Scattered records (A. lanceolatus x A. novi-belgii)	
Aster x versicolor	Late Michaelmas-daisy	Neo	Scattered records (A. laevis x A. novi-belgii)	
Astragalus glycyphyllos	Wild Liquorice	Native	Rare & local perennial on calc. banks, scrub, S Warks, 8 recent sites 1982-2004	WR
Astrantia major	Masterwort	Neo	Perennial garden escape, 2 sites	
Athyrium filix-femina	Lady-fern	Native	Common perennial fern, damp shade, shaded walls etc.	
Atriplex hortensis	Garden Orache	Cas	Uncommon annual, usually a relic of cultivation	
Atriplex littoralis	Grass-leaved Orache	Cas	Roads in B/m 2006, salt-tolerant annual	
Atriplex patula	Common Orache	Native	Widespread & frequent annual of arable, roadsides, farmyards etc, tolerates salt & manure	
Atriplex prostrata	Spear-leaved Orache	Native	Frequent & increasing annual, habitats as for above, but less common	
Atriplex x gustafssonia	Kattegat Orache	Cas	Annual, L/Spa 2006 only (A. prostrata x A. longipes)	
Atropa belladonna	Deadly Nightshade	Native	Occasional perennial, often in urban places	WN
Aubrieta deltoidea	Aubretia	Neo	Rock-garden perennial, uncommon escape	
Avena fatua	Wild-oat	Arch	Annual arable weed, widespread but declining	
Avena sativa	Oat	Cas Neo	Relic of cultivation & bird-seed annual, arable, tips etc.	
Avena sterilis	Winter Wild-oat	Cas Neo	Occasional annual arable weed, declining? (ssp. ludoviciana)	
Avena strigosa	Bristle Oat	Ext Neo	Extinct annual, Moreton Morrell 1878	
Azolla filiculoides	Water Fern	Neo	Floating annual fern, usually forming short-lived populations in ponds & rivers	
Baldellia ranunculoides	Lesser Water-plantain	Ext Native	Extinct wetland perennial, last found Monks Kirby 1957	NT
Ballota nigra	Black Horehound	Arch	Widespread perennial, esp. hedges, roadsides & disturbed ground (ssp. meridionalis)	

Scientific Name	Popular Name	Cat.	Notes	Rarity
Barbarea intermedia	Medium-flowered Winter-cress	Neo	Occasional biennial, esp. waste places & field margins usually not persisting for long	
Barbarea verna	American Winter-cress	Neo	Infrequent biennial, relic, esp. allotments	
Barbarea vulgaris	Winter-cress	Native	Scattered, usually biennial, roadsides, tips, hedges	
Bellis perennis	Daisy	Native	Widespread & frequent perennial of short grassland (incl. garden lawns)	
Berberis darwinii	Darwin's Barberry	Cas	Bird-sown shrub, B/m 2006, often grown as prickly hedge	
Berberis julianae	Chinese Barberry	Cas	Self-sown shrub, pavement B/m 2007, often grown as a prickly hedge	
Berberis vulgaris	Barberry	Neo	Scarce shrub, NE & E Warks, planted & naturalised	
Berteroa incana	Hoary Alison	Ext Cas	Extinct casual annual, Boldmere, Sutton Park -1874	
Berula erecta	Lesser Water-parsnip	Native	Widespread but local waterside perennial	WN
Beta vulgaris	Beet	Ext Cas	Extinct casual annual/biennial, K/worth 1959 (ssp. vulgaris)	
Betula pendula	Silver Birch	Native	Widespread native tree most frequent in N Warks on acid & neutral poor soils, widely planted too	
Betula pubescens ssp. pubescens	Downy Birch ssp.	Native	Less common than above, mainly wet woods, heathland & acid grassland of NW Warks	
Betula pubescens ssp. tortuosa	Downy Birch ssp.	Native	Seemingly scarce, 4 locations in 1960-70, probably under-recorded	
Betula x aurata	A hybrid birch	Native	Probably under-recorded (B. pendula x B. pubescens)	
Bidens cernua	Nodding Bur-marigold	Native	Very local waterside annual	WN
Bidens frondosa	Beggarticks	Neo	Locally abundant waterside annual, especially canalsides	
Bidens tripartita	Trifid Bur-marigold	Native	Occasional waterside annual, increasing along canals	
Biscutella auriculata	A buckler-mustard	Cas Neo	Escape annual (a spice), L/Spa 1990	
Blackstonia perfoliata	Yellow-wort	Native	Infrequent annual of calc. grassland & disturbed ground	WN
Blechnum spicant	Hard-fern	Native	Infrequent perennial fern, esp. acid ancient woodland	WN
Blysmus compressus	Flat-sedge	Native	V. rare perennial, marsh, Lower Lark Stoke 1998 only	NV
Bolboschoenus maritimus	Sea Club-rush	Native	Rare perennial, saline pools mid Warks, 5 recent sites 1986-1997	WR

Scientific Name	Popular Name	Cat.	Notes	Rarity
Borago officinalis	Borage	Neo	Relic of cultivation & garden escape annual, arable, roadsides, disturbed ground etc.	
Botrychium lunaria	Moonwort	Native	V. rare perennial fern, only recent site Draycote Meadows 1995	WR
Brachypodium pinnatum	Tor-grass	Native	Perennial of calc. grassland, S Warks	WN
Brachypodium sylvaticum	False Brome	Native	Widespread perennial grass of hedges & woods	
Brassica juncea	Chinese Mustard	Cas	Uncommon bird-seed & spice annual, transient	
Brassica napus ssp. oleifera	Oil-seed Rape	Cas	Relic of cultivation annual, sometimes persisting on roadsides, field margins etc for a few years, also from bird-seed.	
Brassica napus ssp. rapifera	Swede	Cas	Relic of cultivation annual, 1 record 1996	
Brassica nigra	Black Mustard	Native	Occasional annual of arable & roadsides esp. S Warks	
Brassica oleracea	Cabbage	Ext Cas	Relic of cultivation, no records since 1963-7, also a rare British native, but not of Warks	(NS)
Brassica rapa	Wild Turnip	Arch	Scattered biennial, arable, watersides & waste places (ssp. campestris)	
Brassica tournefortii	Pale Cabbage	Cas Neo	Uncommon 'Asian' pot-herb annual, transient	
Briza maxima	Greater Quaking-grass	Cas Neo	Ornamental annual, self-sown escape, urban	
Briza media	Quaking-grass	Native	Perennial of relatively unimproved grassland, local & decreasing	WN
Bromopsis erecta	Upright Brome	Native	Perennial of calc. grassland, esp. S Warks	WN
Bromopsis inermis	Hungarian Brome	Neo	Occasional perennial of roadsides & waste places (ssp. inermis)	
Bromopsis ramosa	Hairy-brome	Native	Local perennial esp. of hedges & woodland, declining	
Bromus arvensis	Field Brome	Cas Neo	Rare annual casual, 2 sites 1964, 1996	
Bromus commutatus	Meadow Brome	Native	Annual of old wet meadows, esp. S Warks	WN
Bromus hordeaceus ssp. hordeaceus	Soft-brome ssp.	Native	Widespread & abundant annual of roadsides, waste places, etc.	
Bromus hordeaceus ssp. longipedicellatus	Soft-brome ssp.	Native	Recently recognised ssp., grass-seed ingredient, occasional on roadsides, fields etc. 1994-	
Bromus lepidus	Slender Soft-brome	Neo	Widespread but local annual of grassland, declining?	

Scientific Name	Popular Name	Cat.	Notes	Rarity
Bromus pseudosecalinus	Smith's Brome	Ext Neo	Extinct annual, 5 sites 1960-70, S Warks	
Bromus racemosus	Smooth Brome	Native	Occasional annual of grassland, S Warks	
Bromus secalinus	Rye Brome	Arch	Rare annual of arable land, S Warks, only 3 recent sites 1991-	NV
Bromus squarrosus	Corn Brome	Ext Cas	Extinct casual annual, Waverley Wood 1961	
Bromus commutatus x B. racemosus	A hybrid brome	Native	V. rare annual hybrid, Southam 1963, Napton 1991	
Bromus x pseudothominei	Lesser Soft-brome	Neo	Frequent annual hybrid, grassland, roads etc., mid Warks (B. hordaceus x B. lepidus)	
Brunnera macrophylla	Great Forget-me-not	Cas Neo	Garden escape perennial, 1 record 1991	
Bryonia dioica	White Bryony	Native	Widespread climbing perennial, esp. hedgerows	
Buddleja davidii	Butterfly-bush	Neo	Widespread shrub of disturbed land, old buildings, railways etc., esp. urban	
Bupleurum longifolium	A hare's-ear	Cas	Garden perennial escape, S/Avon 2005, first GB record	
Bupleurum rotundifolium	Thorow-wax	Ext Arch & Cas Neo	Rare annual, extinct as an arable weed, last recorded 1960s, now a scarce casual	NC
Bupleurum subovatum	False Thorow-wax	Cas Neo	Rare bird-seed annual	
Butomus umbellatus	Flowering-rush	Native	Waterside perennial, widespread	
Buxus sempervirens	Box	Neo	Widely planted evergreen shrub, occasionally naturalised, E & mid Warks (rare as a British native)	(NR)
Cakile maritima	Sea Rocket	Ext Neo	Extinct annual, introduced with imported sea-sand, Emscote, Bedworth 1963-4	
Calamagrostis canescens	Purple Small-reed	Native	V. rare perennial, marsh & wet woods, only modern site a railway bank near Binley 1990-96	WR
Calamagrostis epigejos	Wood Small-reed	Native	Scattered local perennial, woodland rides, ditches, roadsides	
Calendula officinalis	Pot Marigold	Cas Neo	Scattered transient annual/ perennial escape	
Calla palustris	Bog Arum	Neo	Escape/planted perennial, Sutton Park 1979-	
Callitriche species	Water-starworts		Difficult group of aquatic annuals/ perennials, fruits essential for identification, scarce due to habitat loss & fertilisers	
Callitriche brutia	Pedunculate Water-starwort	Native	Rare aquatic annual, shallow ponds, decreasing, 3 recent sites 1974-97	WR

Scientific Name	Popular Name	Cat.	Notes	Rarity
Callitriche hamulata	Intermediate Water-starwort	Native	Rare aquatic annual, acid ponds, only 3 recent sites 1987-91	WR
Callitriche hermaphroditica	Autumnal Water-starwort	Native?	V. rare aquatic annual, lakes & pools, only recently recorded from Sutton Park (ssp. hermaphroditica)	WR
Callitriche obtusangula	Blunt-fruited Water-starwort	Native	Scattered aquatic perennial, ponds, rivers	
Callitriche platycarpa	Various-leaved Water-starwort	Native	Rare aquatic annual/perennial, streams, ponds, 3 recent sites 1991-98	WR
Callitriche stagnalis	Common Water-starwort	Native	Frequent aquatic annual/perennial, mud, pools, ruts etc.	
Calluna vulgaris	Heather	Native	Dwarf shrub of heathland and a few acid woodland and acid grassland sites, much declined	WN
Caltha palustris	Marsh-marigold	Native	Widespread but local waterside perennial, much planted in created ponds	
Calystegia pulchra	Hairy Bindweed	Neo	Scattered climbing perennial, esp. hedgerows	
Calystegia sepium	Hedge Bindweed	Native	Frequent climbing perennial, esp. hedges, urban & rural (ssp. sepium)	
Calystegia silvatica	Large Bindweed	Neo	Frequent climbing perennial, hedges, gardens, esp. urban	
Calystegia soldanella	Sea Bindweed	Ext Cas	Extinct transient perennial, Streetly 1895	
Calystegia x lucana	A hybrid bindweed	Native	Occasional hybrid, hedges etc. (C. sepium x C. silvatica)	
Camelina sativa	Gold-of-pleasure	Ext Neo	Extinct arable annual, Hams Hall 1939	(NS)
Campanula glomerulata	Clustered Bellflower	Native	Rare perennial of calc. grassland, also an escape, 3 recent sites 1980-95	WR
Campanula lactiflora	Milky Bellflower	Cas	Perennial with 1 record, Edgehill 1995	
Campanula latifolia	Giant Bellflower	Native	Scarce perennial, woods, hedges, waterside etc.	WN
Campanula patula	Spreading Bellflower	Native	V. rare perennial, mainly hedges, last record Shustoke 1999	NE
Campanula persicifolia	Peach-leaved Bellflower	Neo	Garden escape perennial, well-naturalised, esp. urban	
Campanula portenschlagiana	Adria Bellflower	Neo	Garden escape perennial, L/Spa pavement & B/m walls 2007	
Campanula poscharskyana	Trailing Bellflower	Neo	Occasional perennial garden escape, mainly urban walls	
Campanula rapunculoides	Creeping Bellflower	Neo	Occasional perennial garden escape	

Scientific Name	Popular Name	Cat.	Notes	Rarity
Campanula rapunculus	Rampion Bellflower	Ext Neo	Extinct perennial escape, Blacklow Hill 1935	(NE)
Campanula rotundifolia	Harebell	Native	Widespread but local perennial of grassland & heathland, declining	WN
Campanula trachelium	Nettle-leaved Bellflower	Native	Infrequent & local perennial of woods hedges etc, occasionally a garden escape	
Cannabis sativa	Hemp	Neo	Transient annual of bird-seed, fish-bait, also an illegal crop (plus the source of hemp fibre)	
Capsella bursa-pastoris	Shepherd's-purse	Arch	Widespread & common annual of disturbed ground, arable etc.	
Capsella rubella	Pink Shepherd's -purse	Neo	Introduced annual, esp. roads & towpaths 1991-, possibly over-looked	
Capsella x gracilis	A hybrid shepherd's-purse	Native	V. rare annual hybrid, canal towpath, Bushwood 1996 (C. bursa-pastoris x C. rubella)	
Cardamine amara	Large Bitter-cress	Native	Scattered perennial, watersides, wet grassland etc., N & mid Warks	
Cardamine corymbosa	New Zealand Bitter-cress	Neo	Biennial/annual, escape from rock-gardens, alpine pot-plants, B/m, L/Spa 1990- 2007, over-looked? (v. similar to next 2 spp.)	
Cardamine flexuosa	Wavy Bitter-cress	Native	Abundant annual/biennial, cultivated soil & wet places	
Cardamine hirsuta	Hairy Bitter-cress	Native	Frequent annual/perennial grassland, gardens, disturbed ground etc.	
Cardamine impatiens	Narrow-leaved Bitter-cress	Ext Native	Extinct v. rare biennial, last record near Atherstone 1963	NT
Cardamine pratensis	Cuckooflower	Native	Common perennial of wet grassland, marshes, sometimes lawns	
Cardamine x fringsii	A hybrid bitter-cress	Native	V. rare sterile perennial hybrid, Balsall Common 1989 (C. pratensis x C. flexuosa)	
Carduus crispus	Welted Thistle	Native	Occasional biennial, rich soil, hedges, waterside etc (ssp. multiflorus)	
Carduus nutans	Musk Thistle	Native	Scarce biennial, calcareous grassland and disturbed ground, esp. S Warks	WN
Carduus tenuiflorus	Slender Thistle	Ext Neo	Extinct biennial of coastal areas, last found Wellesbourne 1961	
Carduus x stangii	A hybrid thistle	Native	V. rare biennial hybrid, partially fertile, 2 recent sites, Wasperton 1973, Withybrook 2003 (C. crispus x nutans)	

Scientific Name	Popular Name	Cat.	Notes	Rarity
Carex species	Sedges		Perennials of dry and wet habitats, some widespread and common, others rare & local, flowers/fruits usually needed for identification.	
Carex acuta	Slender Tufted-sedge	Native	Occasional, watersides, possibly declining	WN
Carex acutiformis	Lesser Pond-sedge	Native	Fairly common esp. watersides & canals	
Carex arenaria	Sand Sedge	Neo	A native of coastal dunes, introduced with sea-sand, only Warwick 1995-	
Carex binervis	Green-ribbed Sedge	Native	Rare, wet woodland, possibly declining, 5 recent sites, 1986-2007	WR
Carex caryophyllea	Spring Sedge	Native	Scattered records, wet & dry grassland	WN
Carex curta	White Sedge	Native	V. rare, boggy watersides, recent records only for Sutton Park 1984-2007, Coleshill 1990	WR
Carex diandra	Lesser Tussock-sedge	Native	V. rare, bog and mire, only Sutton Park	NNT
Carex dioica	Dioecious Sedge	Native	V. rare, poor-fen, only Sutton Park	WR
Carex distans	Distant Sedge	Native	V. rare, wetlands, Chesterton 1981, Southam 1988	WR
Carex disticha	Brown Sedge	Native	Scattered, old meadows	WN
Carex divulsa ssp. divulsa	Grey Sedge ssp.	Native	Dry/damp banks, scattered	WN
Carex divulsa ssp. leersii	Grey Sedge ssp.	Native	V. rare, roadside, Loxley 1987 only recent record	WR
Carex echinata	Star Sedge	Native	V. rare, wetlands, Ufton 1976, Sutton Park 1990-2007	WR
Carex elongata	Elongated Sedge	Native	V. rare, 1 recent site, Clowes Wood 1984-92	NS
Carex flacca	Glaucous Sedge	Native	Widespread & frequent, wet & dry calc. grassland	
Carex hirta	Hairy Sedge	Native	Widespread & frequent, waste places, grassland etc.	
Carex hostiana	Tawny Sedge	Native	V. rare, wet heath, Sutton Park 1987-2007	WR
Carex laevigata	Smooth-stalked Sedge	Native	V. rare, Clowes Wood 1992, Sutton Park 2007	WR
Carex muricata	Prickly-sedge	Native	Scattered, dry grassland, urban & rural (ssp. lamprocarpa)	
Carex nigra	Common Sedge	Native	Local & declining, wetlands, watersides, grasslands etc.	WN
Carex otrubae	False Fox-sedge	Native	Widespread & frequent, wetlands, waterside, wet grassland, etc.	
Carex ovalis	Oval Sedge	Native	Local, wetlands, damp meadows, etc.	WN

Scientific Name	Popular Name	Cat.	Notes	Rarity
Carex pallescens	Pale Sedge	Native	Rare wet grassland, waterside, wet woodland, 6 recent sites 1987-2000 (the first GB record is probably a John Ray one from Warks)	WR
Carex panicea	Carnation Sedge	Native	Local, wetlands, watersides & wet grassland	WN
Carex paniculata	Greater Tussock-sedge	Native	Local, mainly waterside & wetland	WN
Carex pendula	Pendulous Sedge	Native	Widespread in wet woods, wetlands, tips etc. sometimes a garden escape	
Carex pilulifera	Pill Sedge	Native	Rare, heathy grassland, 3 recent sites 1990-2007	WR
Carex pseudocyperus	Cyperus Sedge	Native	Occasional waterside, scattered, also planted	
Carex pulicaris	Flea Sedge	Native	V. rare, poor-fen & wet heath, Sutton Park only	WR
Carex remota	Remote Sedge	Native	Local, esp. watersides &, damp woods	WN
Carex riparia	Greater Pond-sedge	Native	Widespread & locally abundant, watersides & wetlands	
Carex rostrata	Bottle Sedge	Native	V. rare, wetlands & bogs, only recent records Hampton in A. 1987, Bedworth 2001 (the first GB record is possibly a John Ray one from Warks)	WR
Carex spicata	Spiked Sedge	Native	Local, dry/wet grassland, banks etc.	WN
Carex strigosa	Thin-spiked Wood-sedge	Native	V. rare, 1 recent record K/worth 1995	WN
Carex sylvatica	Wood-sedge	Native	Scattered, woodland & hedgerows	
Carex vesicaria	Bladder-sedge	Native	Rare, marshes & waterside, mid Warks, 5 recent sites 1985-2004	WR
Carex viridula ssp. brachyrrhyncha	Yellow-sedge ssp.	Ext Native	Extinct, last found in rough pasture near Meriden 1955	
Carex viridula ssp. oedocarpa	Yellow-sedge ssp.	Native	Rare, marshes, bogs & woodland, 7 recent sites 1985-2007	WR
Carex x csomadensis	A hybrid sedge	Ext Native	Extinct hybrid, Brinklow 1922 only (C. riparia x C. vesicaria)	NV
Carex x fulva	A hybrid Sedge	Native	V. rare hybrid, re-found Sutton Park 2006, the commonest sedge hybrid in Britain (C. hostiana x C. viridula)	
Carex x pseudoaxillaris	A hybrid Sedge	Ext Native	Extinct hybrid, v. rare, last found c.1960, Earlswood, Snitterfield & Nunhold Grange (C. otrubae x C. remota)	
Carlina vulgaris	Carline Thistle	Native	Scarce biennial, calc. grassland & quarries, mid & S Warks, 9 sites 1971-97	WN

Scientific Name	Popular Name	Cat.	Notes	Rarity
Carpinus betulus	Hornbeam	Neo	Frequent planted tree, occasionally naturalised in woods, a native of S Britain but not Warks	
Carum carvi	Caraway	Arch & Cas	Transient annual, only recent record Bidford 1990	(NE)
Castanea sativa	Sweet Chestnut	Arch	Widely planted tree, naturalised in some woods	
Catabrosa aquatica	Whorl-grass	Native	Rare waterside perennial, 5 recent sites 1978-2006	WR
Catapodium rigidum	Fern-grass	Native	Local annual, calc. roadsides, quarries, paths etc., esp. S Warks	
Caucalis platycarpos	Small Bur-parsley	Ext Neo	Extinct arable annual, Alcester 1875	
Centaurea aspera	Rough Star-thistle	Ext Neo	Extinct transient, perennial, introduced with sea-sand, Emscote 1966	
Centaurea cyanus	Cornflower	Arch & Cas	Very rare arable annual & garden/ wildflower seed mix escape, 5 recent sites 1986-97	WR
Centaurea diluta	Lesser Star-thistle	Cas	Rare annual/perennial Wellesbourne 1961 & 1993	
Centaurea jacea	Brown Knapweed	Ext Neo	Extinct (also extinct in UK?), Milverton 1898 (also an occasional garden plant)	
Centaurea macrocephala	Giant Knapweed	Cas	Garden escape perennial, near Cov 2005	
Centaurea montana	Perennial Cornflower	Neo	Garden escape perennial, 3 recent sites	
Centaurea nigra	Common Knapweed	Native	Widespread & frequent perennial, grasslands, quarries, disturbed ground, roadsides etc.	
Centaurea scabiosa	Greater Knapweed	Native	Local perennial, calc. grassland, quarries & roadsides, S & E Warks	WN
Centaurea solstitialis	Yellow Star-thistle	Cas	Rare casual annual, 2 recent sites 1979 & 1987	
Centaurea x moncktonii	A hybrid knapweed	Ext Native	Extinct perennial, Edgbaston 1951 (C. nigra x C. jacea)	
Centaurium erythraea	Common Centaury	Native	Widespread but local biennial, disturbed land, dry grassland, railways etc.	
Centaurium pulchellum	Lesser Centaury	Native	Rare local annual, damp grassland, woodland etc., 7 recent sites 1972-2004	WR
Centranthus ruber	Red Valerian	Neo	Widespread perennial, urban escape, walls, pavements etc.	
Cephalanthera damasonium	White Helleborine	Ext Native	Extinct perennial, a Farnborough coppice 1887	NV

Scientific Name	Popular Name	Cat.	Notes	Rarity
Cephalanthera longifolia	Narrow-leaved Helleborine	Native	V. rare woodland perennial, only recent records Oversley Wood 2005-7	NV
Cephalaria gigantea	Giant Scabious	Cas	Rare garden escape perennial, Hams Hall 1993	
Cerastium arvense	Field Mouse-ear	Ext Native	Extinct perennial, last record calc. grassland at Little Compton 1960	
Cerastium diffusum	Sea Mouse-ear	Native	Native annual of coast, recent colonist of Warks spreading inland along railways 1978-2000	
Cerastium fontanum	Common Mouse-ear	Native	Widespread & frequent perennial, grassland, etc., urban & rural, 2 ssp. probably present	
Cerastium glomeratum	Sticky Mouse-ear	Native	Widespread & frequent annual, waste-ground, grassland, arable etc.	
Cerastium pumilum	Dwarf Mouse-ear	Ext Cas	Extinct annual, Terry's Green 1951	(NT)
Cerastium semidecandrum	Little Mouse-ear	Native	V. rare annual, Ufton 1996 only recent record	WR
Cerastium tomentosum	Snow-in-summer	Neo	Localised perennial escape, disturbed ground, dumps etc.	
Ceratocapnos claviculata	Climbing Corydalis	Native	Rare annual, woods, banks, 4 recent sites 1995-2004	WR
Ceratochloa carinata	California Brome	Cas	Rare perennial, B/m 1961 & 2007	
Ceratochloa cathartica	Rescue Brome	Neo	Perennial, from bird-seed, L/Spa 1978-95	
Ceratophyllum demersum	Rigid Hornwort	Native	Widespread & locally abundant aquatic perennial	
Ceratophyllum submersum	Soft Hornwort	Native	Rare perennial aquatic, 7 recent sites 1985-91	WR
Cerinthe major	Honeywort	Cas	Occasional garden escape annual, Cov allotment & L/Spa pavement 2006	
Ceterach officinarum	Rustyback	Native	Infrequent wall-fern, S & mid Warks	
Chaenorhinum minus	Small Toadflax	Arch	Widespread but declining annual, railways roadsides etc.	
Chaerophyllum temulum	Rough Chervil	Native	Widespread biennial, esp. hedges.	
Chamaemelum nobile	Chamomile	Ext Native	Extinct perennial, last record Yarningale 1901	NV
Chamerion angustifolium	Rosebay Willowherb	Neo	Widespread & locally abundant perennial, esp. disturbed ground, roadsides & railways, first record 1830, probably not native to Warks	
Chelidonium majus	Greater Celandine	Arch	Widespread & frequent biennial, disturbed ground, hedges etc.	
Chenopodium album	Fat-hen	Native	Widespread annual, arable, farmyards, disturbed land, gardens etc.	

Scientific Name	Popular Name	Cat.	Notes	Rarity
Chenopodium ambrosioides	Mexican-tea	Cas	Transient bird-seed annual, B/m 1983 only	
Chenopodium bonus-henricus	Good-King-Henry	Arch	Rare perennial, waste ground, farmyards, arable etc. 7 recent sites 1982-2007	NV
Chenopodium capitatum	Strawberry-blite	Ext Cas	Extinct escape annual, Warwick 19th century	
Chenopodium ficifolium	Fig-leaved Goosefoot	Arch	Scarce annual, manure, tips etc.	
Chenopodium foliosum	Strawberry Goosefoot	Ext Cas	Extinct casual annual, S/Avon 1823	
Chenopodium hircinum	Foetid Goosefoot	Ext Cas	Extinct casual annual, Milverton 1898	
Chenopodium hybridum	Maple-leaved Goosefoot	Arch	Infrequent annual, arable, allotments, tips etc.	
Chenopodium murale	Nettle-leaved Goosefoot	Ext Cas	Extinct casual annual, last record from a Napton garden 1956	(NV)
Chenopodium opulifolium	Grey Goosefoot	Ext Cas	Extinct casual annual, Sutton Park & Milverton 1891	
Chenopodium polyspermum	Many-seeded Goosefoot	Arch	Widespread & frequent annual, arable, waste, farmyards etc.	
Chenopodium quinoa	Quinoa	Cas	Increasingly planted annual birdseed crop, occasionally persisting, Hampton-in-Arden 2004, Claverdon 2006	
Chenopodium rubrum	Red Goosefoot	Native	Widespread & frequent annual, manure, tips, arable etc.	
Chenopodium suecicum	Swedish Goosefoot	Ext Cas	Extinct annual casual, Cov 1854	
Chenopodium urbicum	Upright Goosefoot	Arch	Nationally rare annual, also a casual, only recent record L/Spa roadside 2004-7	NC
Chenopodium vulvaria	Stinking Goosefoot	Ext Arch	Extinct annual, last record Langley Hall 1960	NE
Chrysanthemum segetum	Corn Marigold	Arch	Rare arable annual, also escape from wild-flower mixes, 9 recent arable sites, usually in v. small numbers	NV
Chrysosplenium alternifolium	Alternate-leaved Golden-saxifrage	Native	Rare perennial of wet woods, 4 recent sites 1982-2005	WR
Chrysosplenium oppositifolium	Opposite-leaved Golden-saxifrage	Native	Scattered local perennial, old wet woods	WN
Cicerbita macrophylla	Common Blue Sow-thistle	Neo	Localised but increasing perennial, persistent invader	
Cichorium intybus	Chicory	Arch	Widespread occasional transient perennial, esp. roadsides & disturbed ground	
Circaea lutetiana	Enchanter's-nightshade	Native	Widespread perennial, woods, hedgerows & shaded areas of gardens	

Scientific Name	Popular Name	Cat.	Notes	Rarity
Circaea x intermedia	Upland Enchanter's-nightshade	Ext Native	Extinct hybrid, Temple Balsall 1848 only (C. lutetiana x C. alpina)	
Cirsium acaule	Dwarf Thistle	Native	Scarce perennial, calc. grassland, banks & quarries	WN
Cirsium arvense	Creeping Thistle	Native	Widespread frequent perennial, grasslands, hedges, disturbed ground, woods etc	
Cirsium dissectum	Meadow Thistle	Native	Rare perennial, wet acid grassland & mire, 3 recent sites 1987-98	WR
Cirsium eriophorum	Woolly Thistle	Native	Local perennial of calc. grassland, roadsides, field margins etc. in S Warks	WN
Cirsium palustre	Marsh Thistle	Native	Scattered perennial, wet grassland, marsh, wet heath, damp woodland rides etc.	
Cirsium vulgare	Spear Thistle	Native	Widespread frequent perennial, grasslands, hedges, disturbed ground, field margins etc.	
Cirsium x celakovskianum	A hybrid thistle	Ext Native	Extinct perennial, only site Myton c.1870 (C. arvense x C. palustre)	
Cirsium x forsteri	A hybrid thistle	Ext Native	Extinct, Sutton Park 1937 (C. dissectum x C. palustre)	
Cladium mariscus	Great Fen-sedge	Ext Native	Extinct v. rare perennial, fens, only site Tamworth area 1670	
Claytonia perfoliata	Springbeauty	Neo	Widespread annual escape, ditches, arable, gardens etc.	
Claytonia sibirica	Pink Purslane	Neo	Increasing annual escape, esp. in woods where invasive, also gardens	
Clematis vitalba	Traveller's-joy	Native	Perennial climber, hedges, wood-edge, walls etc. usually on calc. soil	
Clinopodium acinos	Basil Thyme	Native	Rare perennial, calc. grassland & quarries, 4 recent sites 1979-97	NV
Clinopodium ascendens	Common Calamint	Native	Rare perennial, esp. hedges, 7 recent sites 1981-2004	WR
Clinopodium calamintha	Lesser Calamint	Ext Native	Extinct perennial, only site Lighthorne 1851	NV
Clinopodium vulgare	Wild Basil	Native	Scarce perennial, calc. grassland, quarries etc.	WN
Cochlearia danica	Danish Scurvygrass	Neo	Widespread & increasing annual of salted roadsides	
Coeloglossum viride	Frog Orchid	Ext Native	Extinct perennial, calc. grassland, Ipsley 1878	
Coincya monensis	Wallflower Cabbage	Cas	Perennial casual, railways, 2 sites 1963, 1979, extinct?	
Colchicum autumnale	Meadow Saffron	Native	Rare perennial, mainly woods, 5 recent sites 1971-1990	NNT
Colutea arborescens	Bladder-senna	Neo	Infrequent escape shrub, esp. tips	

Scientific Name	Popular Name	Cat.	Notes	Rarity
Conium maculatum	Hemlock	Arch	Widespread & frequent perennial, fertile soil of roadsides, watersides, disturbed ground, field margins, farmyards etc	
Conopodium majus	Pignut	Native	Widespread perennial, less-improved grassland, sometimes wood-edge	
Conringia orientalis	Hare's-ear Mustard	Ext Cas	Extinct annual casual, last record 1897	
Consolida ajacis	Larkspur	Ext Neo & Cas	Extinct arable annual, now a rare casual garden escape 1991	
Convallaria majalis	Lily-of-the-valley	Native	Rare perennial, woods, NW Warks, 5 native sites 1987-2005, also a garden escape	WR
Convolvulus arvensis	Field Bindweed	Native	Widespread perennial, arable, roadsides, gardens etc.	
Conyza bonariensis	Argentine Fleabane	Cas	Casual annual, pavement, L/Spa 2005 only	
Conyza bilbaoana	'Bilbao' Fleabane	Cas	Biennial/annual, urban roads & tips 2004-7-	
Conyza canadensis	Canadian Fleabane	Neo	Widespread biennial/annual, established 1946-, disturbed ground, roadsides, esp. urban	
Conyza sumatrensis	Guernsey Fleabane	Cas	Biennial/annual, roadsides, tips, urban only 2004-7	
Coriandrum sativum	Coriander	Cas	Scarce annual spice-herb, escape of allotments & gardens	
Corispermum leptopterum	Bugseed	Neo	Annual introduced with sea-sand, Warwick 1962-93, possibly extinct now	
Cornus mas	Cornelian-cherry	Neo	Widely-planted shrub, possibly self-seeded at 1 site, Ravenshaw 1997	
Cornus sanguinea	Dogwood	Native	Widespread & frequent shrub, esp. woods, & hedges, also planted elsewhere	
Cornus sericea	Red-osier Dogwood	Neo	Occasional escape shrub, watersides, park shrubberies	
Coronilla scorpioides	Annual Scorpion-vetch	Cas	Transient bird-seed annual, 3 sites 1965-2003	
Coronopus didymus	Lesser Swine-cress	Neo	Widespread & increasing recently-arrived annual, disturbed ground, gardens, tips, roadsides etc.	
Coronopus squamatus	Swine-cress	Arch	Widespread but local annual, arable, disturbed ground, gateways etc.	
Cortaderia selloana	Pampas-grass	Cas	Ornamental perennial, Lea Marston 2005	

Scientific Name	Popular Name	Cat.	Notes	Rarity
Corydalis solida	Bird-in-a-bush	Neo	Occasional perennial garden escape in a variety of habitats	
Corylus avellana	Hazel	Native	Frequent shrub of ancient woods (frequently as coppice stools) and older hedges, also planted elsewhere, sometimes for its nuts	
Cotoneaster species	Cotoneasters		Escaped shrubs/small trees, bird-sown & garden escapes, walls, tips, 70+ spp. established in UK, flowers/fruit needed to identify	
Cotoneaster bullatus	Hollyberry Cotoneaster	Neo	1 tree + seedlings, quarry, Bishop's Itchington 2005	
Cotoneaster conspicuus	Tibetan Cotoneaster	Neo	3 shrubs, quarry, Bishop's Itchington 2005	
Cotoneaster dielsianus	Diels' Cotoneaster	Neo	1 shrub on wall, B/m 2006	
Cotoneaster henryanus	Henry's Cotoneaster	Neo	1 shrub by pit, Sutton Coldfield 2006	
Cotoneaster horizontalis	Wall Cotoneaster	Neo	Commonest naturalised Cotoneaster in Warks, walls, roadsides, quarries etc. 1989-, popular in gardens	
Cotoneaster integrifolius	Entire-leaved Cotoneaster	Ext Neo	1 record 1932, no location	
Cotoneaster lacteus	Late Cotoneaster	Neo	1 tree & seedlings, derelict site Rugby 2006	
Cotoneaster mairei	Maire's Cotoneaster	Neo	5 shrubs, canalside wall, L/Spa 2005	
Cotoneaster rehderi	Bullate Cotoneaster	Neo	1 shrub by pit, Sutton Coldfield 2006	
Cotoneaster salicifolius	Willow-leaved Cotoneaster	Neo	2 records, Cov canalside 1996, Rugby tip 2006	
Cotoneaster salicifolius x ?	A hybrid cotoneaster	Neo	Hybrid shrub, uncertain parentage, Rugby tip 2006	
Cotoneaster simonsii	Himalayan Cotoneaster	Neo	3 shrubs, walls, Walsgrave Hospital 1989	
Cotula coronopifolia	Buttonweed	Cas Neo	Annual, wetlands, Cov 1991 & 1998	
Cotula squalida	Leptinella	Cas Neo	Perennial lawn weed, only Knowle 1997	
Crassula helmsii	New Zealand Pigmyweed	Neo	Invasive aquatic/waterside perennial, widespread, increasing since 1986	
Crataegus laevigata	Midland Hawthorn	Native	Widespread but local native shrub of woods and hedges, also widely planted in red-flowering form	
Crataegus monogyna	Hawthorn	Native	Widespread and abundant shrub, esp. in hedges and scrub, also widely planted	

Scientific Name	Popular Name	Cat.	Notes	Rarity
Crataegus x media	A hybrid hawthorn	Native	Rare, probably under-reported hybrid, 4 sites 1991-2004 (C. monogyna x C. laevigata)	
X Crataemespilus grandiflora	Haw-medlar	Neo	Unusual planted hybrid shrub, possible escape, B/m 2006 (Mespilus germanica x Crataegus laevigata)	
Crepis biennis	Rough Hawk's-beard	Native	Rare biennial, rough grassland, Preston on Stour 1996, Little Kineton 1999	WR
Crepis capillaris	Smooth Hawk's-beard	Native	Widespread biennial, disturbed land, grassland, arable, roadsides etc.	
Crepis nicaeensis	French Hawk's-beard	Ext Neo	Extinct biennial, Berkswell 1892	
Crepis paludosa	Marsh Hawk's-beard	Ext Native	Extinct perennial, wetlands & watersides, Sutton Park 1882, S/Avon 1960	
Crepis setosa	Bristly Hawk's-beard	Cas	Rare annual, Rugby 1962, Snitterfield 1991	
Crepis vesicaria	Beaked Hawk's-beard	Neo	Widespread & frequent perennial, roadsides, disturbed land, arable etc. (ssp. taraxifolia)	
Crocosmia x crocosmiiflora	Montbretia	Neo	Infrequent perennial escape, roadside, scrub, woodland etc., can be invasive (C. pottsia x C. aurea)	
Crocus chrysanthus	Golden Crocus	Neo	Established perennial, Lapworth Church 1997	
Crocus nudiflorus	Autumn Crocus	Neo	Established perennial, Warwick, 2 sites 1812-1974- (formerly grown as a source of saffron substitute)	WN
Crocus speciosus	Bieberstein's Crocus	Neo	Established perennial, Solihull Church 1997	
Crocus tommasinianus	Early Crocus	Neo	Established perennial, Stivichall 1996	
Crocus vernus	Spring Crocus	Neo	Established perennial, 3 sites, 1891-1996	
Cruciata laevipes	Crosswort	Native	Scattered perennial, roadsides, grassland, hedges etc., declining	WN
Cuscuta australis	Australian Dodder	Ext Cas	Extinct annual parasite of Chrysanthemums, K/worth 1933	
Cuscuta campestris	Yellow Dodder	Ext Cas	Extinct annual Carrot parasite, Wellesbourne 1973	
Cuscuta epilinum	Flax Dodder	Ext Cas	Extinct annual Flax parasite, 3 sites 1834-1851	
Cuscuta epithymum	Dodder	Ext Native	Extinct rare annual parasite, many native hosts 1854-1959	NV

Scientific Name	Popular Name	Cat.	Notes	Rarity
Cuscuta europaea	Greater Dodder	Ext Native	Extinct rare annual parasite, many native hosts 1805-1962	
Cuscuta suaveolens	Lucerne Dodder	Ext Cas	Extinct annual Lucerne parasite, Rugby 1864	
Cyclamen hederifolium	Sowbread	Neo	Established perennial, Knowle 1996	
Cymbalaria muralis	Ivy-leaved Toadflax	Neo	Widespread perennial of urban walls (ssp. muralis)	
Cymbalaria pallida	Italian Toadflax	Neo	Extinct perennial, wall L/Spa 1985-1998	
Cynoglossum germanicum	Green Hound's-tongue	Ext Native	Extinct biennial, last recorded at Kenilworth and S/Avon in 1875	
Cynoglossum officinale	Hound's-tongue	Native	Rare biennial, calc. scrub & grassland, S Warks 9 recent sites 1986-2003	NNT
Cynosurus cristatus	Crested Dog's-tail	Native	Widespread perennial, old & less improved grassland	WN
Cynosurus echinatus	Rough Dog's-tail	Ext Cas	Extinct casual annual, 2 sites B/m 1946	
Cyperus eragrostis	Pale Galingale	Cas	Rare transient perennial, Cov 1984, L/Spa 2007	
Cyperus longus	Galingale	Neo	Introduced waterside perennial, 6+ sites 1973-2007	(NT)
Cystopteris fragilis	Brittle Bladder-fern	Native	Rare perennial fern, walls, mid Warks, 4 recent sites 1983-91	WR
Cytisus scoparius	Broom	Native	Scattered perennial, disturbed ground, acid grassland, roadsides, avoids lime, esp. N Warks, also a garden escape	
Dactylis glomerata	Cock's-foot	Native	Widespread & frequent perennial, grassland, roadsides, disturbed land etc.	
Dactylorhiza fuchsii	Common Spotted-orchid	Native	Widespread but local perennial, less improved grassland, disturbed land, damp woodland & scrub	
Dactylorhiza incarnata	Early Marsh-orchid	Native	V. rare perennial, damp grassland & marsh, 7 sites 1884-1964, refound Depper's Bridge 2002 (ssp. pulchella)	WR
Dactylorhiza maculata	Heath Spotted-orchid	Native	Rare perennial, acid grassland, wet heath, boggy woods etc., 9 recent sites 1975-2000 (ssp. ericetorum)	WR
Dactylorhiza praetermissa	Southern Marsh-orchid	Native	Widespread local perennial, wet grassland, marsh etc.	WN
Dactylorhiza x grandis	A hybrid orchid	Native	Scarce perennial hybrid found usually with parents, 7 recent sites 1975-1998 (D. fuchsii x D. praetermissa)	

Scientific Name	Popular Name	Cat.	Notes	Rarity
Dactylorhiza x hallii	A hybrid orchid	Ext Native	Extinct perennial hybrid, only record Sutton Park 1944 (D. maculata x D. praetermissa)	
Dactylorhiza x wintoni	A hybrid orchid	Native	V. rare perennial hybrid, only record Depper's Bridge 2002 (D. incarnata x D. praetermissa)	
Danthonia decumbens	Heath-grass	Native	Rare perennial, acid grassland, 8 records 1977-2001	WR
Daphne laureola	Spurge-laurel	Native	Scarce small evergreen shrub, calc. woods and scrub, mostly S Warks	WN
Daphne mezereum	Mezereon	Ext Cas	Escape/planted/bird-sown evergreen shrub 1864-1933, not native to Warks, but rare as a British native	(NV)
Datura stramonium	Thorn-apple	Neo	Scattered, bird-seed annual, gardens, waste ground etc., regularly found	
Datura ferox	Angel's-trumpets	Cas	Scarce annual, possibly from bird-seed, soil-heap, B/m 2007	
Daucus carota	Wild Carrot	Native	Biennial of calc. grassland, quarries & roadsides in S Warks, sometimes on disturbed ground elsewhere, avoids acid soils (ssp. carota)	
Deschampsia cespitosa ssp. cespitosa	Tufted Hair-grass ssp.	Native	Widespread perennial, esp. damp grassland & scrub on former pasture, ssp. rarely given, recently 2 ssp. recognised	
Deschampsia cespitosa ssp. parviflora	Tufted Hair-grass ssp.	Native	Under-recorded, woods etc., seemingly the less common ssp. in Warks	
Deschampsia flexuosa	Wavy Hair-grass	Native	Scarce perennial, heathland, acid grassland, acid woodland	WN
Descurainia sophia	Flixweed	Arch + Cas	Rare annual, usually casual, 4 recent sites 1981-2004	WN
Dianthus armeria	Deptford Pink	Ext Native, Neo	Extinct as a native, biennial, Myton 1832, refound as garden escape, Water Orton 1980-92	(NE)
Dianthus deltoides	Maiden Pink	Ext Cas	Extinct perennial, 2 records, 1830 as a possible native, 1960 as an escape	(NT)
Dianthus gratianopolitanus	Cheddar Pink	Ext Cas	Extinct perennial, garden wall, Barford c.1900	(NV)
Digitalis lutea	Straw Foxglove	Neo	Naturalised perennial, Newbold Pacey 1993-	
Digitalis purpurea	Foxglove	Native	Widespread biennial/perennial, native of acid woods, hedges & roadverges in N & W Warks, also a frequent garden escape	

Scientific Name	Popular Name	Cat.	Notes	Rarity
Digitaria ciliaris	Tropical Finger-grass	Neo	Bird-seed annual, Warwick 1992-2007-	
Digitaria sanguinalis	Hairy Finger-grass	Cas	Bird-seed annual, B/m 1983, K/worth 1874	
Diplotaxis muralis	Annual Wall-rocket	Neo	Local annual, roadsides, railways, walls, tips etc.	
Diplotaxis tenuifolia	Perennial Wall-rocket	Arch	Rare perennial, roadsides, railways etc., 4 recent sites 1989-2006	WR
Dipsacus fullonum	Wild Teasel	Native	Widespread & frequent biennial, roadsides, disturbed ground, rough grassland, watersides etc.	
Dipsacus laciniatus	Cut-leaved Teasel	Cas	Biennial, possibly from wild flower mix, a Wylde Green park 2007	
Dipsacus x pseudosilvester	A hybrid teasel	Cas	V. rare biennial hybrid, found with both parents, Wylde Green 2007 (D. fullonum x D. laciniatus)	
Dipsacus pilosus	Small Teasel	Native	Scarce waterside biennial, mid Warks	WN
Dipsacus sativus	Fuller's Teasel	Cas	Perennial, railway, Minworth 1978	
Doronicum columnae	Eastern Leopard's-bane	Cas	Perennial escape, woodland, Farnborough 1996	
Doronicum pardalianches	Leopard's-bane	Neo	Occasional perennial garden escape, esp. woods & hedges	
Doronicum x willdenowii	Willdenow's Leopard's-bane	Neo	Hybrid perennial escape, copse Shottery 1999 (D. pardalianches x D. plantagineum)	
Draba muralis	Wall Whitlowgrass	Ext Neo	Extinct escape perennial, 2 sites 1930, 1959	(NS)
Drosera rotundifolia	Common Sundew	Native	V. rare insectivorous perennial, bog & mire, now only at Sutton Park	WR
Dryopteris affinis	Scaly Male-fern	Native	Widespread but local perennial fern, woods, hedges, ssp. rarely provided, but ssp. borreri. probably the commonest, ssp. cambrensis rarest	
Dryopteris carthusiana	Narrow Buckler-fern	Native	Scarce perennial, shady woodland	WN
Dryopteris dilatata	Broad Buckler-fern	Native	Widespread perennial, woods, shaded walls, etc.	
Dryopteris filix-mas	Male-fern	Native	Widespread perennial, woods, shaded walls etc.	
Duchesnea indica	Yellow-flowered Strawberry	Neo	Perennial escape, Frankton 1998, alleys L/Spa 2005-	
Echinochloa colona	Shama Millet	Cas	Annual, bird-seed, Warwick 1995, Dosthill 1996	
Echinochloa crus-galli	Cockspur	Neo	Annual, bird-seed, increasing, scattered urban records	
Echinochloa esculenta	Japanese Millet	Cas	Annual, bird-seed, Warwick 1990	
Echinops exaltatus	Globe-thistle	Cas	Perennial garden escape, roadside Hampton Lucy 1992	

Scientific Name	Popular Name	Cat.	Notes	Rarity
Echinops sphaerocephalus	Glandular Globe-thistle	Neo	Perennial garden escape, occasionally naturalised, 4 sites 1960-	
Echium vulgare	Viper's-bugloss	Native	Scarce biennial, roadsides, disturbed land, quarries etc.	
Elatine hexandra	Six-stamened Waterwort	Native	V. rare annual aquatic, refound Coleshill Pool 1992	WR
Eleocharis acicularis	Needle Spike-rush	Native	V. rare waterside perennial, refound Ryton 1998	WR
Eleocharis multicaulis	Many-stalked Spike-rush	Ext Native	Extinct waterside perennial, last record Bickenhill 1945	
Eleocharis palustris ssp. palustris	Common Spike-rush ssp.	Native	V. rare ssp., only current site a pond in Hunscote 1988, see below	WR
Eleocharis palustris ssp. vulgaris	Common Spike-rush ssp.	Native	Widespread wetland perennial, this is the commoner ssp.	
Eleocharis quinqueflora	Few-flowered Spike-rush	Native	V. rare waterside perennial, only current site Sutton Park 1983	WR
Eleocharis uniglumis	Slender Spike-rush	Native	Rare waterside perennial, 3 recent sites 1990-7	WR
Eleogiton fluitans	Floating Club-rush	Native	V. rare aquatic perennial, now only at a Packington marsh 1997	WR
Elodea canadensis	Canadian Waterweed	Neo	Widespread abundant aquatic perennial, possibly becoming replaced by the next sp.	
Elodea nuttallii	Nuttall's Waterweed	Neo	Similar to above, increasing (popular garden pond plant)	
Elymus caninus	Bearded Couch	Native	Widespread but local perennial, roadsides, hedges, watersides etc.	
Elytrigia juncea	Sand Couch	Ext Neo	Extinct perennial, a native of the coast imported with sea sand, Emscote, Bedworth	
Elytrigia repens	Common Couch	Native	Widespread & abundant perennial, arable, hedges, grassland etc. (ssp. repens)	
Empetrum nigrum	Crowberry	Native	V. rare dwarf shrub, dry heath, only site Sutton Park 1990 (ssp. nigrum)	WR
Epilobium species	Willowherbs		Difficult group of perennials, hybrids probably under-recorded, extinction & rarity class not assigned to these. 8 hybrids found at Burton Green in 2007, possibly a British record.	
Epilobium brunnescens	New Zealand Willowherb	Neo	V. rare, base of a wall, Wroxall Abbey 1965-83, Warwick 1989-90	WR
Epilobium ciliatum	American Willowherb	Neo	Widespread & abundant, gardens, roadsides, disturbed ground, tips, etc.	

Scientific Name	Popular Name	Cat.	Notes	Rarity
Epilobium hirsutum	Great Willowherb	Native	Widespread & abundant, esp. marshes, ditches and waterside	
Epilobium lanceolatum	Spear-leaved Willowherb	Native	V. rare, S/Avon racecourse 1953, Atherstone quarry 1990	WR
Epilobium montanum	Broad-leaved Willowherb	Native	Widespread & abundant, roadsides, disturbed land, waterside, hedges, tips etc.	
Epilobium obscurum	Short-fruited Willowherb	Native	Widespread but local, roadsides, railways, watersides, hedges etc.	
Epilobium palustre	Marsh Willowherb	Native	Rare, watersides & marshes, NW Warks, 5 recent sites 1981-7	WR
Epilobium parviflorum	Hoary Willowherb	Native	Widespread but local, watersides, marshes, roadsides, railways etc.	
Epilobium roseum	Pale Willowherb	Native	Widespread but local, watersides, wetlands, roadsides etc.	
Epilobium tetragonum	Square-stalked Willowherb	Native	Widespread but local, watersides, wetlands, roadsides, hedges, cultivated ground etc.	
Epilobium x aggregatum	A hybrid willowherb	Native	Hybrid, Birdingbury 1996 (E. montanum x E. obscurum)	
Epilobium x brevipilum	A hybrid willowherb	Native	Hybrid, Burton Green 2007 (E. hirsutum x E. tetragonum)	
Epilobium x dacicum	A hybrid willowherb	Native	Hybrid, B/m 1874, Cov 2007 (E.parviflorum x E. obscurum)	
Epilobium x erroneum	A hybrid willowherb	Native	Hybrid, 4 sites 1955-58, possibly extinct (E. hirsutum x E. montanum)	
Epilobium x floridulum	A hybrid willowherb	Native	Hybrid, Warwick 1980, Wilmcote 1997, Burton Green 2007 (E. parviflorum x E. ciliatum)	
Epilobium x interjectum	A hybrid willowherb	Native	Hybrid, Westwood Heath 2007 (E. montanum x E. ciliatum)	
Epilobium x limosum	A hybrid willowherb	Native	Hybrid, 6 sites 1950-62 (E. parviflorum x E. montanum)	
Epilobium x mentiens	A hybrid willowherb	Native	Hybrid, Warwick 1965, Cov 2007 (E.tetragonum x ciliatum)	
Epilobium x mutabile	A hybrid willowherb	Native	Hybrid Edgbaston 1901, possibly extinct (E. montanum x E. roseum)	
Epilobium x palatinum	A hybrid willowherb	Native	Hybrid, Burton Green 2007 (E. tetragonum x E. parviflorum)	
Epilobium x schmidtianum	A hybrid willowherb	Native	Hybrid Sutton Park 1951, possibly extinct (E. obscurum x E. palustre)	
Epilobium x semiobscurum	A hybrid willowherb	Native	Hybrid, Burton Green 2007, (E. tetragonum x E. obscurum)	
Epilobium x subhirsutum	A hybrid willowherb	Native	Hybrid, Burton Green 2007 (E. hirsutum x E. parviflorum)	
Epilobium x vicinum	A hybrid willowherb	Native	Hybrid, 5 sites 1950-2007 (E. ciliatum x E. obscurum)	

Scientific Name	Popular Name	Cat.	Notes	Rarity
Epipactis helleborine	Broad-leaved Helleborine	Native	Scarce perennial mostly of ancient woodland	WN
Epipactis palustris	Marsh Helleborine	Native	V. rare perennial, wet grassland & marsh, one recent site Lea Marston 1986-	WR
Epipactis phyllanthes	Green-flowered Helleborine	Ext Native	Extinct perennial, only site Charlecote 1857	NS
Epipactis purpurata	Violet Helleborine	Native	Rare perennial of shaded woodland, only recent records Moreton Morrell 1979, Bannam's Wood 1977, Wolford Wood 2007	WR
Equisetum arvense	Field Horsetail	Native	Widespread & abundant perennial in a range of open habitats, often a garden weed	
Equisetum fluviatile	Water Horsetail	Native	Localised waterside perennial	WN
Equisetum hyemale	Rough Horsetail	Ext Native	Extinct perennial, only record Middleton 1695	
Equisetum palustre	Marsh Horsetail	Native	Localised waterside perennial	WN
Equisetum sylvaticum	Wood Horsetail	Native	Rare perennial, acid woods, N Warks, 5 sites 1974-2007	WR
Equisetum telmateia	Great Horsetail	Native	Localised perennial, esp. associated with seepages and damp areas in woods, hedges, also marshes	WN
Equisetum x litorale	Shore Horsetail	Native	V. rare perennial hybrid, Warwick canalside 1995 (E. fluviatile x E. arvense)	
*Equisetum x rothmaleri	A hybrid horsetail	Native	V. rare perennial hybrid, canalsides, Bascote 1995, Longford 1998 (E. arvense x E. palustre)	
Eragrostis cilianensis	Stink-grass	Ext Cas	Extinct bird-seed annual, B/m 1983 only	
Eranthis hyemalis	Winter Aconite	Neo	Naturalised perennial garden escape, scattered, woods, parks etc.	
Erica cinerea	Bell Heather	Native	V. rare dwarf shrub, dry heathland, Coleshill 1981, Baddesley 1996	WR
Erica tetralix	Cross-leaved Heath	Native	Rare perennial, heaths, N Warks, 3 sites 1987-2007	WR
Erigeron acer	Blue Fleabane	Native	Localised annual of quarries, railways, quarries tips etc.	WN
Erigeron glaucus	Seaside Daisy	Cas	Garden escape perennial, roads, Wylde Green 2007	
Erigeron karvinskianus	Mexican Fleabane	Neo	Garden escape perennial, urban walls, pavement etc., increasing	
Erinus alpinus	Fairy Foxglove	Neo	Perennial, walls, Winterbourne Botanic Garden, B/m 2007, spreading nationally	

Scientific Name	Popular Name	Cat.	Notes	Rarity
Eriophorum angustifolium	Common Cotton-grass	Native	Rare perennial, mire and marshy grassland, recent records Kingsbury 1987, Sutton Park 2007, declining	WR
Eriophorum vaginatum	Hare's-tail Cotton-grass	Native	V. rare perennial, bog & mire, recent records Coleshill 1987, Kingsbury 2002, Sutton Park 2007, declining	WR
Erodium botrys	Mediterranean Stork's-bill	Ext Cas	Extinct annual, Bedworth colliery tip 1964	
Erodium cicutarium	Common Stork's-bill	Native	Localised annual, esp. arable, rough grassland etc.	
Erodium lebelii	Sticky Stork's-bill	Ext Cas	Extinct annual, introduced with sea-sand, Emscote 1963	(NS)
Erodium maritimum	Sea Stork's-bill	Ext Cas	Extinct annual, Oscott c.1891	
Erodium moschatum	Musk Stork's-bill	Arch	Rare annual, 3 recent sites 1984-2007, arable etc., possibly native	WR
Erophila glabrescens	Glabrous Whitlowgrass	Native	Rare, but v. similar to E. verna, gravel, walls, 8 recent sites 1987-2002	WR
Erophila majuscula	Hairy Whitlowgrass	Native	V. rare but v. similar to E. verna, Warwick 1987 only	WR
Erophila verna	Common Whitlowgrass	Native	Widespread, disturbed land, railways, roadsides etc (records could include the previous 2 spp.)	
Eruca vesicaria	Garden Rocket	Cas Neo	Annual garden & allotment escape, roadsides, 3 recent records (ssp. sativa)	
Erucastrum gallicum	Hairy Rocket	Ext Cas	Extinct annual/biennial, Edgbaston 1935	
Erucastrum nasturtiifolium	Watercress-leaved Rocket	Ext Cas	Extinct annual/perennial, Sutton Park casual 1877	
Erysimum cheiranthoides	Treacle Mustard	Arch	Rare annual, rough grassland, arable, quarries etc., 8 recent sites 1981-91	WR
Erysimum cheiri	Wallflower	Arch	Infrequent escape perennial, walls, disturbed land, roadside etc.	
Erysimum repandum	Spreading Treacle-mustard	Ext Cas	Extinct casual annual, 1 record Milverton 1900	
Escallonia macrantha	Escallonia	Cas	Garden escape shrub, 1 record Cov 1996	
Escallonia x langleyensis	A hybrid escallonia	Cas	Garden escape shrub, 1 record Sutton Coldfield 2006 (E. macrantha x E. virgata)	
Eschscholzia californica	Californian Poppy	Cas	Garden escape annual, urban roads 1966, 2004-	
Euonymus europaeus	Spindle	Native	Localised small tree of hedges & woods, also planted	WN

Scientific Name	Popular Name	Cat.	Notes	Rarity
Euonymus latifolius	Large-leaved Spindle	Ext Neo	Extinct garden escape shrub, Farnborough 1954	
Eupatorium cannabinum	Hemp-agrimony	Native	Localised perennial, wet woodland edge, hedges, banks etc.	
Euphorbia amygdaloides	Wood Spurge	Native	Scarce perennial mainly in ancient woods and hedges of SW Warks, (ssp. amygdaloides)	WN
Euphorbia cyparissias	Cypress Spurge	Ext Cas	Garden escape, last record as a casual Wellesbourne 1964	
Euphorbia esula agg.	Leafy Spurge	Ext Cas	Extinct perennial, Leek Wootton & Myton 1871	
Euphorbia exigua	Dwarf Spurge	Arch	Scarce annual arable weed, calc. soils, S Warks, declining	NNT
Euphorbia helioscopia	Sun Spurge	Arch	Widespread & frequent annual, allotments, gardens, disturbed land, roadsides etc.	
Euphorbia lathyris	Caper Spurge	Neo	Localised garden escape, disturbed land, roadsides, tips etc.	
Euphorbia peplus	Petty Spurge	Arch	Widespread & frequent annual, allotments, gardens etc.	
Euphorbia platyphyllos	Broad-leaved Spurge	Arch	V. rare arable annual weed, calcareous soils, S Warks, 3 recent sites 1988-2002	WR
Euphorbia boissieriana x E. esula	A hybrid spurge	Neo	Perennial escape established at Small Heath sidings, B/m 1989, first UK record?	
Euphorbia x pseudovirgata	Twiggy Spurge	Neo	Garden escape perennial, Stockton 1983, Shipston-on-Stour 1996 (E. waldsteinii x E. esula)	
Euphrasia arctica	An eyebright	Ext Native	Extinct annual, Kineton 1964 (ssp. borealis)	
Euphrasia confusa	An eyebright	Native	V. rare annual, only recent record Burton Dassett 1979	WR
Euphrasia micrantha	An eyebright	Ext Native	Extinct annual, last found Olton c.1960	
Euphrasia nemorosa	An eyebright	Native	Scarce annual, a few calc. quarries but most records unconfirmed – eyebrights are difficult to identify	WR
Fagopyrum esculentum	Buckwheat	Neo	Scarce annual, arable escape, bird-seed, disturbed ground, roadsides, tips etc.	
Fagus sylvatica	Beech	Neo	Widely planted tree, naturalised in some woods, native to S Britain but not Warks	
Falcaria vulgaris	Longleaf	Neo	V. rare perennial, arable, Newbold-on-Stour 1928-2005	WR
Fallopia baldschuanica	Russian-vine	Neo	Climbing perennial, garden escape, esp. hedges, scrub, mainly urban	

Scientific Name	Popular Name	Cat.	Notes	Rarity
Fallopia convolvulus	Black-bindweed	Arch	Widespread annual, arable, roadsides, disturbed land etc.	
Fallopia japonica	Japanese Knotweed	Neo	Widespread & increasing invasive perennial, esp. roadsides & watersides (the planting of it is illegal)	
Fallopia sachalinensis	Giant Knotweed	Neo	Invasive & increasing perennial, esp. roadsides, but less frequent than previous sp.	
Fallopia x bohemica	Hybrid Japanese Knotweed	Native	Rare perennial hybrid, watersides, L/Spa, Solihull, Guy's Cliffe 1993-1995 (F. japonica x F. sachalinensis)	
Festuca species	Fescues		Large group of perennial grasses, some v. distinctive, some need expert identification, hybrids sown & spontaneous.	
Festuca altissima	Wood Fescue	Native	V. rare, only Bentley Park Wood 1972-98-	WR
Festuca arundinacea	Tall Fescue	Native	Localised on roadsides, in woods, roads, grassland etc.	
Festuca brevipila	Hard Fescue	Cas	Grass-seed casual, only Copt Green 1996	
Festuca filiformis	Fine-leaved Sheep's-fescue	Native	Rare, tips, acid soil, NW Warks, 3 recent sites 1984-2001	WR
Festuca gigantea	Giant Fescue	Native	Localised, hedges, woods, watersides etc.	
Festuca heterophylla	Various-leaved Fescue	Ext Cas	Extinct, Edgbaston garden 1975	
Festuca longifolia	Blue Fescue	Ext Native & Cas Neo	Extinct as a native, heaths, last site Leek Wootton 1897, casual garden escape L/Spa, B/m 2007	NR
Festuca ovina ssp. hirtula	Sheep's-fescue ssp.	Native	Rare, acid grassland & heathland, NW Warks, locally abundant at Sutton Park	WR
Festuca ovina ssp. ophioliticola	Sheep's-fescue ssp.	Native	Rare or possibly overlooked, calc. grassland, Shipston-on-Stour 1997	WR
Festuca ovina ssp. ovina	Sheep's-fescue ssp.	Native	Probably the most frequent ssp., scarce, acid grassland (could include records of the other ssp.)	WN
Festuca pratensis	Meadow Fescue	Native	Localised & decreasing, old meadows, roadsides etc.	WN
Festuca rubra ssp. commutata	Chewing's Red Fescue	Native	Rare or possibly overlooked, 3 recent sites 1983-93	WR
Festuca rubra ssp. megastachys	Red Fescue ssp.	Cas	3 sites, Warwick & S/Avon 1983-94	
Festuca rubra ssp. rubra	Red Fescue ssp.	Native	Widespread & abundant, grasslands, roadsides etc., grass-seed mixtures too	

Scientific Name	Popular Name	Cat.	Notes	Rarity
Festuca x aschersoniana	A hybrid fescue	Native	V. rare hybrid, Moreton Morrell 1990, Fenny Compton 1997 (F. pratensis x F. arundinacea)	
X Festulolium braunii	A hybrid fescue/ rye-grass	Native	V. rare hybrid, S/Avon meadow 1996 (F. pratensis x Lolium multiflorum)	
X Festulolium holmbergii	A hybrid fescue/ rye-grass	Native	V. rare hybrid, Knowle meadow 1981 (F. arundinacea x Lolium perenne)	
X Festulolium loliaceum	A hybrid fescue/ rye-grass	Neo	Occasional scattered records, 1857-1998-, grass-seed mixtures (F. pratensis x Lolium perenne)	
X Festulolium un-named	A hybrid fescue/ rye-grass	Native	V. rare hybrid, Butler's Marston 1977 (F. arundinacea x Lolium multiflorum)	
Ficus carica	Fig	Neo	Small tree widely planted, possibly bird-sown at some sites, L/Spa walls 2006, canalside B/m 2007	
Filago minima	Small Cudweed	Native	Rare annual, disturbed ground, railway, 6 recent sites 1985-2007	WR
Filago vulgaris	Common Cudweed	Native	Rare annual, heathland, banks, disturbed ground etc., 7 recent records 1990-2007	NNT
Filipendula ulmaria	Meadowsweet	Native	Widespread perennial, wet meadows, marshes, hedges-ditches	
Filipendula vulgaris	Dropwort	Native	Rare perennial, calc. grassland, S Warks	WR
Foeniculum vulgare	Fennel	Arch	Localised perennial garden escape, roadsides, tips etc.	
Fragaria ananassa	Garden Strawberry	Neo	Localised perennial, garden escape, tips etc.	
Fragaria moschata	Hautbois Strawberry	Neo	Scarce perennial garden escape, mainly woods, 3 recent sites	
Fragaria vesca	Wild Strawberry	Native	Widespread but localised perennial, woods, banks, roadsides, quarries etc.	
Frangula alnus	Alder Buckthorn	Native	Localised shrub, mostly woodland, occasionally planted	WN
Fraxinus excelsior	Ash	Native	Widespread and common tree, woods, hedges, fields, parks, frequently planted	
Fritillaria meleagris	Fritillary	Neo	Scarce perennial, long-naturalised at some sites, also a garden escape 1817-1999-	(NV)
Fumaria bastardii	Tall Ramping-fumitory	Ext Cas	Extinct annual casual, last found Bilton 1875	

Scientific Name	Popular Name	Cat.	Notes	Rarity
Fumaria capreolata	White Ramping-fumitory	Native	V. rare annual, Warwick Castle 1981-89, Bedworth 1996 (ssp. babingtonii)	WR
Fumaria densiflora	Dense-flowered Fumitory	Neo	V. rare arable annual, Wellesbourne 1959-2003-	WR
Fumaria muralis	Common Ramping-fumitory	Native	Rare annual, tips, allotment, 4 recent sites 1987-2006 (ssp. boraei)	WR
Fumaria officinalis ssp. officinalis	Common Fumitory ssp.	Arch	Widespread annual, arable, gardens, roadsides etc, the much commoner ssp. but possibly declining	
Fumaria officinalis ssp. wirtgenii	Common Fumitory ssp.	Arch	V. rare ssp., possibly overlooked, only Ufton 1987	WR
Gagea lutea	Yellow Star-of-Bethlehem	Ext Native	Extinct perennial, woodlands, last found Edgehill 1965	
Galanthus nivalis	Snowdrop	Neo	Widespread naturalised perennial, garden escape, woods, hedges etc.	
Galega officinalis	Goat's-rue	Neo	Localised perennial, tips, roads etc. (some records may refer to garden hybrids)	
Galeopsis angustifolia	Red Hemp-nettle	Arch	V. rare annual arable weed, only recent records Little Compton 1986, Ratley 1992	NC
Galeopsis bifida	Bifid Hemp-nettle	Native	Scarce annual, rough grassland, disturbed ground etc., easily overlooked as G. tetrahit	WN
Galeopsis speciosa	Large-flowered Hemp-nettle	Arch	V. rare annual arable weed, only recent record Maxstoke 2004	NV
Galeopsis tetrahit	Common Hemp-nettle	Native	Widespread annual, woods, roadsides, arable, grassland etc.	
Galinsoga parviflora	Gallant-soldier	Neo	Scattered annual, allotments, disturbed ground etc., increasing 1955-	
Galinsoga quadriradiata	Shaggy-soldier	Neo	Scattered annual often occurring alongside the previous similar sp. 1971-	
Galium aparine	Cleavers	Native	Widespread & abundant annual, hedges, arable, disturbed land etc.	
Galium mollugo	Hedge Bedstraw	Native	Infrequent perennial, roadsides, hedges, rough grassland, disturbed land etc.	
Galium odoratum	Woodruff	Native	Infrequent & declined perennial, old woods & hedges	WN
Galium palustre ssp. elongatum	Common Marsh-bedstraw ssp.	Native	Rare ssp., but possibly over-looked, last record Bushwood 1996	WR
Galium palustre ssp. palustre	Common Marsh-bedstraw ssp.	Native	Infrequent perennial, waterside & marshes, declining	WN

Scientific Name	Popular Name	Cat.	Notes	Rarity
Galium pumilum	Slender Bedstraw	Ext Native?	Extinct perennial, calc. grassland, Tredington 1904, doubtfully native	(NE)
Galium saxatile	Heath Bedstraw	Native	Infrequent perennial, acid grassland, woods & hedges, N & W Warks	WN
Galium spurium	False Cleavers	Ext Cas	Extinct annual, last found S/Avon tip 1955	
Galium tricornutum	Corn Cleavers	Ext Arch	Extinct arable annual weed, S Warks., last records c.1960	NC
Galium uliginosum	Fen Bedstraw	Native	Infrequent perennial, watersides & wetland	WN
Galium verum	Lady's Bedstraw	Native	Widespread perennial, grassland, hedges, roadsides etc.	
Galium x pomeranicum	A hybrid bedstraw	Native	Rare perennial hybrid, 3 sites SW Warks 1986-96- (G. verum x G. mollugo)	
Gastridium ventricosum	Nit-grass	Ext Neo	Extinct annual, arable, last record Alcester 1957	(NS)
Genista anglica	Petty Whin	Native	Rare shrub, heathland districts, N Warks, 2 recent sites 1972-97	NNT
Genista hispanica	Spanish Gorse	Neo	Naturalised escape, 2 recent sites (ssp. occidentalis)	
Genista tinctoria	Dyer's Greenweed	Native	Rare shrub, calc. grassland, 3 recent sites 1980-90 (ssp. tinctoria)	WR
Gentianella amarella	Autumn Gentian	Native	Scarce biennial, calc. grassland and quarries, (ssp. amarella)	WN
Geranium columbinum	Long-stalked Crane's-bill	Native	Rare annual, rough grassland, 6 recent records 1988-2007-	WR
Geranium dissectum	Cut-leaved Crane's-bill	Arch	Widespread & abundant annual, disturbed ground, arable, grassland, hedges etc.	
Geranium endressii	French Crane's-bill	Neo	Perennial garden escape, Tamworth 1986, Goldicote 1987	
Geranium lucidum	Shining Crane's-bill	Native	Widespread but local annual, gardens, roadsides, hedges etc.	
Geranium molle	Dove's-foot Crane's-bill	Native	Widespread & frequent annual, roadsides, arable, disturbed land, hedges etc.	
Geranium phaeum	Dusky Crane's-bill	Neo	Perennial garden escape, Leamington Hastings 1835-1971-	
Geranium pratense	Meadow Crane's-bill	Native	Widespread but local perennial, roadsides, watersides, damp meadows, hedges etc.	WN
Geranium pusillum	Small-flowered Crane's-bill	Native	Localised annual, roadsides, disturbed ground, hedges, grassland etc.	

Scientific Name	Popular Name	Cat.	Notes	Rarity
Geranium pyrenaicum	Hedgerow Crane's-bill	Neo	Localised perennial, esp. roadsides, possibly increasing	
Geranium robertianum	Herb-Robert	Native	Widespread & common biennial, hedges, woods, shaded banks etc.	
Geranium rotundifolium	Round-leaved Crane's-bill	Native	Scarce annual of W Warks, roadsides, disturbed ground etc., increasing in B/m where 5+ sites 1995-2007	WR
Geranium sanguineum	Bloody Crane's-bill	Neo	Perennial garden escape, 3 recent sites	
Geranium sylvaticum	Wood Crane's-bill	Ext Native	V. rare perennial, Oversley Wood & Middleton 1817-66	
Geranium versicolor	Pencilled Crane's-bill	Neo	Garden escape perennial hybrid, 1 recent site, Farnborough Hall 1983	
Geranium x magnificum	Purple Crane's-bill	Cas Neo	Garden escape perennial hybrid, Ettington 2002, Griff 2005, Kingsbury 2006 (G. ibericum x G. platypetalum)	
Geranium x oxonianum	Druce's Crane's-bill	Neo	Garden escape perennial hybrid, 3 sites, Ettington 1990-7-, B/m 2007 (G. endresssi x G. versicolor)	
Geum rivale	Water Avens	Native	V. rare perennial, now only Arbury Park 1983-	WR
Geum urbanum	Wood Avens	Native	Widespread & frequent perennial, hedgerows, woods, roadsides etc.	
Geum x intermedium	A hybrid avens	Native	V. rare perennial hybrid, Brandon Wood 1993, Ufton Wood 1987 (G. rivale x G. urbanum)	
Glaucium flavum	Yellow Horned-poppy	Ext Cas	Extinct biennial, Shipston-on-Stour 1867 only	
Glaux maritima	Sea-milkwort	Ext Neo	Extinct perennial, Stoke (Cov) only 1962-5	
Glechoma hederacea	Ground-ivy	Native	Widespread perennial, hedges, disturbed ground, woods etc.	
Glyceria declinata	Small Sweet-grass	Native	Localised waterside perennial	
Glyceria fluitans	Floating Sweet-grass	Native	Widespread waterside perennial	
Glyceria maxima	Reed Sweet-grass	Native	Locally dominant perennial of river margins, swamp & watersides	
Glyceria notata	Plicate Sweet-grass	Native	Localised waterside perennial	
Glyceria x pedicellata	Hybrid Sweet-grass	Native	Sterile perennial hybrid, watersides (G. fluitans x G. notata)	
Gnaphalium luteoalbum	Jersey Cudweed	Cas	Rare annual, roadside L/Spa 2004-7, allotment B/m 2007	
Gnaphalium sylvaticum	Heath Cudweed	Native	V. rare annual, heathland & acid grassland, recent records Hampton-in-Arden 2004, Berkswell 2005	NE

Scientific Name	Popular Name	Cat.	Notes	Rarity
Gnaphalium uliginosum	Marsh Cudweed	Native	Localised annual, damp arable land, marshes, disturbed ground etc.	
Groenlandia densa	Opposite-leaved Pondweed	Native	Rare submerged aquatic, rivers & canals, 4 recent sites 1977-97-	NV
Guizotia abyssinica	Niger	Cas	Bird-seed annual, 3 sites 1962-90	
Gymnadenia conopsea	Fragrant Orchid	Ext Native	Extinct perennial of calcareous soils, last confirmed record Snitterfield 1948	
Gymnocarpium dryopteris	Oak Fern	Ext Cas	Extinct perennial, only record Sutton Park 1866, probably planted	
Gymnocarpium robertianum	Limestone Fern	Native	Rare perennial, walls, last record Tanworth-in-Arden 1979, possibly extinct	NS
Hebe dieffenbachii	Diffenbach's Hebe	Neo	Perennial garden escape, wall, Sutton Coldfield 2006	
Hedera helix ssp. helix	Ivy	Native	Widespread & abundant climbing perennial, trees, woods, hedges, walls etc	
Hedera helix ssp. hibernica	Atlantic Ivy	Neo	Garden escape, probably under-recorded, can grow in similar locations to normal Ivy	
Helianthemum nummularium	Common Rockrose	Native	Rare perennial, calc. grassland, Aston Grove 1980, Little Compton 1987, roadside near Chesterton Wood 2006	WR
*Helianthus annuus	Sunflower	Cas	Bird-seed annual or garden escape, B/m 2007, crop & garden plant	
Helianthus tuberosus	Jerusalem Artichoke	Neo	Perennial garden escape, 3 recent sites	
Helianthus x laetiflorus	Perennial Sunflower	Cas	Perennial garden escape, 3 sites (H. rigidus x H. tuberosus)	
Helictotrichon pratense	Meadow Oat-grass	Native	Localised perennial, calc. grassland, S Warks	WN
Helictotrichon pubescens	Downy Oat-grass	Native	Occasional perennial, calc. grassland, S & E Warks	WN
Helleborus foetidus	Stinking Hellebore	Native	Rare perennial of calc. woods & scrub, also a garden escape, 6 recent sites 1977-2006	NS
Helleborus viridis	Green Hellebore	Native	V. rare perennial, Bannam's Wood 2003 (ssp. occidentalis)	WR
Heracleum mantegazzianum	Giant Hogweed	Neo	Localised invasive perennial, esp. watersides & roadsides (the planting of it is illegal)	
Heracleum sphondylium	Hogweed	Native	Widespread & abundant perennial, roadsides, hedges, woods, grassland, disturbed ground, riverbanks etc.	
Herniaria glabra	Smooth Rupturewort	Cas	Annual/perennial, garden escape, Finham 1996	

Scientific Name	Popular Name	Cat.	Notes	Rarity
Herniaria hirsuta	Hairy Rupturewort	Ext Cas	Extinct annual, K/worth tanyards 1891	
Hesperis matronalis	Dame's-violet	Neo	Widespread biennial garden escape, esp. roadsides & hedges, increasing	
Hieracium	Hawkweeds		A difficult group of perennials without popular names & with confusing nomenclature, they need expert identification.	
Hieracium acuminatum	A hawkweed	Neo	Occasional, tips, railways etc.	
Hieracium diaphanum	A hawkweed	Native	Seemingly rare, only recent records, Leek Wootton, Wolfhampcote 1984, 1992	WR
Hieracium eboracense	A hawkweed	Ext Native	Extinct, only record Brailes 1886	
Hieracium exotericum agg.	A hawkweed aggregate	Neo	Seemingly rare, only 4 sites 1977-84-, an 'aggregate' of several microspecies	WR
Hieracium maculatum	A hawkweed	Neo	Rare, only recent record Wellesbourne 1998	WR
Hieracium sabaudum	A hawkweed	Native	Widespread, roads, railway, woods etc.	
Hieracium salticola	A hawkweed	Neo	Localised, urban roads & railway, esp. B/m area	
Hieracium speluncarum	A hawkweed	Neo	Escape, Edgbaston 1983 only	
Hieracium umbellatum	A hawkweed	Native	V. rare, Little Compton 1980, Kenilworth 1982 (ssp. umbellatum)	WR
Hieracium vagum	A hawkweed	Native	Widespread, railways, tips, scrub etc.	
Hieracium vulgatum	A hawkweed	Ext Native	Seemingly extinct, last record Botley Hill 1965	
Hippocrepis comosa	Horseshoe Vetch	Native	V. rare perennial, calc. grassland, only recent record Little Compton 1994	WR
Hippophae rhamnoides	Sea-buckthorn	Neo	Widely planted, also self-sown along roads, Cov 2007	
Hippuris vulgaris	Mare's-tail	Native	Aquatic perennial, scattered mid & S Warks	
Hirschfeldia incana	Hoary Mustard	Cas	Recently arrived perennial, tips, roadsides, 4 sites 1983-90-	
Holcus lanatus	Yorkshire-fog	Native	Widespread & common perennial, grasslands, roadsides etc.	
Holcus mollis	Creeping Soft-grass	Native	Frequent perennial, hedges, disturbed ground, grassland, woods, etc.	
Hordelymus europaeus	Wood Barley	Ext Native	Extinct perennial, only record Aston Grove 1955	NS
Hordeum distichon	Two-rowed Barley (Barley)	Neo	Relic of cultivation annual, arable, tips etc.	

Scientific Name	Popular Name	Cat.	Notes	Rarity
Hordeum jubatum	Foxtail Barley	Cas	Bird-seed escape, perennial, roadsides, grasslands etc. 1973-88	
Hordeum murinum	Wall Barley	Arch	Widespread & frequent annual, roadsides, grasslands, hedges esp. urban areas (ssp. murinum)	
Hordeum secalinum	Meadow Barley	Native	Perennial mainly in SE Warks, old calc. meadows & roadsides, seemingly decreasing	
Hordeum vulgare	Six-rowed Barley	Cas	Rare annual, only record S/Avon 1996	
Hottonia palustris	Water-violet	Native	Rare aquatic perennial, 4 sites N Warks 1820-1991, translocated to Kingsbury 1991	WR
Humulus lupulus	Hop	Native	Localised climbing perennial, mainly in hedges	
Huperzia selago	Fir Clubmoss	Ext Native	Extinct perennial, Coleshill Pool 1817-46	
Hyacinthoides hispanica	Spanish Bluebell	Neo	Perennial garden escape, not always distinguished from Hybrid Bluebell	
Hyacinthoides non-scripta	Bluebell	Native	Widespread perennial, locally abundant in ancient woods & hedges, with much of its world population within Britain	
Hyacinthoides x massartiana	Hybrid Bluebell	Neo	Widespread & increasing perennial, esp. hedges & wood-margins in the vicinity of both parents (H. non-scripta x H. hispanica)	
Hydrocharis morsus-ranae	Frogbit	Cas	V. rare aquatic perennial, only record Glascote 1986 where probably an escape. Rare as a British native	(NV)
Hydrocotyle ranunculoides	Floating Pennywort	Neo	Aquatic perennial escape, Wixford 1994, Burton Green 2006, Wootton Spinnies 2007	
Hydrocotyle vulgaris	Marsh Pennywort	Native	Rare perennial, marsh & mire, 6 recent sites 1987-2000	WR
Hyoscyamus niger	Henbane	Arch	Scarce biennial, 9 recent sites 1979-2003	NV
Hypericum androsaemum	Tutsan	Native	Rare small shrub, woods & hedges, also garden escape, recent records 1988-2007	WR
Hypericum calycinum	Rose-of-Sharon	Neo	Garden escape small shrub, widely planted, 4 recent sites	
Hypericum elodes	Marsh St John's-wort	Ext Native	Extinct perennial, last recorded from Bickenhill Plantation and Coleshill Pool in the 1950s	
Hypericum hircinum	Stinking Tutsan	Neo	Garden escape shrub, Foleshill 1998, Hillmorton 1958 (ssp. majus)	

Scientific Name	Popular Name	Cat.	Notes	Rarity
Hypericum hirsutum	Hairy St John's-wort	Native	Scarce perennial, mainly calc. scrub & grassland in SW Warks	WN
Hypericum humifusum	Trailing St John's-wort	Native	Localised perennial, grassland, road sides, woods etc., avoids calc. soils	
Hypericum maculatum	Imperforate St John's-wort	Native	Localised perennial, disturbed ground, rough grassland, watersides etc (ssp. obtusiusculum)	
Hypericum olympicum	A Greek St John's-wort	Cas	Perennial garden escape, roadside, B/m 2007	
Hypericum perforatum	Perforate St John's-wort	Native	Widespread & frequent perennial, disturbed ground, hedges, grassland, woods etc.	
Hypericum pulchrum	Slender St John's-wort	Native	Localised perennial, hedges, woods etc.	WN
Hypericum tetrapterum	Square-stalked St John's-wort	Native	Widespread perennial, esp. wet grassland, marshes & watersides	WN
Hypericum x desetangsii	A hybrid St John's-wort	Native	Rare perennial hybrid, 3 sites 1989-98- (H. perforatum x H. maculatum)	WR
Hypochaeris glabra	Smooth Cat's-ear	Ext Native	Extinct perennial, acid grassland 1670-1830 (Ray's record is the first GB one)	NV
Hypochaeris radicata	Common Cat's-ear	Native	Widespread perennial, grassland, heathland, disturbed land, roadsides, hedges etc.	
Iberis amara	Wild Candytuft	Ext Neo	Extinct arable annual weed, 3 sites 1847-75	NV
Iberis umbellata	Garden Candytuft	Cas	Garden escape annual, only record Warmington 1990	
Ilex aquifolium	Holly	Native	Widespread evergreen shrub/tree, native in acid woods and many hedges, but widely planted elsewhere	
Ilex x altaclarensis	Highclere Holly	Neo	A widely planted hybrid holly naturalised in some woods (I. aquifolium x I. perado)	
Impatiens capensis	Orange Balsam	Neo	Widespread waterside annual, increasing	
Impatiens glandulifera	Indian Balsam	Neo	Widespread annual of watersides & wet woodland, highly invasive & increasing	
Impatiens noli-tangere	Touch-me-not Balsam	Neo	Garden escape annual, wetlands & wet woodland, Berkswell 1852-2000-	(NS)
Impatiens parviflora	Small Balsam	Neo	Scarce but increasing annual, roads, tips, wet woods etc.	
Inula conyzae	Ploughman's-spikenard	Native	Scarce perennial, calc. grassland & scrub, disturbed land	WN

Scientific Name	Popular Name	Cat.	Notes	Rarity
Inula helenium	Elecampane	Arch & Cas	Garden escape perennial, esp. roadsides, hedges, urban areas etc, 5 recent sites 1979-2006	
Iris foetidissima	Stinking Iris	Native	Localised perennial, calc. woods, hedges, roadsides etc., also a garden escape	WN
Iris pseudacorus	Yellow Iris	Native	Widespread & frequent perennial, waterside, marshes etc	
Isolepis setacea	Bristle Club-rush	Native	Rare annual/perennial, wetlands & watersides, esp. N Warks, 6 sites 1982-2005	WR
Jasione montana	Sheep's-bit	Native	V. rare perennial, heathland & acid grassland, only recent record Middleton 1989	WR
Juglans regia	Walnut	Neo	Widely planted tree, occasionally self-seeding in hedges etc.	
Juncus species	Rushes		A difficult group of perennials (except the annual J. bufonius) of wet or heathy places, hybrids very hard to identify	
Juncus acutiflorus	Sharp-flowered Rush	Native	Rare, wetland & mire, 6 recent records 1986-2000	WR
Juncus articulatus	Jointed Rush	Native	Widespread & frequent, wetlands & watersides	
Juncus bufonius	Toad Rush	Native	Frequent (only annual rush Warks), watersides, wetlands, roadsides, disturbed land, arable etc.	
Juncus bulbosus	Bulbous Rush	Native	Scarce in N & W Warks, acidic wetlands	
Juncus compressus	Round-fruited Rush	Native	Rare, S & E Warks, marshes, watersides, wet grassland on calc. soils, 5 recent sites 1982-1990	NNT
Juncus conglomeratus	Compact Rush	Native	Most frequent in NW Warks, wetlands, damp grassland, damp woods etc.	
Juncus effusus	Soft-rush	Native	Widespread & frequent, esp. marshes and wet meadows	
Juncus inflexus	Hard Rush	Native	Widespread & frequent, esp. marshes & wet meadows	
Juncus squarrosus	Heath Rush	Native	Rare, dry heathland, mostly NW Warks, 4 recent sites 1984-2000	WR
Juncus subnodulosus	Blunt-flowered Rush	Native	Rare, marshy areas and watersides, S Warks, 7 recent sites 1983-1992	WR
Juncus tenuis	Slender Rush	Neo	Localised, marshes, watersides esp. canalsides	
Juncus x diffusus	A hybrid rush	Ext Native	Seemingly extinct hybrid, scattered records 1848-1965, perhaps overlooked (J. inflexus x J. effusus)	

Scientific Name	Popular Name	Cat.	Notes	Rarity
Juncus x surrejanus	A hybrid rush	Native	V. rare hybrid, 1 recent record Wappenbury Wood 1983 (J. articulatus x J. acutiflorus)	
Juniperus communis	Common Juniper	Cas Neo	Garden escape shrub, old plantation Ansty 1998, widely planted (ssp. communis)	
Kickxia elatine	Sharp-leaved Fluellen	Arch	Scarce arable annual weed, calc. soils, S Warks	WN
Kickxia spuria	Round-leaved Fluellen	Arch	Scarce arable annual weed, calc. soils, S Warks	WN
Knautia arvensis	Field Scabious	Native	Scattered perennial, grassland, roadsides, hedges etc. on calc. soils, mainly S Warks, declining	WN
Koeleria macrantha	Crested Hair-grass	Native	Rare perennial, calc. grassland, limestone quarries etc. S Warks, 3 sites 1981-97	WR
Laburnum anagyroides	Laburnum	Neo	Widely planted tree, occasionally self-sown along roadsides, hedges etc. (most planted ones now are the hybrid Voss's Laburnum)	
Lactuca serriola	Prickly Lettuce	Neo	Widespread annual/biennial, disturbed ground, arable, roadsides etc. 1951-	
Lactuca virosa	Great Lettuce	Native?	Widespread annual/biennial, disturbed ground, arable, roadsides etc., increasing and possibly not native to Warks 1985-	
Lagarosiphon major	Curly Waterweed	Neo	Aquatic perennial pond escape, increasing 1986-	
Lagurus ovatus	Hare's-tail	Cas	Garden escape annual (an ornamental grass), 3 sites 1973-	
Lamiastrum galeobdolon ssp. argentatum	Yellow Archangel ssp.	Neo	Perennial garden escape, scattered records, esp. hedges, invasive	
Lamiastrum galeobdolon ssp. montanum	Yellow Archangel ssp.	Native	Widespread perennial, mainly ancient woods & hedges, possibly declining	WN
Lamium album	White Dead-nettle	Arch	Widespread & frequent perennial, disturbed land, roadsides, hedges, grassland, arable etc.	
Lamium amplexicaule	Henbit Dead-nettle	Arch	Localised annual, arable, disturbed land, garden etc., declining	WN
Lamium hybridum	Cut-leaved Dead-nettle	Arch	Scarce arable & garden annual	WN
Lamium maculatum	Spotted Dead-nettle	Neo	Localised garden escape perennial, hedges, disturbed ground, roadsides etc.	

Scientific Name	Popular Name	Cat.	Notes	Rarity
Lamium purpureum	Red Dead-nettle	Arch	Widespread & common annual, arable, hedges, roadsides, disturbed ground, gardens etc.	
Lappula squarrosa	Bur Forget-me-not	Ext Cas	Extinct annual, only record Kenilworth 1891	
Lapsana communis	Nipplewort	Native	Widespread & frequent annual, disturbed ground, hedges, roadsides etc. (ssp. communis)	
Larix decidua	European Larch	Neo	Widely planted tree, 3 recent records for self-sown trees	
Lathraea clandestina	Purple Toothwort	Neo	Scarce garden escape perennial, root-parasite of various trees e.g. Alder, willows & poplars, 5 sites 1983-	
Lathraea squamaria	Toothwort	Native	Rare perennial, root-parasite of various trees e.g. willows, Hazel, Ash & elms, 4 recent sites 1987-96	WR
Lathyrus aphaca	Yellow Vetchling	Neo	Scarce annual, arable & disturbed land, recent records, Alvecote 1976, Wellesbourne 1993	NV
Lathyrus clymenum	A mediterranean pea	Cas	Bird-seed annual, Cov 1979	
Lathyrus grandiflorus	Two-flowered Everlasting-pea	Neo	Localised garden escape perennial, disturbed ground, hedges etc. 1960-	
Lathyrus latifolius	Broad-leaved Everlasting-pea	Neo	Similar to above & sometimes confused with it, widespread but local garden escape	
Lathyrus linifolius	Bitter-vetch	Native	Rare perennial, hedges, roadsides, ancient woods etc., 4 recent sites 1985-92	WR
Lathyrus hirsutus	Hairy Vetchling	Ext Cas	Extinct annual, only record Baginton 1957	
Lathyrus niger	Black Pea	Ext Cas	Extinct garden escape perennial, Southam, 1913 only	
Lathyrus nissolia	Grass Vetchling	Native	Localised annual, grassland, roadsides, hedges, increasing	WN
Lathyrus pratensis	Meadow Vetchling	Native	Widespread & frequent perennial, disturbed ground, grassland, hedges etc.	
Lathyrus sylvestris	Narrow-leaved Everlasting-pea	Native	Localised perennial, also garden escape, disturbed ground, hedges, woods, roadsides, grassland etc.	
Lathyrus tuberosus	Tuberous Pea	Neo	Scarce garden escape perennial, hedges, banks etc., usually short-lived, 3 recent sites	
Lavatera cretica	Smaller Tree-mallow	Cas	Garden escape perennial, L/Spa 1994, Cov 1997	
Lavatera trimestris	Royal Mallow	Cas	Garden escape annual, L/Spa 1994 only	

Scientific Name	Popular Name	Cat.	Notes	Rarity
Lavatera x clementii	A hybrid mallow	Cas	Garden escape perennial, Coleshill 1996, Cov 1997 (L. olbia x L. thuringiaca, includes 'L. thuringiaca')	
Legousia hybrida	Venus's-looking-glass	Arch	Rare annual arable weed, 8 recent sites 1980-92, declining	WR
Lemna gibba	Fat Duckweed	Native	Localised floating aquatic annual	
Lemna minor	Common Duckweed	Native	Widespread & frequent floating aquatic annual	
Lemna minuta	Least Duckweed	Neo	Widespread & common floating aquatic annual 1989-, increasing & invasive	
Lemna trisulca	Ivy-leaved Duckweed	Native	Widespread & frequent submerged annual	
Leontodon autumnalis	Autumn Hawkbit	Native	Widespread & frequent perennial, grasslands of various sorts, roadsides, disturbed ground, lawns etc.	
Leontodon hispidus	Rough Hawkbit	Native	Localised perennial, grassland, disturbed land, esp. on calcareous soils in S Warks	WN
Leontodon saxatilis	Lesser Hawkbit	Native	Localised perennial, grassland, disturbed land, esp. on calcareous soils in S Warks	WN
Leonurus cardiaca	Motherwort	Ext Cas	Extinct perennial, last found Wilmcote 1960	
Lepidium campestre	Field Pepperwort	Arch	Localised biennial/annual, arable, roadsides, farmyards etc.	
Lepidium draba	Hoary Cress	Neo	Widespread but localised perennial, disturbed ground, roadsides, grassland etc, increasing (ssp. draba)	
Lepidium heterophyllum	Smith's Pepperwort	Native	V. rare perennial, roadsides, farmyards, grassland, recent records S/Avon 1996, Wappenbury 2003	WR
Lepidium latifolium	Dittander	Neo	Scarce perennial, disturbed ground & roadside, 6 sites, possibly increasing	(NS)
Lepidium perfoliatum	Perfoliate Pepperwort	Ext Cas	Extinct biennial/annual, only record Hillmorton 1923	
Lepidium ruderale	Narrow-leaved Pepperwort	Arch	Localised biennial/annual, disturbed ground, roadsides, gardens etc., salt-tolerant	
Lepidium sativum	Garden Cress	Cas	Garden escape annual mostly disturbed land, last record Cov 1985	

Scientific Name	Popular Name	Cat.	Notes	Rarity
Lepidium virginicum	Least Pepperwort	Cas	Casual biennial/annual, disturbed ground, last record Lea Marston 1974	
Leucanthemum vulgare	Oxeye Daisy	Native	Widespread perennial, frequent in S Warks, esp. calc. grassland & roadsides, limestone quarries & disturbed calc. ground	
Leucanthemum x superbum	Shasta Daisy	Neo	Occasional garden escape perennial, esp. urban roadsides, railway & disturbed ground (L. lacustre x L. maximum)	
Leucojum aestivum	Summer Snowflake	Neo	Garden escape perennial, woods, watersides etc., 2 recent sites, rare native of southern England	(NS)
Levisticum officinale	Lovage	Cas	Garden escape perennial, only record Warwick 1996	
Leycesteria formosa	Himalayan Honeysuckle	Neo	Bird-sown perennial shrub, L/Spa walls 2007	
Leymus arenarius	Lyme-grass	Neo	Perennial escape, 2 sites, B/m canalsides 1987, 2007	
Ligustrum ovalifolium	Garden Privet	Neo	Popular garden shrub, occasionally found on disturbed ground & roadsides (but means of establishment not always clear)	
Ligustrum vulgare	Wild Privet	Native	Localised shrub, calc. scrub, woodland & hedges, mainly S Warks	
Lilium martagon	Martagon Lily	Neo	Scarce garden escape perennial, esp. woods	
Limnanthes douglasii	Meadow-foam	Cas	Garden escape annual, disturbed ground 1996-7	
Limosella aquatica	Mudwort	Native	Rare annual of waterside mud, 4 recent sites 1986-2004	NS
Linaria pelisseriana	Jersey Toadflax	Ext Cas	Extinct annual, Rugby 1869 only	
Linaria purpurea	Purple Toadflax	Neo	Widespread perennial, walls, disturbed ground, roadsides etc. esp. urban areas	
Linaria repens	Pale Toadflax	Arch	Localised perennial disturbed ground, roadsides, railways, etc.	WN
Linaria vulgaris	Common Toadflax	Native	Widespread & frequent perennial, disturbed ground, roadsides, railways etc.	
Linaria x dominii	A hybrid toadflax	Native	V. rare perennial, rough grassland & roadsides, B/m 2007, with parents (L. purpurea x L. repens)	
Linaria x sepium	A hybrid toadflax	Native	Rare perennial hybrid, railways, 4 sites 1977-2006- (L. vulgaris x L. repens)	

Scientific Name	Popular Name	Cat.	Notes	Rarity
Linum bienne	Pale Flax	Cas	Escape biennial/perennial, esp. disturbed ground, 4 recent records	
Linum catharticum	Fairy Flax	Native	Localised annual, calc. grassland, roadsides & quarries, esp. S Warks	WN
Linum usitatissimum	Flax	Cas Neo	Relic of cultivation & bird-seed annual, roadsides, arable, disturbed land etc.	
Listera ovata	Common Twayblade	Native	Localised perennial, calc. woods, scrub & grassland, mainly S Warks	WN
Lithospermum arvense	Corn Gromwell	Arch	Scarce arable annual weed, calc. soils, S Warks, 9 recent sites 1986-1995, decreasing	NE
Lithospermum officinale	Common Gromwell	Native	Scarce perennial, mainly calc. scrub & hedges, S Warks	WN
Littorella uniflora	Shoreweed	Native	Rare waterside annual, esp. mesotrophic lakes, NW & mid Warks, 3 recent sites 1983-6	WR
Lobelia erinus	Garden Lobelia	Cas	Annual/biennial, escape from urban 'hanging baskets', selfsown 1996-	
Lobularia maritima	Sweet Alison	Neo	Garden escape annual, disturbed ground, roadsides, esp. urban, increasing	
Lolium multiflorum	Italian Rye-grass	Neo	Frequent annual/biennial, arable, grassland (esp. grass leys), roadsides, disturbed land etc.	
Lolium perenne	Perennial Rye-grass	Native	Widespread & abundant perennial, grasslands (esp. grass leys), disturbed land, amenity grassland etc.	
Lolium temulentum	Darnel	Ext Arch & Ext Cas	Extinct annual, once an arable weed, subsequently a bird-seed casual of disturbed ground, last record Rugby 1965	NC
Lolium x boucheanum	A hybrid rye-grass	Neo	Scarce annual/perennial (L. perenne x L. multiflorum)	
Lonicera caprifolium	Perfoliate Honeysuckle	Ext Neo	Extinct perennial climber, garden escape, Chadshunt 1892 only	
Lonicera henryi	Henry's Honeysuckle	Cas	Perennial climber, bird-sown escape, Rugby 2006	
Lonicera japonica	Japanese Honeysuckle	Neo	Perennial climber, garden escape, S/Avon 1998, B/m 2006-	
Lonicera nitida	Wilson's Honeysuckle	Neo	Garden escape shrub, Cov, L/Spa, B/m 2006-	
Lonicera periclymenum	Honeysuckle	Native	Widespread & frequent perennial climber, esp. woods & hedges	
Lonicera pileata	Box-leaved Honeysuckle	Neo	Garden escape shrub, Rugby tip, L/Spa towpath 2006-7	

Scientific Name	Popular Name	Cat.	Notes	Rarity
Lonicera xylosteum	Fly Honeysuckle	Ext Cas	Extinct shrub, Edgbaston Park 1812	
Lotus corniculatus	Common Bird's-foot-trefoil	Native	Widespread perennial, grasslands of various sorts, disturbed land, lawns, roadsides etc.	
Lotus glaber	Narrow-leaved Bird's-foot-trefoil	Native	Scarce perennial, calc. grassland & quarries, S Warks	WN
Lotus pedunculatus	Greater Bird's-foot-trefoil	Native	Localised perennial wet grassland, ditches, marshes, damp woods etc.	
Lunaria annua	Honesty	Neo	Widespread & frequent garden escape, disturbed ground, hedges, roadsides, woods etc.	
Lupinus arboreus	Tree Lupin	Neo	Garden escape perennial, disturbed ground & roadsides, 3 sites 1979-92	
Lupinus x regalis	Russell Lupin	Neo	Garden escape perennial, roadsides, railways, disturbed land (L. arboreus x L. polyphyllus)	
Luzula campestris	Field Wood-rush	Native	Widespread perennial, grasslands, roadsides, lawns etc.	
Luzula luzuloides	White Wood-rush	Ext Cas	Extinct perennial garden escape, only record 1932 (no location given)	
Luzula multiflora ssp. congesta	Heath Wood-rush ssp.	Native	V. rare perennial, Sutton Park only 1990, possibly over-looked for next ssp.	WR
Luzula multiflora ssp. multiflora	Heath Wood-rush ssp	Native	Localised perennial, woods & grassland on more acid soils of NW Warks	WN
Luzula pilosa	Hairy Wood-rush	Native	Rare perennial, woods & grassland on more acid soils of NW Warks, 3 recent sites 1975-2001	WR
Luzula sylvatica	Great Wood-rush	Native	Scarce perennial, ancient woods	WN
Lychnis flos-cuculi	Ragged-robin	Native	Widespread but localised perennial, marshes, wet meadows, watersides, damp woods	WN
Lychnis viscaria	Sticky Catchfly	Cas	Garden escape perennial, Edgbaston 1990, also a very rare British native elsewhere	(NT)
Lycium barbarum	Duke of Argyll's Teaplant	Neo	Garden escape shrub, occasional in hedges, disturbed ground etc., rarely bird-sown	
Lycopersicon esculentum	Tomato	Cas	Garden escape annual, probably not self-sowing 1996, 1998	
Lycopodiella inundata	Marsh Clubmoss	Ext Native	Extinct perennial, wet heath, mire & peaty watersides, last record Coleshill Pool 1842	NE
Lycopodium clavatum	Stag's-horn Clubmoss	Ext Native	Extinct perennial, dry heathland & acid grassland, last record Sutton Park 1884	

Scientific Name	Popular Name	Cat.	Notes	Rarity
Lycopus europaeus	Gipsywort	Native	Widespread but localised perennial, marshes & watersides	
Lysichiton americanus	American Skunk-cabbage	Neo	Garden escape perennial, naturalised in 4 wetland sites 1967-2007-	
Lysimachia ciliata	Fringed Loosestrife	Ext Cas	Extinct garden escape perennial, Berkswell 1851 only record	
Lysimachia nemorum	Yellow Pimpernel	Native	Scattered perennial, damp ancient woodland, hedgerows etc.	
Lysimachia nummularia	Creeping-jenny	Native	Localised perennial, esp. wet grassland & marshes, also a frequent garden escape	
Lysimachia punctata	Dotted Loosestrife	Neo	Frequent garden escape perennial, much confused with L. ciliata	
Lysimachia vulgaris	Yellow Loosestrife	Native	Scarce perennial, waterside & marsh	WN
Lythrum junceum	False Grass-poly	Cas	Birdseed annual, 2 sites, last Bedworth 1978	
Lythrum portula	Water-purslane	Native	Rare annual, woodland rides, marshes, watersides etc., 4 recent sites 1979-95	WR
Lythrum salicaria	Purple-loosestrife	Native	Localised perennial, watersides	
Mahonia aquifolium	Oregon-grape	Neo	Localised garden escape shrub, woods, hedges, disturbed ground etc.	
Maianthemum bifolium	May Lily	Neo	Garden escape perennial, Leek Wootton 1961-84-, a rare native elsewhere	(NV)
Malcolmia maritima	Virginia Stock	Cas	Garden escape annual, Edgbaston 1990 only record	
Malus pumila	Apple	Neo	Widespread escape tree, hedges, roadsides, disturbed ground etc. (formerly M. domestica)	
Malus sylvestris	Crab Apple	Native	Widespread tree, mainly woods & hedges, hybridises with previous sp.	
Malva alcea	Greater Musk-mallow	Cas	Garden escape perennial, Erdington 2006 only (but v.similar to next sp.)	
Malva moschata	Musk-mallow	Native	Widespread but localised perennial, roadsides, grassland, hedges etc.	
Malva neglecta	Dwarf Mallow	Arch	Scattered local biennial/annual, roadsides, farmyards, arable, grasslands etc., possibly increasing	
Malva nicaeensis	French Mallow	Ext Cas	Extinct biennial/annual, Milverton 1876, K/worth 1891	
Malva parviflora	Least Mallow	Ext Cas	Extinct annual, Milverton 1902, Offchurch 1963	
Malva pusilla	Small Mallow	Cas	Annual, K/worth 1881, L/Spa allotments 1990	

Scientific Name	Popular Name	Cat.	Notes	Rarity
Malva sylvestris	Common Mallow	Arch	Widespread perennial, roadsides, disturbed ground, hedges, grassland etc.	
Marrubium vulgare	White Horehound	Ext Cas	Extinct, 8 records 1817-1957, also an archaeological record, a scarce native elsewhere	(NS)
Matricaria discoidea	Pineappleweed	Neo	Widespread & frequent annual, paths, disturbed ground, roadsides, cultivated land etc.	
Matricaria recutita	Scented Mayweed	Arch	Widespread but declining annual, arable, roadsides, farmyards etc.	
Matteucia struthiopteris	Ostrich Fern	Neo	Perennial fern, naturalised Guy's Cliffe 1961-, Leek Wootton 1998	
Meconopsis cambrica	Welsh Poppy	Neo	Localised perennial garden escape, esp. urban roads, a rare native elsewhere	(NS)
Medicago arabica	Spotted Medick	Neo	Localised annual, roadsides, grassland, arable, S & mid Warks	
Medicago laciniata	Tattered Medick	Ext Cas	Extinct annual, Bidford 1957-8, Nuneaton 1958	
Medicago lupulina	Black Medick	Native	Widespread & frequent annual, disturbed ground, roadsides, grassland etc.	
Medicago minima	Bur Medick	Ext Cas	Extinct annual, railways, disturbed ground, last record Warwick 1972	(NV)
Medicago polymorpha	Toothed Medick	Cas	Rare annual, last record Warwick 1981, possibly extinct, a scarce native of the coast	(NS)
Medicago sativa ssp. falcata	Sickle Medick	Neo	Scarce perennial, roadsides, disturbed ground, 6 recent sites 1975-95	NS
Medicago sativa ssp. sativa	Lucerne	Neo	Localised perennial, roadsides, arable, disturbed ground etc., a crop relic	
Medicago sativa ssp. varia	Sand Lucerne	Neo	Perennial, Cov canalside 1997 only record	
Melampyrum pratense	Common Cow-wheat	Native	Rare annual root hemi-parasite, ancient acid woods, 5 recent sites 1974-2000	WR
Melica uniflora	Wood Melick	Native	Localised perennial, ancient woods & hedgerows	WN
Melilotus albus	White Melilot	Neo	Scattered annual/biennial, esp. roadsides & disturbed ground	
Melilotus altissimus	Tall Melilot	Arch	Frequent biennial/perennial, esp. roadsides & disturbed ground	
Melilotus indicus	Small Melilot	Neo	Scarce annual, roadsides, disturbed ground, allotments etc., 4 recent sites	

Scientific Name	Popular Name	Cat.	Notes	Rarity
Melilotus officinalis	Ribbed Melilot	Neo	Frequent biennial, esp. roadsides & disturbed ground	
Melissa officinalis	Balm	Neo	Occasional garden escape perennial, esp. roadsides, railways, disturbed ground etc.	
Mentha species	Mints		Aromatic perennials, distinctive scents. Hybrids difficult to identify, arise spontaneously, and may be escape cultivars	
Mentha aquatica	Water Mint	Native	Widespread & frequent, mainly waterside & wetlands	
Mentha arvensis	Corn Mint	Native	Scarce & declined, woodland rides, arable, watersides etc.	
Mentha pulegium	Pennyroyal	Ext Native & Cas	Extinct native, wet heaths 1787-1866, also a garden escape, 3 sites, hedge, tips 1991-2006-	NE
Mentha requienii	Corsican Mint	Cas	Escape, lawn, paving, Winterbourne Botanic Gardens 2007	
Mentha spicata	Spear Mint	Neo	Occasional escape, esp. roadsides & disturbed ground	
Mentha suaveolens	Round-leaved Mint	Ext Native	Extinct, 2 records Sutton Park 1870-3	
Mentha x gracilis	Bushy Mint	Native	Rare hybrid, wetlands & allotment, 4 recent sites 1986-91- (M. arvensis x M. spicata)	
Mentha x piperita	Peppermint	Neo	Garden escape hybrid, 2 recent sites, Alveston 1988, Bedworth 1992 (M. aquatica x M. spicata)	
Mentha x verticillata	Whorled Mint	Native	Rare hybrid, watersides, 4 recent sites 1986-91- (M. arvensis x M. aquatica)	
Mentha x villosa	Apple-mint	Neo	Localised garden escape hybrid, roadsides, tips, allotments etc. (M. spicata x M. suavolens)	
Mentha x villosonervata	Sharp-toothed Mint	Neo	Garden escape hybrid, L/Spa 1986, Sutton Park 1997 (M. spicata x M. longifolia)	
Menyanthes trifoliata	Bogbean	Native	Scarce perennial, mesotrophic watersides & shallow pools, also a garden pond escape	WN
Mercurialis annua	Annual Mercury	Neo	Scarce annual, disturbed land, mainly urban, possibly increasing	WN
Mercurialis perennis	Dog's Mercury	Native	Widespread perennial, esp. woods & hedges	
Mespilus germanica	Medlar	Cas	Scarce shrub, usually planted	
Milium effusum	Wood Millet	Native	Localised perennial, ancient woods & hedges	WN
Mimulus guttatus	Monkeyflower	Neo	Localised perennial, watersides	

Scientific Name	Popular Name	Cat.	Notes	Rarity
Minuartia hybrida	Fine-leaved Sandwort	Native	Rare annual, disturbed ground, 3 recent sites 1988-1994	NE
Misopates orontium	Weasel's-snout	Arch	V. rare arable annual weed, recent records Binley 1996, nr. Kineton 1986	NV
Moehringia trinervia	Three-nerved Sandwort	Native	Widespread but localised annual, esp. woodland rides & hedges	
Moenchia erecta	Upright Chickweed	Ext Native	Extinct annual, heaths, last record Yarningale Common 1898	
Molinia caerulea	Purple Moor-grass	Native	Scarce perennial, wet heath, mire, boggy woodland clearings, declining	WN
Monotropa hypopitys ssp. hypophegea	Yellow Bird's-nest ssp.	Native	Rare perennial root-parasite, shaded woodland, only confirmed site for this ssp. Ufton Fields 1986- (both ssp. v.similar)	NE
Monotropa hypopitys ssp. hypopitys	Yellow Bird's-nest ssp.	Native	As above, only confirmed site for this ssp. Wilmcote Rough 1974- (records for Compton Verney 1848 & Hams Hall 2001 have not been checked for ssp.)	NE
Montia fontana ssp. amporitana	Blinks ssp.	Native	V. rare annual, wetlands, only recent records Sutton Park 1986, Cornet's End 1987	WR
Montia fontana ssp. chondrosperma	Blinks ssp.	Native	As above, only recent records nr. K/worth 1985, Dorridge 1998	WR
Montia fontana ssp. variabilis	Blinks ssp.	Native	As above, only record Sutton Park 1874-1986-	WR
Muscari armeniacum	Garden Grape-hyacinth	Neo	Occasional garden escape perennial, 6 recent sites	
Muscari neglectum	Grape-hyacinth	Cas	Garden escape perennial, Maxstoke (NV) 1987, a rare native of East Anglia	
Mycelis muralis	Wall Lettuce	Native	Widespread perennial, walls, hedges, woods etc., esp. urban	
Myosotis arvensis	Field Forget-me-not	Arch	Widespread annual/perennial, roadsides, disturbed ground, arable, grassland etc.	
Myosotis discolor	Changing Forget-me-not	Native	Scarce annual, grassland, roadsides, railways, paths, disturbed ground etc.	
Myosotis laxa	Tufted Forget-me-not	Native	Localised annual/biennial, watersides & marshes (ssp. caespitosa)	
Myosotis ramosissima	Early Forget-me-not	Native	Scarce annual, grassland, disturbed land, roadsides & railways, mainly calc. soils, S Warks	
Myosotis scorpioides	Water Forget-me-not	Native	Widespread & frequent perennial, waterside & wetlands	

Scientific Name	Popular Name	Cat.	Notes	Rarity
Myosotis secunda	Creeping Forget-me-not	Native	Rare annual/perennial, mire & boggy waterside, NW Warks, 3 recent sites	WR
Myosotis sylvatica	Wood Forget-me-not	Native	Widespread perennial, woods, hedges, roadsides etc., also a garden escape	
Myosotis x suzae	A hybrid forget-me-not	Native	V. rare hybrid, 2 records, Lower Shuckburgh canal 1963, Farnborough lake 1985 (M. scorpioides x M. laxa)	
Myosoton aquaticum	Water Chickweed	Native	Widespread perennial, watersides & marshes, esp. in river valleys	
Myosurus minimus	Mousetail	Native	Scarce arable annual weed, 6 recent sites 1983-2001, declining	NV
Myriophyllum alterniflorum	Alternate Water-milfoil	Ext Native	Extinct submerged perennial aquatic, mesotrophic pools, last record Sutton Park 1968	
Myriophyllum aquaticum	Parrot's-feather	Neo	Submerged perennial aquatic, 6 sites 1991-2007, invasive pond escape	
Myriophyllum spicatum	Spiked Water-milfoil	Native	Frequent submerged perennial aquatic, possibly declining	
Myriophyllum verticillatum	Whorled Water-milfoil	Ext Native	Extinct submerged perennial aquatic, last record Rugby 1955	NV
Myrrhis odorata	Sweet Cicely	Neo	Scarce garden escape perennial, hedges, railways, watersides etc., 2 recent sites 1984, 1996	
Narcissus poeticus	Pheasant's-eye Daffodil	Neo	Garden escape perennial, esp. hedges, 2 sites 1984, 2004 (ssp. poeticus)	
Narcissus pseudonarcissus	Wild Daffodil	Native	Rare perennial woods, hedges etc., also planted, 6 sites 1983-2005 as a native	WR
Narcissus x incomparabilis	Nonesuch Daffodil	Ext Neo	Extinct garden escape perennial, only record Guy's Cliffe 1876-91 (N. poeticus x N. pseudonarcissus)	
Narcissus x medioluteus	Primrose-peerless	Neo	Uncommon garden escape perennial, only recent record Snitterfield 1987 (N. tazetta x N. poeticus)	
Nardus stricta	Mat-grass	Native	V. rare perennial, acid grassland & heathland, Cov 1994, Nuneaton 2001	WR
Narthecium ossifragum	Bog Asphodel	Ext Native	Extinct perennial, bog & mire, last site Coleshill Bog 1962	
Neottia nidus-avis	Bird's-nest Orchid	Native	Rare perennial, shaded woodland, 4 recent sites 1969-2003	NNT

Scientific Name	Popular Name	Cat.	Notes	Rarity
Nepeta cataria	Cat-mint	Arch	V. rare perennial, mainly hedges on calc. soils, only recent record Shilton 1998	NV
Nepeta x faassenii	Garden Cat-mint	Neo	Garden escape perennial, S/Avon 1992, B/m 2006 (N. racemosa x N. nepetella)	
Neslia paniculata	Ball Mustard	Ext Cas	Extinct bird-seed annual, Rugby 1897, 1957	
Nicandra physalodes	Apple-of-Peru	Neo	Localised bird-seed annual, esp. disturbed ground & gardens	
Nicotiana x sanderae	A sweet tobacco hybrid	Cas	Garden escape annual, derelict garden, B/m 2006-7	
Nigella damascena	Love-in-a-mist	Cas	Scarce garden escape annual, esp. urban areas 1999-2007	
Nuphar lutea	Yellow Water-lily	Native	Widespread aquatic perennial, rivers, lakes, ponds, canals, introduced at some sites	
Nymphaea alba	White Water-lily	Native	Localised aquatic perennial, esp. lakes, introduced at some sites (ssp. alba)	
Nymphoides peltata	Fringed Water-lily	Neo	Localised aquatic perennial, an increasing & invasive escape, but a rare native in parts of Britain	(NS)
Odontites vernus ssp. serotinus	Red Bartsia ssp.	Native	Localised annual root hemi-parasite, grassland, disturbed land etc., esp. calc. soils in S & E Warks (ssp. often not provided)	
Odontites vernus ssp. vernus	Red Bartsia ssp.	Native	As for above, same distribution, possibly the more common ssp. in Warks	
Oenanthe aquatica	Fine-leaved Water-dropwort	Native	V. rare aquatic annual/biennial, only modern record Frankton 1995	WR
Oenanthe crocata	Hemlock Water-dropwort	Native	Localised perennial, mainly watersides incl. wooded streams	
Oenanthe fistulosa	Tubular Water-dropwort	Native	Scarce perennial, watersides & marshes, 9 recent sites 1972-2004	NV
Oenanthe fluviatilis	River Water-dropwort	Native	Rare partially-submerged aquatic perennial, R. Leam, R. Avon, 6 recent sites	WR
Oenanthe lachenalii	Parsley Water-dropwort	Native	Rare perennial, waterside & marshes, 3 recent sites, Wilmcote 1987, S/Avon 1987, Alvecote 1992	WR
Oenanthe silaifolia	Narrow-leaved Water-dropwort	Ext Native	Extinct perennial, watersides & marshes, last record S/Avon 1854	NT
Oenothera species	Evening-primroses		Escapes, naturalised on disturbed ground, railways, roadsides etc., annual or biennial, hybrids much studied locally	

Scientific Name	Popular Name	Cat.	Notes	Rarity
Oenothera biennis	Common Evening-primrose	Neo	Localised in Warks, 13 recent sites 1979-1990	
Oenothera cambrica	Small-flowered Evening-primrose	Neo	Scarce, introduced with sea-sand, Emscote 1963-, decreasing during this period	
Oenothera glazioviana	Large-flowered Evening-primrose	Neo	Widespread, probably the commonest species in Warks, but easily confused with hybrids, 1952-	
Oenothera stricta	Fragrant Evening-primrose	Cas	Rare, Coleshill 1871, refound L/Spa 1989, not hybridising	
Oenothera x britannica	A hybrid evening-primrose	Neo	Rare, 6 sites 1979-90, both hybrid combinations found (O. cambrica x O. glazioviana, and vice-versa)	
Oenothera x fallax	Intermediate Evening-primrose	Neo	Localised 1988-2000, both hybrid combinations found (O. glazioviana x O. biennis and vice-versa)	
Oenothera biennis x O. cambrica	A hybrid evening-primrose	Native	Frequent 1978-97, both hybrid combinations found	
Oenothera x O. fallax x O. cambrica	A hybrid evening-primrose	Native	V. rare, triple hybrid, 2 records Warwick 1979, Rugby 1989	
Omphalodes verna	Blue-eyed-Mary	Neo	Rare perennial garden escape, esp. roadside 1982-96	
Onobrychis viciifolia	Sainfoin	Neo	Scarce perennial seed-mix escape, rare crop, mainly roadsides & disturbed land, 7 recent sites, a rare native of southern Britain, but not Warks	(NT)
Onoclea sensibilis	Sensitive Fern	Ext Neo	Extinct perennial, Leek Wootton 1964 only record	
Ononis repens	Common Restharrow	Native	Localised perennial, grassland, roadsides, quarries, disturbed ground, mainly on calc. soils in S & E Warks (ssp. repens)	
Ononis spinosa	Spiny Restharrow	Native	Scarce perennial, grassland, roadsides, quarries, disturbed ground, mainly on calc. soils in S & E Warks	WN
Onopordum acanthium	Cotton Thistle	Arch	Localised biennial, roadsides, grassland, watersides, disturbed ground etc., some records garden escapes	
Ophioglossum vulgatum	Adder's-tongue	Native	Scarce perennial fern, mostly old relatively unimproved grassland	WN
Ophrys apifera	Bee Orchid	Native	Widespread local perennial, esp. disturbed ground & roadsides; Wasp Orchid (var. trollii) is rare in S Warks on calc. roadsides	WN

Scientific Name	Popular Name	Cat.	Notes	Rarity
Ophrys insectifera	Fly Orchid	Native	V. rare perennial, only recent record Snitterfield Bushes 1988 but possibly now extinct here	NV
Orchis mascula	Early-purple Orchid	Native	Scarce perennial, mostly ancient calc. woods in S Warks, occasionally hedges & roadsides	WN
Orchis morio	Green-winged Orchid	Native	Scarce perennial, old relatively unimproved grassland, 15 sites 1971-2004, strong population at Draycote Meadows	NNT
Oreopteris limbosperma	Lemon-scented Fern	Native	V. rare perennial fern, acid grassland & heaths, only recent site Earlswood 1999	WR
Origanum vulgare	Marjoram	Native	Scarce perennial, calc. grassland, roadsides, railways, hedges & open scrub, S Warks, also a garden escape	WN
Ornithogalum angustifolium	Star-of-Bethlehem	Neo	Scarce perennial formerly cultivated, esp. woods & roadsides	
Ornithogalum nutans	Drooping Star-of-Bethlehem	Neo	Scarce garden escape perennial, churchyards & roadsides, 3 recent sites 1974-90	
Ornithogalum pyrenaicum	Spiked Star-of-Bethlehem	Neo	Scarce garden escape perennial, orchards, hayfield, roadsides, 4 sites 1985-92, a rare native elsewhere in Britain	(NS)
Ornithopus perpusillus	Bird's-foot	Native	Rare annual, disturbed sandy ground, dry heath etc., avoiding calc. soils, N Warks, 8 recent sites 1968-2007	WR
Orobanche elatior	Knapweed Broomrape	Ext Native	Extinct perennial root-parasite (of Greater Knapweed), calc. grassland, last record Whichford 1957	
Orobanche minor	Common Broomrape	Native	Rare perennial root-parasite (various hosts), esp. grassland & arable land, 9 recent sites 1974-2004	WR
Orobanche rapum-genistae	Greater Broomrape	Ext Native	Extinct perennial root-parasite (of Broom & gorses), heathland & acid grassland, last record Whitley 1847	NT
Oryzopsis miliacea	Smilo-grass	Cas	Garden escape perennial, roadside L/Spa 2005	
Osmunda regalis	Royal Fern	Ext Native & Neo	Perennial fern, native of water margins in heathland districts but extinct in Warks by 1908; now a neophyte naturalised or self-sown in B/m, L/Wootton, Rugby 1988-2006	

Scientific Name	Popular Name	Cat.	Notes	Rarity
Oxalis acetosella	Wood-sorrel	Native	Scattered perennial, mostly ancient woods & hedges	
Oxalis articulata	Pink-sorrel	Cas	Uncommon garden escape perennial, mainly disturbed ground & roadsides in urban areas	
Oxalis corniculata	Procumbent Yellow-sorrel	Neo	Widespread & frequent perennial, roadsides, walls, urban paths etc.	
Oxalis exilis	Least Yellow-sorrel	Neo	Similar to above, increasing since 1988	
Oxalis incarnata	Pale Pink-sorrel	Cas	Garden escape perennial, walls etc., 3 sites 1987-	
Oxalis latifolia	Garden Pink-sorrel	Neo	Garden escape perennial, waste, Henley-in-Arden 1996	
Oxalis stricta	Upright Yellow-sorrel	Neo	Garden escape perennial, walls & disturbed ground, 6 recent sites	
Panicum capillare	Witch-grass	Cas	Annual, disturbed ground, tips etc. from birdseed, agricultural seed etc., B/m 1983, 2007	
Panicum miliaceum	Common Millet	Cas	Occasional annual of disturbed land, pheasant feeding areas etc., bird-seed and agricultural seed escape, increasingly planted on farmland as a wild bird crop	
Papaver argemone	Prickly Poppy	Arch	Scarce & declining annual, mainly arable & disturbed ground, 9 recent sites 1980-2007	NV
Papaver atlanticum	Atlas Poppy	Neo	Perennial garden escape, roadsides, Rugby, B/m 2006-	
Papaver dubium ssp. dubium	Long-headed Poppy ssp.	Arch	Widespread & frequent annual, mainly arable & disturbed ground	
Papaver dubium ssp. lecoqii	Babington's Poppy	Arch	Localised annual, arable, roadsides & disturbed ground, esp. on calcareous soils of S Warks	
Papaver hybridum	Rough Poppy	Arch	V. rare arable annual, Wellesbourne 1990 only	WR
Papaver rhoeas	Common Poppy	Arch	Widespread & locally abundant annual, arable, disturbed ground, grassland etc.	
Papaver somniferum	Opium Poppy	Arch	Widespread annual, roadsides, disturbed ground, allotments etc. (ssp. somniferum)	
Parapholis incurva	Curved Hard-grass	Ext Cas	Extinct annual, K/worth 1902 only, a scarce native of the coast	(NS)
Parentucellia viscosa	Yellow Bartsia	Neo	Annual root hemi-parasite, disturbed land & grasslands, a recent colonist spreading inland from use of grassland seed mixtures, 4 sites 1995-2001	

Scientific Name	Popular Name	Cat.	Notes	Rarity
Parietaria judaica	Pellitory-of-the-wall	Native	Localised perennial, mostly urban walls	
Paris quadrifolia	Herb-Paris	Native	Rare perennial, ancient calc. woods, 9 recent sites 1979-2000	WR
Parnassia palustris	Grass-of-Parnassus	Native	V. rare perennial, mire, Sutton Park only 1812-2007	WR
Passiflora caerulea	Blue Passion-flower	Cas	Garden escape perennial climber, pavements, B/m & L/Spa 2007	
Pastinaca sativa	Wild Parsnip	Native	Localised biennial, calc. grassland, quarries & roadsides, mainly S Warks (var. sativa)	WN
Pedicularis palustris	Marsh Lousewort	Native	V. rare annual/biennial, root hemi-parasite, mire & bog, Sutton Park only 1812-2007	WR
Pedicularis sylvatica	Lousewort	Native	Rare biennial root hemi-parasite, wet heath & poor-fen, NW Warks, 3 recent sites 1985-2007 (ssp. sylvatica)	WR
Pentaglottis sempervirens	Alkanet	Neo	Widespread perennial, roadsides, disturbed ground, hedges, grassland etc.	
Persicaria amphibia	Amphibious Bistort	Native	Widespread wetland perennial, often watersides and open water, but also as a terrestrial plant on roadsides & disturbed ground	
Persicaria amplexicaulis	Red Bistort	Neo	Uncommon garden escape perennial, recent records Ashlawn, Portway, B/m	
Persicaria bistorta	Common Bistort	Native	Infrequent perennial, roadsides, watersides, marshes, grassland, hedges, etc.	
Persicaria campanulata	Lesser Knotweed	Neo	Uncommon garden escape perennial, Sutton Park, B/m	
Persicaria capitata	A knotweed	Neo	Garden escape perennial (used in hanging-baskets), Cov 1992, L/Spa 2002-7	
Persicaria hydropiper	Water-pepper	Native	Localised annual, mainly waterside	
Persicaria lapathifolia	Pale Persicaria	Native	Localised annual, arable, roadsides, disturbed ground, watersides etc.	
Persicaria maculosa	Redshank	Native	Widespread & frequent annual, roadsides, disturbed ground, arable, watersides, grasslands etc.	
Persicaria minor	Small Water-pepper	Native	V. rare annual, wetlands, Sutton Park only 1880-1995	NV
Persicaria mitis	Tasteless Water-pepper	Ext Native	Extinct annual, only record Bourton 1892	NV

Scientific Name	Popular Name	Cat.	Notes	Rarity
Persicaria wallichii	Himalayan Knotweed	Neo	Scarce perennial, roadside, watersides etc., 5 recent sites 1980-95, increasing	
Petasites albus	White Butterbur	Neo	Uncommon garden escape perennial, 3 recent sites 1985-9	
Petasites fragrans	Winter Heliotrope	Neo	Frequent garden escape perennial, roadsides, disturbed ground, hedges etc., increasing	
Petasites hybridus	Butterbur	Native	Localised perennial, mainly watersides & roadside ditches	
Petasites japonicus	Giant Butterbur	Neo	Garden escape perennial, 1 recent record, Combrook	
Petrorhagia nanteuilii	Childing Pink	Ext Cas	Extinct annual escape, L/Spa 1966, (NV) a rare native of the S coast	
Petroselinum crispum	Garden Parsley	Cas	Uncommon garden escape biennial, only recent record Warmington	
Petroselinum segetum	Corn Parsley	Ext Native	Extinct annual/biennial arable weed, calc. soils, last site Newbold 1950	
Petunia x hybrida	Petunia	Cas	Garden escape annual, B/m 1997 (P. axillaris x P. integrifolia)	
Phacelia tanacetifolia	Phacelia	Cas	Occasional garden or agricultural escape (increasingly grown on farmland as a nectar source for bees), 5 recent sites	
Phalaris aquatica	Bulbous Canary-grass	Neo	Perennial used for game-cover & game-bird food, mainly arable, 4 sites	
Phalaris arundinacea	Reed Canary-grass	Native	Widespread & frequent perennial, watersides, marshes, damp grassland etc.	
Phalaris canariensis	Canary-grass	Neo	Frequent annual, esp. disturbed ground & roadsides, escape from bird-seed, agricultural seed etc.	
Phalaris minor	Lesser Canary-grass	Cas	Annual, game cover & bird-seed escape, arable & disturbed ground, 4 sites	
Phalaris paradoxa	Awned Canary-grass	Cas	Annual, game-bird seed, arable 1993, 2005	
Phegopteris connectilis	Beech Fern	Ext Native	Extinct fern, Berkswell 1848	
Philadelphus coronarius	Mock-orange	Neo	Garden escape shrub, 3 recent sites 1983-93	
Philadelphus x virginalis	Hairy Mock-orange	Neo	Garden escape shrub, 1 site Minworth 2006 (a hybrid possibly involving P. coronarius x P. microphyllus x P. pubescens)	

Scientific Name	Popular Name	Cat.	Notes	Rarity
Phleum arenarium	Sand Cat's-tail	Neo	Annual, introduced with sea-sand, Warwick 1964-97, possibly extinct now	
Phleum bertolonii	Smaller Cat's-tail	Native	Localised perennial, mainly grassland and roadsides, possibly over-looked	
Phleum pratense	Timothy	Native	Widespread & frequent perennial, grassland, roadsides and disturbed ground	
Phragmites australis	Common Reed	Native	Localised perennial, watersides, marshes & ditches	
Phyllitis scolopendrium	Hart's-tongue	Native	Frequent perennial fern, shaded walls, watersides & woodland	
Physalis alkekengi	Japanese-lantern	Neo	Garden escape perennial, 1 recent record B/m 2006	
Physalis peruviana	Cape-gooseberry	Cas	Garden escape perennial, Wolvey 1997	
Phyteuma spicatum	Spiked Rampion	Ext Cas	Extinct garden escape, Hill Wootton (EN) 1863, 1865, a rare native of Sussex	
Phytolacca acinosa	Indian Pokeweed	Cas	Garden escape perennial, Warwick 1973	
Picea abies	Norway Spruce	Neo	Widely planted tree, occasionally self-sowing?, 11 doubtful records	
Picris echioides	Bristly Oxtongue	Arch	Localised annual/biennial, roadsides, disturbed ground, field margins etc., esp. on calc. soils of S Warks, increasing	
Picris hieracioides	Hawkweed Oxtongue	Native	Scarce biennial/perennial, calc. grassland, scrub & disturbed land, S Warks	WN
Pilosella aurantiaca	Fox-and-cubs	Neo	Localised garden escape perennial, esp. lawns & churchyards	
Pilosella flagellaris	Shetland Mouse-ear-hawkweed	Ext Neo	Extinct garden escape, Ryton 1963 (ssp. flagellaris)	
Pilosella officinarum	Mouse-ear-hawkweed	Native	Widespread perennial, grassland, disturbed ground, lawns, hedges etc.	
Pilularia globulifera	Pillwort	Ext Native	Extinct perennial fern, Sutton Park, Coleshill 1818-98	NT
Pimpinella major	Greater Burnet-saxifrage	Native	Scarce perennial, grassland, roadsides, hedges etc. mainly NE Warks	WN
Pimpinella saxifraga	Lesser Burnet-saxifrage	Native	Localised perennial, dry & usually calc. grassland, disturbed land, roadsides & hedges. Mainly S Warks	WN
Pinguicula vulgaris	Common Butterwort	Native	V. rare insectivorous perennial, bog & mire, a few old records for NW Warks, now only surviving at Sutton Park	WR

Scientific Name	Popular Name	Cat.	Notes	Rarity
Pinus sylvestris	Scots Pine	Neo	Widely planted tree, possibly self-seeding in a few places, native of Scotland but not England	(NS)
Pisum sativum	Garden Pea	Cas	Garden escape & crop relic annual, 3 sites	
Plantago arenaria	Branched Plantain	Ext Cas	Extinct annual, bird-seed, Myton 1882, Rugby 1965	
Plantago coronopus	Buck's-horn Plantain	Native	Localised annual/perennial, salted roads, increasing	
Plantago lanceolata	Ribwort Plantain	Native	Widespread & frequent perennial, mainly roadsides, grassland & disturbed ground	
Plantago major ssp. intermedia	Greater Plantain ssp.	Native	Rare perennial (possibly over-looked), Hampton-in-Arden 1989, Snitterfield 1996, but ssp. usually not distinguished	WR
Plantago major ssp. major	Greater Plantain ssp.	Native	Widespread & frequent perennial, grassland, paths, roadsides, gardens etc., the commoner ssp. in GB	
Plantago media	Hoary Plantain	Native	Scarce perennial, mainly in older, less improved grasslands, decreasing	WN
Platanthera bifolia	Lesser Butterfly-orchid	Native	V. rare perennial, calc. woodland & scrub, Ufton Wood 1984-95, Moreton Morrell 2002	NV
Platanthera chlorantha	Greater Butterfly-orchid	Native	Rare perennial, calc. grassland, quarries, scrub & woods, S Warks	NNT
Poa angustifolia	Narrow-leaved Meadow-grass	Native	Localised perennial, grasslands, roadsides, railways, disturbed ground etc. esp. on calc soils, possibly over-looked	
Poa annua	Annual Meadow-grass	Native	Widespread & frequent annual, road verges, disturbed land, grassland, arable etc.	
Poa chaixii	Broad-leaved Meadow-grass	Neo	Scarce garden escape perennial, 2 recent records, L/Spa canalside 1987, Walton 1988	
Poa compressa	Flattened Meadow-grass	Native	Localised perennial, disturbed ground, walls, roadsides & railways	
Poa humilis	Spreading Meadow-grass	Native	Localised perennial, esp. old damp meadows	WN
Poa nemoralis	Wood Meadow-grass	Native	Scarce perennial, mainly ancient woods & hedges	WN
Poa palustris	Swamp Meadow-grass	Neo	Rare perennial, unknown site 1932, Astley Castle moat 1996	WR
Poa pratensis	Smooth Meadow-grass	Native	Widespread & frequent perennial, various grassland types, roadsides, disturbed ground etc.	

Scientific Name	Popular Name	Cat.	Notes	Rarity
Poa trivialis	Rough Meadow-grass	Native	Widespread & frequent perennial, grassland, roadsides, arable, disturbed ground, waterside, marshes, hedges etc.	
Polemonium caeruleum	Jacob's-ladder	Neo	Scarce garden escape perennial, tips, etc. 6 recent sites, a scarce native elsewhere in Britain	(NR)
Polygala serpyllifolia	Heath Milkwort	Native	Rare perennial, mainly heathland & acid grassland, 6 sites 1982-2001	WR
Polygala vulgaris	Common Milkwort	Native	Localised perennial, esp. calc grassland in S Warks, also some acid sites (ssp. only once provided, ssp. vulgaris)	WN
Polygonatum multiflorum	Solomon's-seal	Neo	Scarce garden escape perennial, mainly woods & roadsides	
Polygonatum odoratum	Angular Solomon's-seal	Neo	Garden escape perennial, 2 recent sites 1983, 1989, a scarce native elsewhere in Britain	(NS)
Polygonatum x hybridum	Garden Solomon's-seal	Neo	Garden escape perennial, 2 recent sites, Sutton Park 1990, Earlswood 1992 (P. multiflorum x P. odoratum)	
Polygonum arenastrum	Equal-leaved Knotgrass	Arch	Widespread but localised annual, roadsides, disturbed ground, arable, farmyards etc.	
Polygonum aviculare	Knotgrass	Native	Widespread & frequent annual, disturbed ground, roadsides, farmyards, arable, grassland etc.	
Polygonum patulum	Red-knotgrass	Ext Cas	Extinct annual similar to above, only Saltley 1964	
Polygonum rurivagum	Cornfield Knotgrass	Arch	Rare arable weed, calc. soils, 4 recent sites 1989-92	WR
Polypodium interjectum	Intermediate Polypody	Native	Frequent perennial fern, limestone & lime-mortared walls, banksides, esp. S Warks	
Polypodium vulgare	Polypody	Native	Scarce perennial fern, walls, hedges, tree-stumps in woodland & scrub	WN
Polypodium x mantoniae	A hybrid polypody	Native	Rare hybrid perennial fern, 4 sites 1983-1996 (P. vulgare x P. interjectum)	
Polypogon monspeliensis	Annual Beard-grass	Neo	Annual from bird-seed etc., locally frequent at Salford Priors 2005-7, a scarce native of coastal areas	(NS)
Polypogon viridis	Water Bent	Neo	Annual/perennial, L/Spa roads 2005-, B/m Botanical Garden 2007	
Polystichum aculeatum	Hard Shield-fern	Native	Localised perennial fern, mostly woods & hedges, mid & S Warks	

Scientific Name	Popular Name	Cat.	Notes	Rarity
Polystichum setiferum	Soft Shield-fern	Native	Localised perennial fern, woods & hedges, more frequent & widespread than previous sp.	
Populus alba	White Poplar	Neo	Frequently planted tree, sometimes naturalising by suckering	
Populus nigra ssp. betulifolia	Black-poplar	Native	Widespread but localised tree, WN usually planted, but naturalised or possibly native along certain rivers, streams and ditches (esp. Alne & Tame valleys)	WN
Populus tremula	Aspen	Native	Widespread but localised tree, mainly in ancient woods, occasionally planted elsewhere	
Populus x canescens	Grey Poplar	Neo	Widely planted hedge & field tree in S & E Warks, but naturalised along some riverbanks and hedges by suckering (P. alba x P. tremula)	
Potamogeton species	Pondweeds		Floating and submerged perennial aquatics, diminishing due to water pollution, river engineering etc. Identification can be v. difficult and occasional hybrids complicate matters further.	
Potamogeton acutifolius	Sharp-leaved Pondweed	Ext Native	Extinct, only record canal Rugby c.1859	NC
Potamogeton alpinus	Red Pondweed	Ext Native	Extinct, several records 1842-1967, the last at Newton	
Potamogeton berchtoldii	Small Pondweed	Native	Scarce submerged aquatic, ponds & lakes, commonest of the v. small spp. in Warks	
Potamogeton compressus	Grass-wrack Pondweed	Ext Native	Extinct, many records canals 1837-1965, last at Napton	NE
Potamogeton crispus	Curled Pondweed	Native	Widespread submerged aquatic, ponds, canals & rivers	
Potamogeton friesii	Flat-stalked Pondweed	Native	V. rare submerged aquatic, Coventry Canal 1992-7, Oxford Canal, Wormleighton 1985	NNT
Potamogeton lucens	Shining Pondweed	Native	Rare, unpolluted canals, rivers & ponds, 7 recent sites	WR
Potamogeton natans	Broad-leaved Pondweed	Native	Widespread & locally frequent in ponds, canals & rivers	
Potamogeton nodosus	Loddon Pondweed	Ext Native	Extinct, R. Stour at Alderminster 1856 only record	NV
Potamogeton obtusifolius	Blunt-leaved Pondweed	Native	Rare submerged aquatic, ponds & lakes, 8 recent sites	WR

Scientific Name	Popular Name	Cat.	Notes	Rarity
Potamogeton pectinatus	Fennel Pondweed	Native	Widespread submerged aquatic, canals, rivers & ponds, the commonest narrow-leaved pondweed in Warks, pollution-tolerant	
Potamogeton perfoliatus	Perfoliate Pondweed	Native	Localised submerged aquatic, canals, rivers & ponds, possibly favouring larger waterbodies	
Potamogeton polygonifolius	Bog Pondweed	Native	V. rare, mesotrophic waterbodies & boggy pools, Bickenhill 1986, Exhall 1997	WR
Potamogeton praelongus	Long-stalked Pondweed	Ext Native	Extinct, Sutton Park 1909, canal Rugby c.1960	NT
Potamogeton pusillus	Lesser Pondweed	Native	Localised, rivers, canals & ponds	
Potamogeton trichoides	Hairlike Pondweed	Native	V. rare, only recent record Bascote 1989	WR
Potamogeton x angustifolius	Long-leaved Pondweed	Ext Native	Extinct, Earlswood Reservoir 1893-1959 (P. lucens x P. gramineus, formerly P. x zizii)	
Potamogeton x cadburyae	'Cadbury's Pondweed'	Ext Native	Extinct endemic, Seeswood Pool, Nuneaton 1948, only known site in world (P. lucens x P. crispus)	
Potamogeton x lintonii	Linton's Pondweed	Ext Native	Extinct, canal Hockley Heath 1962, canal Edgbaston 1961 (P. friesii x P. crispus)	
Potamogeton x salicifolius	A hybrid pondweed	Native	V. rare, canal Warwick 1870, canal Cov 1957, 1996 (P. lucens x P. perfoliatus)	
Potentilla anglica	Trailing Tormentil	Native	Rare perennial, moderately acidic grassland, woodland, roadsides etc. avoiding calc. soils, 6 recent sites	WR
Potentilla anserina	Silverweed	Native	Widespread & frequent perennial, seasonally flooded grassland, disturbed land, roadsides etc.	
Potentilla argentea	Hoary Cinquefoil	Native	V. rare perennial, sidings Water Orton 1982, Woodloes 1983	NNT
Potentilla erecta	Tormentil	Native	Localised perennial, acid grassland, heathland, woodland, roadsides etc. NW Warks	
Potentilla intermedia	Russian Cinquefoil	Neo	Perennial garden escape, sidings Water Orton 1981-3	
Potentilla norvegica	Ternate-leaved Cinquefoil	Ext Cas	Extinct garden escape perennial, Minworth 1940, Wellesbourne 1954	
Potentilla palustris	Marsh Cinquefoil	Native	Rare perennial, waterside, marsh & mire, NW Warks, 4 recent sites	WR
Potentilla recta	Sulphur Cinquefoil	Neo	Scarce garden escape perennial, roadsides, hedges, tips etc., 6 recent sites	

Scientific Name	Popular Name	Cat.	Notes	Rarity
Potentilla reptans	Creeping Cinquefoil	Native	Widespread & frequent perennial, roadsides, disturbed ground, grassland, hedges etc.	
Potentilla sterilis	Barren Strawberry	Native	Localised perennial, roadsides, hedgerows, grassland, woodland & scrub	
Potentilla x mixta	A hybrid cinquefoil	Native	Frequent perennial, much commoner than P. erecta or P. anglica, hedges, roadsides, banks etc., often without a parent (P. erecta x P. reptans or P. anglica x P. reptans)	
Potentilla x suberecta	A hybrid tormentil	Native	Rare perennial hybrid, often with a parent, roadsides, lawns, hedges etc. (P. anglica x P. erecta)	
Primula veris	Cowslip	Native	Frequent but declined perennial, less improved grasslands, roadsides, railway etc.	
Primula vulgaris	Primrose	Native	Frequent perennial of ancient woods, hedges & banks	
Primula x polyantha	False Oxlip	Native	Localised perennial hybrid, usually with both parents, hedges, woods, churchyards etc. (P. vulgaris x P. veris)	
Prunella vulgaris	Selfheal	Native	Widespread & frequent perennial, disturbed ground, grassland (including garden lawns), roadsides etc.	
Prunus avium	Wild Cherry	Native	Widespread tree, native of ancient woods and hedges, widely planted elsewhere	
Prunus cerasifera	Cherry Plum	Neo	Widespread small tree, naturalised in many hedges, also widely planted	
Prunus cerasus	Dwarf Cherry	Arch	Rare small tree, hedges, similar to P. avium, 3 recent sites, possibly overlooked	WR
Prunus domestica ssp. domestica	Wild Plum	Arch	Localised small tree, naturalised in hedges, on road verges etc, ssp. not often given and difficult to distinguish without fruit	
Prunus domestica ssp. insititia	Bullace & Damson	Arch	Occasional in hedges, Damson frequently planted in orchards and gardens	
Prunus domestica ssp. italica	Greengage	Neo	Rare garden escape tree, possibly self-sown at Warwick riverside	
Prunus laurocerasus	Cherry Laurel	Neo	Large evergreen shrub, naturalised in some woods, widely planted	

Scientific Name	Popular Name	Cat.	Notes	Rarity
Prunus lusitanica	Portugal Laurel	Neo	Large evergreen shrub naturalised in some woods, widely planted.	
Prunus padus	Bird Cherry	Neo	•Widely planted but possibly naturalised at some sites	
Prunus spinosa	Blackthorn	Native	Widespread & frequent in hedges, woods and as scrub, said to hybridise with P. domestica (= P. x fruticans)	
Pseudofumaria alba	Pale Corydalis	Neo	Scarce garden escape perennial, wall L/Spa 2005-	
Pseudofumaria lutea	Yellow Corydalis	Neo	Frequent garden escape perennial, esp. urban walls	
Pteridium aquilinum	Bracken	Native	Perennial fern, locally abundant on acid soils of woods, heaths, hedges, esp. NW Warks, locally in parts of S Warks	
Pteris cretica	Ribbon Fern	Neo	Self-sown perennial, wall L/Spa 1991-2007-	
Puccinellia distans	Reflexed Saltmarsh-grass	Neo	Widespread but localised salt-tolerant perennial, roadsides (esp. of major & urban ones), increasing	
Pulicaria dysenterica	Common Fleabane	Native	Widespread but localised perennial, watersides, marshes, roadsides etc.	
Pulicaria vulgaris	Small Fleabane	Ext Native	Extinct annual, last record Myton 1834	NC
Pulmonaria officinalis	Lungwort	Neo	Scarce perennial garden escape	
Pyracantha rogersiana	Asian Firethorn	Neo	Garden escape shrub, probably bird-sown, 2 sites	
Pyrola minor	Common Wintergreen	Ext Native	Extinct perennial, Meriden 1873	
Pyrus communis	Pear	Arch	Frequent as a planted tree, possibly naturalised in some hedges, woods & fields (though difficult to be sure)	
Pyrus pyraster	Wild Pear	Neo	Rare hedgerow tree, reputably 4 sites in S Warks 1995-6	WR
Quercus cerris	Turkey Oak	Neo	Widely planted tree but naturalised and invasive in some woods	
Quercus petraea	Sessile Oak	Native	Localised tree, common in some ancient acid woods of N & W Warks, occasionally planted elsewhere	
Quercus robur	Pedunculate Oak	Native	Widespread & frequent tree, in a variety of habitats both as a wild and planted tree	
Quercus x rosacea	A hybrid oak	Native	Usually present at edges of woods containing Q. petraea or in surrounding land (Q. petraea x Q. robur)	

Scientific Name	Popular Name	Cat.	Notes	Rarity
Radiola linoides	Allseed	Ext Native	Extinct annual of damp acid grassland, wet heath etc., NW Warks, last record Cornet's End 1893	NT
Ranunculus species	Buttercups, Water-crowfoots, Crowfoots and Spearworts		Plants that vary from fully terrestrial (buttercups) to almost fully submerged aquatics of both standing and flowing water (water-crowfoots). Water-crowfoots are much declined and challenging to identify with several hybrids complicating matters further.	
Ranunculus acris	Meadow Buttercup	Native	Widespread & frequent perennial, damp grassland, roadsides, watersides etc.	
Ranunculus aquatilis	Common Water-crowfoot	Native	Widespread but localised aquatic, mainly ponds, the commonest water-crowfoot in Warks	
Ranunculus arvensis	Corn Buttercup	Arch	Scarce annual, mainly arable, declining	NC
Ranunculus auricomus	Goldilocks Buttercup	Native	Widespread but localised, esp. ancient woods & hedges	
Ranunculus bulbosus	Bulbous Buttercup	Native	Widespread & frequent perennial, esp. dry grassland, roadsides and disturbed ground	
Ranunculus circinatus	Fan-leaved Water-crowfoot	Native	Rare aquatic, ponds & canals, 3 recent sites, Edgbaston, Ryton, R. Leam 1975-86	WR
Ranunculus ficaria ssp. bulbifer	Lesser Celandine ssp.	Native	Widespread perennial, hedges, woods, gardens etc. often tolerating damp and disturbed conditions	
Ranunculus ficaria ssp. ficaria	Lesser Celandine ssp.	Native	Widespread & frequent perennial, tolerating more open habitat than previous ssp., and probably the commoner ssp. in Warks	
Ranunculus flammula	Lesser Spearwort	Native	Localised perennial in NW Warks, marshes, watersides, wet meadows, avoiding calc. areas	
Ranunculus fluitans	River Water-crowfoot	Native	Rare aquatic, rivers, 3 recent sites, Rivers Itchen, Nene, Tame	WR
Ranunculus hederaceus	Ivy-leaved Crowfoot	Native	Rare, marshes & watersides, 3 recent sites, mid Warks	WR
Ranunculus lingua	Greater Spearwort	Native	Localised perennial, marshes & watersides, widely planted in ponds & increasing as an escape	
Ranunculus omiophyllus	Round-leaved Crowfoot	Native	V. rare aquatic, boggy pools, only recent site Sutton Park 1989	WR

Scientific Name	Popular Name	Cat.	Notes	Rarity
Ranunculus parviflorus	Small-flowered Buttercup	Native	Rare annual, arable, roadsides, banks, 3 recent sites, mid Warks	WR
Ranunculus peltatus	Pond Water-crowfoot	Native	Scarce aquatic, ponds in mid Warks	WN
Ranunculus penicillatus	Stream Water-crowfoot	Native	Scarce aquatic, locally abundant in Rivers Blythe, Leam, Tame & Itchen (ssp. pseudofluitans where critically checked)	WN
Ranunculus repens	Creeping Buttercup	Native	Widespread & frequent perennial, grasslands, disturbed ground, arable, roadsides, gardens etc.	
Ranunculus sardous	Hairy Buttercup	Neo	V. rare annual, mainly arable, Myton 1891, Wellesbourne 1992	WR
Ranunculus sceleratus	Celery-leaved Buttercup	Native	Widespread but localised annual, marshes, watersides & wet fields (esp. on damp mud)	
Ranunculus trichophyllus	Thread-leaved Water-crowfoot	Native	Scarce aquatic, ponds & rivers, Rivers Blythe & Sowe	WN
Ranunculus trichophyllus x R. peltatus	A hybrid water-crowfoot	Native	V. rare, c.1974 (no site given), apparently the only convincing example of this hybrid in Britain	
Ranunculus x bachii	Wirtgen's hybrid Water-crowfoot	Ext Native	No records since c.1960, R. Alne area (parentage unclear, possibly R. fluitans x R. trichophyllus)	
Ranunculus x lutzii	A hybrid water-crowfoot	Ext Native	Seemingly extinct, 3 sites c.1960 (R. trichophyllus x R. aquatilis)	
Ranunculus x virzionensis	A hybrid water-crowfoot	Native	V. rare endemic, Coleshill pools 1974, possibly the only British record (R. aquatilis x R. peltatus)	
Raphanus raphanistrum	Wild Radish	Arch	Widespread but localised annual, roadsides, arable, farmyards, disturbed land etc. (ssp. raphanistrum)	
Raphanus sativus	Garden Radish	Cas	Escape of cultivation, waste ground B/m 1988-9	
Rapistrum rugosum	Bastard Cabbage	Neo	Scarce annual/perennial, disturbed ground & grassland, 6 sites (ssp. linnaeanum)	
Reseda alba	White Mignonette	Neo	Rare annual/perennial, disturbed ground, 3 recent sites, B/m 1997	WN
Reseda lutea	Wild Mignonette	Native	Widespread but localised biennial/ perennial, mainly disturbed ground, dry grassland & roadsides esp. calc. soils	
Reseda luteola	Weld	Arch	Widespread but localised biennial, mainly disturbed ground of quarries & industrial sites	
Rhagadiolus stellatus	Star Hawkbit	Ext Cas	Extinct birdseed annual, Rugby 1965	

Scientific Name	Popular Name	Cat.	Notes	Rarity
Rhamnus cathartica	Buckthorn	Native	Localised shrub, mainly in hedges on calc. soils of S Warks	
Rheum x hybridum	Rhubarb	Cas Neo	Garden escape perennial, 1 record Warmington 1986	
Rhinanthus alectorolophus	A yellow-rattle	Cas Neo	Presumed escape from wild flower mix used at Wellesbourne by-pass 1986 (possibly first British record)	
Rhinanthus minor ssp. minor	Yellow-rattle ssp.	Native	Scarce annual root hemi-parasite, old and less improved hay meadows, but also used in wildflower seed mixes	WN
Rhinanthus minor ssp. stenophyllus	Yellow-rattle ssp.	Native?	Rare autumnal-flowering ssp., wet grassland (a northern ssp. possibly not native to Warks)	WN
Rhododendron ponticum	Rhododendron	Neo	Invasive evergreen shrub, naturalised & invasive in some acid woods, also widely planted	
Rhus typhina	Stag's-horn Sumach	Neo	Widely planted suckering shrub, 2 records as a naturalised plant, B/m 1993, Cov 1996	
Rhynchospora alba	White Beak-sedge	Ext Native	Extinct perennial, bogs, last record Packington 1885	
Ribes alpinum	Mountain Currant	Neo	Garden escape shrub, last record Fenny Compton 1991, a rare native elsewhere in Britain	(NS)
Ribes nigrum	Black Currant	Neo	Occasional garden escape/relic/ birdsown shrub, woods, watersides and waste places	
Ribes rubrum	Red Currant	Native	Widespread but localised, esp. damp woods, watersides and hedges, prob. native at some sites but also a garden escape/relic/ birdsown shrub	
Ribes sanguineum	Flowering Currant	Neo	Garden escape shrub, 3 sites B/m 2006-7	
Ribes uva-crispa	Gooseberry	Neo	Garden escape shrub, hedges, woods, watersides, roadsides & sometimes bird-sown on walls	
Robinia pseudoacacia	False-acacia	Neo	Widely planted and frequently suckering over a large area to become naturalised, possibly setting seed too	
Rorippa amphibia	Great Yellow-cress	Native	Localised perennial, mainly watersides	
Rorippa microphylla	Narrow-fruited Watercress	Native	Widespread but localised waterside perennial	
Rorippa nasturtium-aquaticum	Watercress	Native	Widespread but localised waterside perennial	

Scientific Name	Popular Name	Cat.	Notes	Rarity
Rorippa palustris	Marsh Yellow-cress	Native	Widespread but localised annual/ perennial, esp. watersides, occasionally roadsides & gardens	
Rorippa sylvestris	Creeping Yellow-cress	Native	Localised perennial, mainly watersides	
Rorippa x anceps	A hybrid yellow-cress	Native	Rare perennial, water-meadow L/Spa 1988, Abbot's Salford 1989 (R. sylvestris x R. amphibia)	
Rorippa x armoracoides	Walthamstow Yellow-cress	Cas	Rare perennial, arable field Clifton 2005, probably not native (R. sylvestris x R. austriaca)	
Rorippa x erythrocaulis	Thames Yellow-cress	Native	Rare hybrid perennial, river bank R. Avon, S/Avon 1989 (R. palustris x R. amphibia)	NV
Rorippa x sterilis	Hybrid Watercress	Native	Scarce waterside perennial, often without parents, also crop escape (R. nasturtium-aquatilis x R. microphylla)	
Rosa species	Roses		Difficult group of shrubs/climbers, with c.100 British species & hybrids, most of which need expert identification	
Rosa agrestis	Small-leaved Sweet-briar	Ext Native	Extinct, Chesterton Wood 1889	NT
Rosa arvensis	Field-rose	Native	Widespread & frequent, hedges, scrub etc., second commonest wild rose in Warks	
Rosa caesia ssp. caesia	Hairy Dog-rose	Ext Native	Extinct, last record Tamworth 1876 (a northern ssp.)	
Rosa caesia ssp. vosagiaca	Glaucous Dog-rose	Native	Rare, limestone quarries Southam, Bishop's Itchington 1997	WR
Rosa canina	Dog-rose	Native	Commonest wild rose in Warks, hedges, scrub, woodland edge etc., all 4 'groups' (Transitorii, Lutetianae, Dumales, Pubescentes) recorded	
Rosa ferruginea	Red-leaved Rose	Neo	Garden escape, probably bird-sown, Rugby 2006, B/m 2006	
Rosa 'Hollandica'	Dutch Rose	Neo	Garden escape, old railway Rugby 1999, Dosthill 2001	
Rosa micrantha	Small-flowered Sweet-briar	Native	V. rare in S Warks, woods, & hedges on calc. soils, last record Wilmcote Rough 1997	WR
Rosa multiflora	Many-flowered Rose	Neo	Garden escape, 4 sites 1966-2006	
Rosa obtusifolia	Round-leaved Dog-rose	Native	Widespread but localised	
Rosa rubiginosa	Sweet-briar	Native	Seemingly scarce as a native but distribution obscured by planted & bird-sown specimens	WN

Scientific Name	Popular Name	Cat.	Notes	Rarity
Rosa rugosa	Japanese Rose	Neo	Garden escape (popular in landscaping), bird-sown, 7 recent sites	
Rosa sherardii	Sherard's Downy-rose	Native	Rare, hedges & scrub, 6 recent sites 1993-2005	WR
Rosa spinosissima	Burnet Rose	Ext Native, Neo	Presumed extinct, last record as a native Aston Grove 1962, 6 recent sites 1992-2006 represent garden escapes or planted specimens	
Rosa stylosa	Short-styled Field-rose	Native	V. rare, usually hedges on calc. soils, 2 recent sites Offchurch 1981, Stockton 1995	WR
Rosa tomentosa	Harsh Downy-rose	Native	Rare, mainly hedges, 3 recent sites 1989, 1996, declining	WR
Rosa virginiana	Virginian Rose	Neo	Garden escape, wall, Hockley, 1996	
Rosa x andegavensis	A hybrid rose	Native	Scarce, 14 sites 1866-2005 (R. stylosa x R. canina)	
Rosa x biturigensis	A hybrid rose	Neo	Possible cultivar, 1 site 1997 (R. spinossisima x R. rubiginosa)	
Rosa x cottettii	A hybrid rose	Ext Native	Extinct, Rugby c.1870 (R. caesia x R. tomentosa)	
Rosa x dumalis	A hybrid rose	Native	Frequent, sometimes planted (R. canina x R. caesia, with both R. caesia ssp. involved)	
Rosa x dumetorum	A hybrid rose	Native	Scarce, 7 recent sites (R. canina x R. obtusifolia)	
Rosa x gallicoides	A hybrid rose	Ext Native	Extinct, 2 sites, Harbury 1877, Chesterton 1890 (R. arvensis x R. rubiginosa)	
Rosa x involuta	A hybrid rose	Ext Native	Extinct, 4 sites 1861-1890 (R. spinosissima x R. sherardii)	
Rosa x nitidula	A hybrid rose	Native	Rare, Harborough Magna 1883, Haselor, c.1960, Wilmcote Rough 1995 (R. canina x R. rubiginosa)	
Rosa x rothschildii	A hybrid rose	Native	Rare, 4 sites 1876-1997 (R. canina x R. sherardii)	
Rosa x sabinii	A hybrid rose	Ext Neo	V. rare, Allesley 1853 (R. spinosissima x R. mollis)	
Rosa x scabriuscula	A hybrid rose	Native	Rare, 4 recent sites (R. canina x R. tomentosa)	
Rosa x toddiae	A hybrid rose	Native	V. rare, Whatcote 1887, Bedworth 2005 (R. canina x R. micrantha)	
Rosa x verticillacantha	A hybrid rose	Native	Widespread & frequent, commonest wild hybrid rose in Warks, (R. arvensis x R. canina, also known as R. x irregularis)	

Scientific Name	Popular Name	Cat.	Notes	Rarity
Rubus species (includes 'Rubus fruticosus' agg.)	Brambles, raspberries etc.		Widespread often abundant shrubs & scramblers, with over 300 British species & microspecies, mostly requiring expert identification. The aggregate name 'R. fruticosus' is not used by experts. Rarity and extinction status uncertain for most, so not noted for most. The number of 10-kilometre squares (km) for each sp. in Warks as shown in the maps of Edees & Newton (1988) is indicated for some species plus any subsequent records.	
Rubus adamsii	A bramble	Native	4 km, no post-1970 records	
Rubus adscitus	A bramble	Native	2 km, plus 1 record 1989	
Rubus adspersus	A bramble	Native	1 km, no post-1970 records	
Rubus albionis	A bramble	Native	4 km, no post-1970 records	
Rubus amplificatus	A bramble	Native	c. 14 km, no post-1970 records	
Rubus anglocandicans	A bramble	Native	c. 9 km (as R. falcatus), 1 recent record	
Rubus anglofuscus	A bramble	Native	8 km (as R. fuscus), 1 record 1988	
Rubus armeniacus	A bramble cultivar	Neo	Escape & birdsown cultivar 'Himalayan Giant' 1982-87 (=R. procerus)	
Rubus armipotens	A bramble	Native	c. 2 km (as R. winteri), no post-1970 records	
Rubus arrheniiformis	A bramble	Native	Last record Sutton Park 1901	
Rubus bagnallianus	A bramble	Native	c. 6 km 1875-1987	
Rubus bartonii	A bramble	Native	c. 2 km, no post-1970 records	
Rubus bertramii	A bramble	Native	c. 2 km (as R. opacus), no post-1970 records	
Rubus bloxamianus	A bramble	Native	c. 7 km (as R. granulatus)	
Rubus bloxamii	A bramble	Native	c. 4 km 1880-1987	
Rubus boraeanus	A bramble	Native	5 km	
Rubus botryeros	A bramble	Native	1 km	
Rubus boudiccae	A bramble	Native	c. 6 km	
Rubus caesius	Dewberry	Native	Widespread in mid & S Warks, calc. scrub & hedges, roadsides, watersides etc.	
Rubus calvatus	A bramble	Native	c. 3 km 1885-c.1950	
Rubus cardiophyllus	A bramble	Native	c. 14 km 1874-1987	
Rubus cissburiensis	A bramble	Native	1 km, no post-1970 records	
Rubus cockburnianus	White-stemmed Bramble	Neo	Garden & birdsown escape, B/m 2007	
Rubus conjungens	A bramble	Native	Scattered records, mainly N, W & mid Warks. 1874-1988	
Rubus criniger	A bramble	Native	c. 2 km, no post-1970 records	
Rubus dasyphyllus	A bramble	Native	Widespread records 1876-1987	

Scientific Name	Popular Name	Cat.	Notes	Rarity
Rubus diversus	A bramble	Native	1 km, no post-1970 records	
Rubus eboracensis	A bramble	Native	1 km	
Rubus echinatoides	A bramble	Native	c. 9 km 1951-1988	
Rubus echinatus	A bramble	Native	Widespread records 1860-1988 (=R. discerptus)	
Rubus eligantispinosus	A bramble cultivar	Cas	Garden escape, 2 km, esp. railways, no post-1970 records	
Rubus euryanthemus	A bramble	Native	2 records 1957-74	
Rubus flexuosus	A bramble	Native	8 records 1870-1974 (=R. foliosus)	
Rubus gratus	A bramble	Native	8 records 1879-c. 1960	
Rubus hylocharis	A bramble	Native	4 km	
Rubus hylonomus	A bramble	Native	2 records 1915-1965, no post-1970 records	
Rubus idaeus	Raspberry	Native	Widespread & locally frequent garden escape/native, hedges, woods, roadsides, banks etc., scarcer in S Warks.	
Rubus infestus	A bramble	Native	2 km, no post-1970 records	
Rubus insectifolius	A bramble	Native	c. 4 records 1878-1974	
Rubus intensior	A bramble	Native	1 record 1988	
Rubus laciniatus	A bramble	Neo	Bird-sown cultivar, 5 sites 1950-1995	
Rubus lanaticaulis	A bramble	Native	1 km, no post-1970 records	
Rubus leightonii	A bramble	Native	Widespread records 1885-1987	
Rubus leyanus	A bramble	Native	2 records 1988	
Rubus lindebergii	A bramble	Native	1 km 1879, no post-1970 records	
Rubus lindleianus	A bramble	Native	Widespread records 1874-1987	
Rubus longithyrsiger	A bramble	Native	2 km 1988	
Rubus macrophyllus	A bramble	Native	3 km, no post-1970 records	
Rubus mercicus	A bramble	Extinct Native	Last record Water Orton 1905	NR
Rubus micans	A bramble	Native	8 km 1891-1987	
Rubus moylei	A bramble	Native	1 km, no post-1970 records	
Rubus mucronulatus	A bramble	Native	5 records 1893-1974	
Rubus murrayi	A bramble	Native	Occasional in W Warks 1883-1988	
Rubus nemoralis	A bramble	Native	6 records 1881-1987	
Rubus nemorosus	A bramble	Native	c. 8 km 1847-1985 (=R. balfourianus)	
Rubus nessensis	A bramble	Native	2 km, no post-1970 records	
Rubus newbridgensis	A bramble	Native	2 records 1988	
Rubus pallidus	A bramble	Native	5 km 1882-1974	
Rubus pampinosus	A bramble	Native	c. 3 km 1965-1988 (=R. favonii)	
Rubus pascuorum	A bramble	Native	2 records c.1885, no post-1970 records	
Rubus platyacanthus	A bramble	Native	11 km N & W Warks 1882-c. 1960 (=R. carpinifolius)	
Rubus plicatus	A bramble	Native	4 km 1884-1954, no post-1970 records	

Scientific Name	Popular Name	Cat.	Notes	Rarity
Rubus polyanthemus	A bramble	Native	c. 10 km 1887- 1987	
Rubus proiectus	A bramble	Native	1 record 1988	
Rubus pruinosus	A bramble	Native	19 km 1852-1987 (=R. sublustris)	
Rubus pyramidalis	A bramble	Native	c. 7 km c.1850-1963	
Rubus radula	A bramble	Native	c. 4 km	
Rubus raduloides	A bramble	Native	c. 2 km, no post-1970 records	
Rubus robiae	A bramble	Native	1 record 1988	
Rubus rossensis	A bramble	Native	c. 3 km 1879-1988 (=R. crassifolius)	
Rubus rubritinctus	A bramble	Native	2 km 1897-c. 1960, no post-1970 records	
Rubus rufescens	A bramble	Native	c. 8 km 1897-1988	
Rubus scaber	A bramble	Native	c. 4 records 1880-1988	
Rubus scabripes	A bramble	Native	c. 6 km 1881-1974	
Rubus scissus	A bramble	Native	c. 10 records 1873-c. 1960, no post-1970 records	
Rubus sprengelii	A bramble	Native	c. 16 records 1873-1988	
Rubus tricolor	Chinese Bramble	Neo	Garden escape & self-sown, canalside, B/m, 2007	
Rubus tuberculatus	A bramble	Native	Widespread except E Warks, 3 records 1987	
Rubus ulmifolius	A bramble	Native	Widespread, the commonest Warks bramble	
Rubus varvicensis	A bramble	Native	c. 7 km 1894-1974, endemic to VC 38 & 39 (=R. mercius)	
Rubus vestitus	A bramble	Native	Widespread & often abundant in woodland 1852-1987	
Rubus warrenii	A bramble	Native	c. 4 km, no post-1970 records	
Rubus watsonii	A bramble	Native	2 km 1949, 1989 (=R. drymophilus)	
Rubus winteri	A bramble	Native	1 km 1884, no post-1970 records	
Rubus wirralensis	A bramble	Native	c. 7 km, 2 records 1988-	
Rubus caesius x R. ulmifolius	A hybrid bramble	Native	V. rare but possibly over-looked, 1 record 1987	
Rubus ulmifolius x R. vestitus	A hybrid bramble	Native	V. rare but possibly over-looked, 2 records 1987, 1988	
Rumex acetosa	Common Sorrel	Native	Widespread & frequent perennial, grassland, roadsides, disturbed ground etc. (ssp. acetosa)	
Rumex acetosella ssp. acetosella	Sheep's Sorrel ssp.	Native	Widespread perennial, most frequent in N Warks, grassland, roadsides, hedgerows etc., esp. on acid soils, ssp. not often provided	
Rumex acetosella ssp. pyrenaicus	Sheep's Sorrel ssp.	Native	Seemingly rare, Snitterfield 1988 only	WR
Rumex conglomeratus	Clustered Dock	Native	Widespread & frequent biennial/ perennial, esp. watersides, marshes & wet grassland	

Scientific Name	Popular Name	Cat.	Notes	Rarity
Rumex crispus	Curled Dock	Native	Widespread & frequent perennial, roadside, farmyards, disturbed ground, grassland, cultivated land etc. (ssp. crispus)	
Rumex hydrolapathum	Water Dock	Native	Localised perennial, mainly watersides	
Rumex maritimus	Golden Dock	Native	Scarce annual/perennial, mainly watersides	WN
Rumex obtusifolius	Broad-leaved Dock	Native	Widespread & frequent perennial, grassland, disturbed land, roadsides, hedgerows, arable land etc.	
Rumex pulcher	Fiddle Dock	Native	Rare perennial, dry grassland & roadsides, S Warks, 3 sites 1984-	WR
Rumex sanguineus	Wood Dock	Native	Widespread & frequent perennial, marshes, hedgerows, roadsides etc., often in shaded & damp places	
Rumex x abortivus	A hybrid dock	Ext Native	V. rare hybrid, pre-1970 record, details unknown (R. conglomeratus x R. obtusifolius)	
Rumex x dufftii	A hybrid dock	Ext Native	Possibly extinct, one doubtful record Meriden 1952 (R. sanguineus x R. obtusifolius)	
Rumex x pratensis	A hybrid dock	Native	Rare but possibly over-looked, Hampton-in-Arden 1992 & 1872-1960, commonest British Rumex hybrid (R. crispus x R. obtusifolius)	
Rumex x ruhmeri	A hybrid dock	Native	V. rare, only records Bramcote 1969 & 1973 (R. conglomeratus x R. sanguineus)	
Rumex x sagorski	A hybrid dock	Ext Native	Possibly extinct, Shustoke 1958 only (R. crispus x R. sanguineus)	
Rumex x schulzii	A hybrid dock	Ext Native	Possibly extinct, only record Rugby 1965 (R. crispus x R. conglomeratus)	
Rumex x weberi	A hybrid dock	Ext Native	One doubtful record Leamington Hastings 1961 (R. hydrolapathum x R. obtusifolium)	
Ruscus aculeatus	Butcher's-broom	Neo	Scarce garden escape shrub, mainly in woods	
Sagina apetala ssp. apetala	Annual Pearlwort ssp.	Native	Widespread but localised annual, roadsides and disturbed ground, ssp. often not provided	
Sagina apetala ssp. erecta	Annual Pearlwort ssp.	Native	As above, possibly the commoner ssp. in Warks	
Sagina nodosa	Knotted Pearlwort	Native	V. rare perennial, only recent site Sutton Park 1982-2006	WR

Scientific Name	Popular Name	Cat.	Notes	Rarity
Sagina procumbens	Procumbent Pearlwort	Native	Widespread & frequent perennial, disturbed ground, pavements, cultivated land etc.	
Sagittaria sagittifolia	Arrowhead	Native	Localised aquatic perennial, rivers & canals	
Salix species	Willows		Native & introduced trees & shrubs, many spp. frequently planted, often difficult to identify due to the existence of many varieties, cultivars, and hybrids (some involving 3 parent spp.)	
Salix alba	White Willow	Arch	Widely planted tree, sometimes naturalised, esp. watersides, wet ditches, ditched hedgerows etc., frequently pollarded	
Salix aurita	Eared Willow	Native	Rare shrub, acid grassland, wet heath, marshes, scrub & woods, esp. on acid soils of NW Warks, only recent records Hay Wood 1983, B/m 2006	WR
Salix caprea	Goat Willow	Native	Widespread but localised shrub/ small tree, damp woods, watersides, marshes, hedges etc. (ssp. caprea)	
Salix cinerea ssp. cinerea	Grey Willow ssp.	Native	Rare, not planted, watersides, damp hedges etc., 4 recent sites 1987-98	WR
Salix cinerea ssp. oleifolia	Grey Willow ssp.	Native	Widespread & frequent, wetlands, disturbed land, watersides, hedges, roadsides, damp woodland etc.	
Salix eriocephala	Heart-leaved Willow	Neo	Naturalised garden escape, Sutton Park 1979-2006	
Salix fragilis	Crack-willow	Arch	Widespread & frequent tree, planted plus naturalised, watersides, wetlands & wet woodland, frequently pollarded	
Salix myrsinifolia	Dark-leaved Willow	Neo	Naturalised escape (possibly planted), Shrewley Pool 1984-92	
Salix pentandra	Bay Willow	Native	Rare shrub, wetlands, watersides & hedges, 6 recent sites 1976-96	WR
Salix purpurea	Purple Willow	Native	Rare shrub, watersides & hedges, 4 recent sites 1983-95	WR
Salix repens	Creeping Willow	Ext Native, Neo	Extinct as a native, last record Sutton Park c. 1960; introduced with sea-sand at Emscote, Warwick c. 1960-1995	
Salix triandra	Almond Willow	Arch	Rare shrub, mainly watersides & hedges, 6 recent records	WR

Scientific Name	Popular Name	Cat.	Notes	Rarity
Salix viminalis	Osier	Arch	Localised shrub, watersides, wetlands and old withy beds etc.	
Salix x alopecuroides	A hybrid willow	Neo?	1 pre-1970 record, no site given (S. fragilis x S. triandra)	
Salix x calodendron	Holme Willow	Neo	Rare triple hybrid, 2 recent sites Shrewley 1984, Cov 1994 (S. viminalis x S. caprea x S. cinerea)	
Salix x forbyana	Fine Osier	Ext Neo	Rare triple hybrid, last sites Edgbaston Pool & Shrewley c.1960, presumed extinct (S. purpurea x S. viminalis x S. cinerea)	
Salix x fruticosa	Shrubby Osier	Ext Neo?	Only record Lowsonford 1965, possibly extinct (S. aurita x S. viminalis)	
Salix x latifolia	A hybrid willow	Ext Neo	Only record Shrewley 1966, possibly extinct (S. caprea x S. mysinifolia)	
Salix x laurina	Laurel-leaved Willow	Ext Neo	Only record Shrewley 1966, possibly extinct (S. cinerea x S. physifolia)	
Salix x mollissima	Sharp-stipuled Willow	Ext Arch	Last record Church Lawford c.1960, possibly extinct (S. triandra x S. viminalis)	
Salix x multinervis	A hybrid willow	Native	V. rare, Earlswood 1982, Hampton-in-Arden 1992 (S. cinerea x S. aurita)	
Salix x reichardtii	A hybrid willow	Native	Localised, the commonest Salix hybrid in Warks (S. caprea x S. cinerea)	
Salix x rubens	Hybrid Crack-willow	Ext Neo	Last records c.1960, formerly planted, possibly extinct (S. alba x S. fragilis)	
Salix x sericans	Broad-leaved Osier	Neo?	V. rare, planted and possibly naturalised, last record Henwood 1999 (S. caprea x S. viminalis)	
Salix x smithiana	Silky-leaved Osier	Neo?	Scarce hybrid, 2 recent sites, Kineton 1977& 1995 (S. viminalis x S. cinerea)	
Salsola kali ssp. kali	Prickly Saltwort	Ext Neo	Extinct annual, introduced with imported sea-sand, only one site in Warwick 1963	(NV)
Salsola kali ssp. ruthenica	Spineless Saltwort	Cas Neo	Annual with only one record, Cov 1994	
Salvia pratensis	Meadow Clary	Ext Native & Cas	Extinct perennial, less improved grasslands, last record as native Birdingbury 1908, subsequently recorded as a possible escape Pillerton Priors 2001-4	NT

Scientific Name	Popular Name	Cat.	Notes	Rarity
Salvia verbenaca	Wild Clary	Native	V. rare perennial, calc. grassland & scrub, Bidford, Alderminster 1995	WR
Sambucus ebulus	Dwarf Elder	Arch	Rare perennial, mainly hedges, 3 recent sites 1990-94	WR
Sambucus nigra	Elder	Native	Widespread & frequent shrub, hedges, woods, scrub, disturbed land etc., sometimes bird-sown on walls and occasionally planted	
Samolus valerandi	Brookweed	Native	Rare perennial, watersides & marshes, 3 recent sites 1984-95	WR
Sanguisorba minor ssp. minor	Salad Burnet	Native	Localised perennial in S Warks, mainly calc. grassland & quarries	WN
Sanguisorba minor ssp. muricata	Fodder Burnet	Neo	Perennial, escaped fodder crop & from wildflower seeds, 2 recent records, Halford 1986, Cov 1988	
Sanguisorba officinalis	Great Burnet	Native	Localised perennial, mainly damp grassland, occasionally watersides, wetlands, roadsides etc.	WN
Sanicula europea	Sanicle	Native	Localised perennial, shady woodland	WN
Saponaria officinalis	Soapwort	Arch	Occasional garden escape perennial, roadsides, disturbed ground etc.	
Saxifraga cymbalaria	Celandine Saxifrage	Neo	Garden escape annual, 2 recent sites, Cov 1996, Wibtoft 1998	
Saxifraga granulata	Meadow Saxifrage	Native	Scarce perennial, older & less improved grassland, cemeteries etc.	WN
Saxifraga hypnoides	Mossy Saxifrage	Ext Neo	Garden escape perennial, only record Cov 1851	(NV)
Saxifraga tridactylites	Rue-leaved Saxifrage	Native	Localised annual, mainly old limestone walls	WN
Scabiosa columbaria	Small Scabious	Native	Rare perennial, mainly calc. grassland, 5 recent records 1980-2006	WR
Scandix pecten-veneris	Shepherd's-needle	Arch	Rare arable annual weed, 5 recent records 1986-2007	NC
Schoenoplectus lacustris	Common Club-rush	Native	Widespread aquatic/waterside perennial, locally frequent along rivers & around lakes	
Schoenoplectus tabernaemontani	Grey Club-rush	Native	Localised waterside perennial, 5 recent records	WN
Schoenus nigricans	Black Bog-rush	Ext Native	Extinct perennial, fens, Dosthill 1670, Coleshill 1817	
Scirpus sylvaticus	Wood Club-rush	Native	Localised perennial, watersides & marshes	
Scleranthus annuus	Annual Knawel	Native	Localised annual, arable & sandy & gravelly places, avoiding calc. soils (ssp. annuus)	NE

Scientific Name	Popular Name	Cat.	Notes	Rarity
Scorpiurus muricatus	Caterpillar-plant	Cas	Annual, from bird-seed, Rugby 1982, allotment L/Spa 1986	
Scorzonera humilis	Viper's-grass	Ext Neo	Extinct perennial, pasture, Portway 1954-1965, probably not native to Warks, though source unclear	(NV)
Scrophularia auriculata	Water Figwort	Native	Frequent perennial, waterside & marshes	
Scrophularia nodosa	Common Figwort	Native	Widespread perennial, woods, marshes, roadsides, hedges etc.	
Scrophularia umbrosa	Green Figwort	Native	V. rare perennial, only modern records from Moreton Morrell 1871-2004	WR
Scrophularia vernalis	Yellow Figwort	Neo	V. rare perennial, possibly from game cover or game feed, Walton 1988-2006	
Scutellaria galericulata	Skullcap	Native	Widespread perennial, watersides, marshes & wet woodland	
Scutellaria minor	Lesser Skullcap	Ext Native	Extinct perennial, bog, mire & damp acid woodland, last site Ryton Wood 1962	
Scutellaria x hybrida	A hybrid skullcap	Ext Native	Extinct hybrid perennial, canal, Sowe Waste 1887 (S. galericulata x S. minor)	
Secale cereale	Rye	Cas	Crop & bird-seed annual, 3 sites 1993-2004	
Securigera varia	Crown Vetch	Neo	Garden escape perennial, 3 recent sites 1977-1990	
Sedum acre	Biting Stonecrop	Native	Scattered perennial, walls, surfaced ground, roofs and disturbed ground	
Sedum album	White Stonecrop	Neo	Localised garden escape perennial, walls, disturbed ground, roadsides, railways, etc.	
Sedum anglicum	English Stonecrop	Cas	2 sites 1996-	
Sedum forsterianum	Rock Stonecrop	Ext Neo	Extinct garden escape perennial, only record Oversley 1872, native to W Britain	(NS)
Sedum rupestre	Reflexed Stonecrop	Neo	Localised garden escape, walls, roofs, disturbed ground etc.	
Sedum sexangulare	Tasteless Stonecrop	Ext Neo	Extinct garden escape perennial, last record 1848	
Sedum spectabile	Butterfly Stonecrop	Neo	Garden escape perennial, W Warks c. 1999	
Sedum spurium	Caucasian-stonecrop	Neo	Localised garden escape, disturbed ground, walls etc.	
Sedum telephium	Orpine	Native	Rare perennial, native & garden escape, woods, hedges & roadsides, 6 recent sites	WR

Scientific Name	Popular Name	Cat.	Notes	Rarity
Selaginella kraussiana	Krauss's Clubmoss	Neo	Garden escape perennial, rockeries, B/m Botanical Garden 2007	
Sempervivum tectorum	House-leek	Neo	Garden escape perennial, roof, Temple Balsall 1989	
Senecio aquaticus	Marsh Ragwort	Native	Widespread but local perennial, marshes, watersides & wet grassland	
Senecio cineraria	Silver Ragwort	Neo	Garden escape perennial, Cov 1994, Kinwarton 1998	
Senecio erucifolius	Hoary Ragwort	Native	Localised perennial, grassland, disturbed ground, roadsides, railways & scrub on calc. soils, mainly S Warks	WN
Senecio inaequidens	Narrow-leaved Ragwort	Neo	Invasive garden escape perennial, 4 sites 2000-7	
Senecio jacobaea	Common Ragwort	Native	Widespread & frequent perennial, roadsides, grasslands, disturbed land, woodland rides, hedges etc. (a notifiable weed that landowners must remove under some circumstances)	
Senecio squalidus	Oxford Ragwort	Neo	Widespread but localised annual/perennial, disturbed ground, railways, old buildings etc.	
Senecio sylvaticus	Heath Groundsel	Native	Localised annual, hedges, roadsides, rough grassland, sandy arable etc., avoiding calc. soils, mainly N Warks	
Senecio viscosus	Sticky Groundsel	Neo	Localised annual, disturbed ground, roadsides, railways etc., avoiding calc. soils, mainly N Warks	
Senecio vulgaris	Groundsel	Native	Widespread & frequent annual, disturbed ground, roadsides, arable, gardens etc.	
Senecio x albescens	A hybrid ragwort	Neo	Rare perennial, 3 sites 2004-2006 (S. cineraria x S. jacobaea)	
Senecio x baxteri	A hybrid ragwort	Ext Neo	Extinct annual, only records B/m 1945, Alvecote 1960 (S. squalidus x S. vulgaris)	
Senecio x ostenfeldii	A hybrid ragwort	Native	V. rare, S/Avon 1988 (S. jacobaea x S. aquaticus)	
Senecio x subnebrodensis	A hybrid ragwort	Neo	Scarce annual hybrid, railway, roadsides etc., 8 recent records (S. squalidus x S. viscosus)	
Serratula tinctoria	Saw-wort	Native	Scarce perennial, grassland, roadsides, wetlands etc.	WN
Setaria italica	Foxtail Bristle-grass	Cas	Bird-seed annual, 2 recent sites, B/m 1983, L/Spa 1989	

Scientific Name	Popular Name	Cat.	Notes	Rarity
Setaria parviflora	Knotroot Bristle-grass	Cas	Bird-seed annual/perennial, K/worth 1999	
Setaria pumila	Yellow Bristle-grass	Cas	Occasional birdseed annual, tips, gardens, game-bird feed	
Setaria verticillata	Rough Bristle-grass	Cas	Bird-seed annual, 3 recent sites 1973-2004	
Setaria viridis	Green Bristle-grass	Neo	Occasional bird-seed annual, self-sowing, increasing	
Sherardia arvensis	Field Madder	Native	Localised annual, arable, short grassland, roadsides etc.	WN
Sida spinosa	Prickly Mallow	Cas	Birdseed annual/perennial, 1 site B/m 1983	
Silaum silaus	Pepper-saxifrage	Native	Localised perennial, old & less improved grassland, roadsides etc., esp. on calc. soils of S Warks	WN
Silene armeria	Sweet-William Catchfly	Cas	Bird-seed annual, only record Rugby 1982	
Silene cretica	A catchfly	Ext Neo	Extinct annual, only record Sutton Park 1877	
Silene dioica	Red Campion	Native	Widespread & frequent perennial, woods, roadsides, hedges etc.	
Silene gallica	Small-flowered Catchfly	Ext Arch & Cas Neo	Extinct annual, sandy arable, last 'native' record 1913, only recent record B/m 1983 (probably from birdseed)	NE
Silene latifolia	White Campion	Arch	Widespread perennial, roadsides, hedges, disturbed land etc. (ssp. alba)	
Silene noctiflora	Night-flowering Catchfly	Arch	Rare annual arable weed, S & E Warks, 3 recent sites 1986-98	NV
Silene nutans	Nottingham Catchfly	Ext Neo	Extinct annual, only record Oscott 1891, not native to Warks	(NT)
Silene vulgaris	Bladder Campion	Native	Localised perennial, roadsides, railways, disturbed land etc. (ssp. vulgaris)	
Silene x hampeana	A hybrid campion	Native	Occasional perennial, esp. roadsides, often in 'hybrid swarms' (S. latifolia x S. dioica)	
Silybum marianum	Milk Thistle	Cas	Scarce annual/biennial, 4 recent sites 1990-2004	
Sinapis alba	White Mustard	Arch	Localised annual, arable, disturbed ground, roadsides etc., diminishing	
Sinapis arvensis	Charlock	Arch	Widespread annual, arable, disturbed ground, roadsides etc.	
Sison amomum	Stone Parsley	Native	Localised biennial, mainly roadsides & hedges on calc. soils in S Warks	WN
Sisymbrium altissimum	Tall Rocket	Neo	Scarce annual, last record 1989	

Scientific Name	Popular Name	Cat.	Notes	Rarity
Sisymbrium officinale	Hedge Mustard	Arch	Widespread & frequent annual/ biennial, roadsides, disturbed land, hedges etc.	
Sisymbrium orientale	Eastern Rocket	Neo	Localised annual, esp. urban roads & disturbed ground, increasing	
Sisymbrium polyceratium	Many-podded Hedge-mustard	Cas	Annual, only record Hams Hall 1987	
Sisymbrium strictissimum	Perennial Rocket	Neo	Possible garden escape perennial, allotment L/Spa 2006	
Sisyrinchium bermudiana	Blue-eyed-grass	Neo	Possible garden escape perennial, Exhall 1989, Middleton 1997	
Sisyrinchium striatum	Pale Yellow-eyed -grass	Cas	Possible garden escape perennial, roadside B/m 2007	
Smyrnium olusatrum	Alexanders	Neo	Scarce biennial, fairly salt-tolerant, roadsides 1989-2007, increasing	
Solanum dulcamara	Bittersweet	Native	Widespread perennial, hedges, marshes, roadsides, etc.	
Solanum nigrum ssp. nigrum	Black Nightshade ssp.	Native	Frequent annual, esp. in S Warks, arable, gardens, roadsides, disturbed land etc., the commoner ssp.	
Solanum nigrum ssp. schultesii	Black Nightshade ssp.	Neo	Scarce annual, 5 sites 1997-2006, possibly overlooked	
Solanum physalifolium	Green Nightshade	Neo	Localised annual, arable, tips & roadsides, a crop seed contaminant 1959-99	
Solanum rostratum	Buffalo-bur	Cas	Scarce annual, esp. arable & disturbed ground, from bird-seed, crop seed 1982-2005	
Solanum tuberosum	Potato	Cas	Relic of cultivation perennial, recent records Henley 1996, B/m 2007	
Soleirolia soleirolii	Mind-your- own-business	Neo	Localised garden escape perennial, urban alleys etc.	
Solidago canadensis	Canadian Goldenrod	Neo	Frequent garden escape perennial, disturbed ground, roadsides, railways, tips etc.	
Solidago gigantea	Early Goldenrod	Neo	As above, but seemingly less common 1980-2007 (ssp. serotina)	
Solidago graminifolia	Grass-leaved Goldenrod	Ext Neo	Extinct garden escape, B/m 1943 only	
Solidago virgaurea	Goldenrod	Native	Rare perennial, hedgerows, roadsides, railways, esp. W Warks, 4 recent sites	WR
Sonchus arvensis	Corn Sow-thistle	Native	Widespread & frequent perennial, roadsides, disturbed ground, arable etc.	
Sonchus asper	Prickly Sow-thistle	Native	Widespread & frequent perennial, roadsides, disturbed ground, arable etc.	

Scientific Name	Popular Name	Cat.	Notes	Rarity
Sonchus oleraceus	Smooth Sow-thistle	Native	Widespread & frequent perennial, roadsides, disturbed ground, arable etc.	
Sonchus tenerrimus	A casual sow-thistle	Cas	Perennial, alley L/Spa 2004-6 only record	
Sorbaria tomentosa	Himalayan Sorbaria	Neo	Garden escape shrub, bird-sown, walls, Rugby 2005-7	
Sorbus aria	Common Whitebeam	Neo	Frequently planted tree, also recorded as self-sown	
Sorbus aucuparia	Rowan	Native	A native tree of ancient acid woods, frequently planted elsewhere	
Sorbus intermedia	Swedish Whitebeam	Neo	Frequently planted tree, also recorded as naturalised at a few sites	
Sorbus torminalis	Wild Service-tree	Native	Scarce tree of ancient woods, occasionally planted	WN
Sorghum bicolor	Great Millet	Cas	Annual, from gamebird-seed at Alscot 2004, bird-seed Cov 2005	
Sorghum halapense	Johnson-grass	Cas	Perennial, from bird-seed, B/m 1983 only record	
Sparganium emersum	Unbranched Bur-reed	Native	Localised aquatic perennial, watersides & swamp of rivers, canals, pools	WN
Sparganium erectum ssp. erectum	Branched Bur-reed ssp.	Native	Widespread aquatic perennial, watersides & swamp, ssp. often not given, 6 recent records for this ssp.	
Sparganium erectum ssp. microcarpum	Branched Bur-reed ssp.	Native	8 recent sites	
Sparganium erectum ssp. neglectum	Branched Bur-reed ssp.	Native	6 recent sites	
Sparganium erectum ssp. oocarpum	Branched Bur-reed ssp.	Native	V. rare ssp. (but possibly overlooked), Welford/Avon 1947, Preston Bagot 1995	WR
Sparganium natans	Least Bur-reed	Ext Native	Extinct aquatic perennial, last record Arbury 1854	
Spartium junceum	Spanish Broom	Neo	Garden escape shrub, Cov 1988	
Spergula arvensis	Corn Spurrey	Arch	Localised annual, esp. arable & allotments, N Warks, avoids calc. soils	NV
Spergularia marina	Lesser Sea-spurrey	Neo	Localised but increasing salt-tolerant annual, roadsides	
Spergularia rubra	Sand Spurrey	Native	Localised annual, mainly disturbed sandy and gravelly ground	
Spiraea douglasii	Steeple-bush	Cas	Garden escape shrub, Fulready 1992 (ssp. menziesii)	
Spiraea japonica	Japanese Spiraea	Cas	Garden escape shrub, pavement, B/m 2007	
Spiraea x pseudosalicifolia	Confused Bridewort	Neo	Garden escape shrub 1992-2006 (S. salicilifolia x S. douglassii)	

Scientific Name	Popular Name	Cat.	Notes	Rarity
Spiraea salicifolia	Bridewort	Neo	Garden escape shrub, only recent record Earlswood 1992	
Spiranthes spiralis	Autumn Lady's-tresses	Ext Native	Extinct perennial, last record K/worth 1873	NT
Spirodela polyrhiza	Greater Duckweed	Native	Rare floating aquatic perennial, ponds & canals, 5 recent sites	WR
Stachys annua	Annual Yellow-woundwort	Ext Neo	Extinct annual, Sutton Park 1877, Hatton 1955	
Stachys arvensis	Field Woundwort	Arch	Rare annual, mainly arable & disturbed ground, 6 recent sites	NNT
Stachys byzantina	Lamb's-ear	Cas	Garden escape perennial, Nuneaton 2005	
Stachys officinalis	Betony	Native	Localised perennial, old & less improved grassland, hedges, roadsides etc.	WN
Stachys palustris	Marsh Woundwort	Native	Localised perennial, esp. watersides (increasingly sold for ponds)	
Stachys sylvatica	Hedge Woundwort	Native	Widespread & frequent perennial, hedges, roadsides, woods etc.	
Stachys x ambigua	A hybrid woundwort	Native	Rare perennial, watersides, 3 recent sites 1986-98 (S. sylvatica x S. palustris)	
Stellaria alsine	Bog Stitchwort	Native	Localised perennial, mainly marshes & watersides	WN
Stellaria graminea	Lesser Stitchwort	Native	Widespread perennial, grassland, woods, hedges, roadsides etc.	
Stellaria holostea	Greater Stitchwort	Native	Widespread perennial, hedges, roadsides, woods etc., declining	
Stellaria media	Common Chickweed	Native	Widespread & frequent annual, arable, disturbed land, gardens, grassland etc.	
Stellaria neglecta	Greater Chickweed	Native	Localised annual/perennial, hedges, roadsides, wet woods etc.	
Stellaria nemorum	Wood Chickweed	Ext Cas?	Extinct perennial, Alcester 1817, Honington 1891, possibly planted	
Stellaria pallida	Lesser Chickweed	Native	Rare annual, Burton Dassett 1985, Fenny Compton 1989	WR
Stellaria palustris	Marsh Stitchwort	Ext Native	Extinct perennial of damp areas, last record Spernall 1884	NV
Stratiotes aloides	Water-soldier	Neo	Aquatic escape perennial, 5 sites 1977-2006, a scarce native of E England	(NT)
Succisa pratensis	Devil's-bit Scabious	Native	Localised perennial, damp meadows, watersides, woods etc.	WN
Sutera cordata	Bacopa 'Snowflake'	Cas	Window-box escape perennial, asphalt, B/m 1997	
Sutera ?cordata	Bacopa sp.	Cas	Garden escape annual/perennial, roadside, Castle Bromwich 2006	

Scientific Name	Popular Name	Cat.	Notes	Rarity
Symphoricarpos albus	Snowberry	Neo	Localised suckering shrub, game cover & garden escape, mainly woods & hedges	
Symphytum asperum	Rough Comfrey	Ext Neo	Extinct garden escape perennial, last record Temple Balsall 1967	
Symphytum grandiflorum	Creeping Comfrey	Neo	Scarce garden escape perennial, roadsides & woodland	
Symphytum officinale	Common Comfrey	Native	Localised perennial, roadsides, watersides, disturbed ground etc.	
Symphytum orientale	White Comfrey	Neo	Scarce perennial garden escape, roadsides, ditches, disturbed ground, walls etc.	
Symphytum tauricum	Crimean Comfrey	Ext Neo	Extinct perennial, Warwick 1879, presumed garden escape	
Symphytum tuberosum	Tuberous Comfrey	Neo	Garden escape perennial, Shipston 1983, Bubbenhall 1987	
Symphytum x uplandicum	Russian Comfrey	Neo	Widespread garden escape perennial, commonest Comfrey in Warks (S. asperum x S. officinale)	
Syringa vulgaris	Lilac	Neo	Popular garden shrub, sometimes naturalising by suckering, hedges, disturbed ground etc.	
Tagetes patula	French Marigold	Cas	Garden escape annual, B/m 2007	
Tamus communis	Black Bryony	Native	Widespread climbing perennial, mainly hedges & scrub	
Tanacetum parthenium	Feverfew	Neo	Widespread perennial, mainly roadsides & disturbed ground, esp. in urban areas	
Tanacetum vulgare	Tansy	Native	Localised perennial, roadsides, tips	
Taraxacum 'officinale' agg.	Dandelions		Widespread perennials of grasslands (incl. garden lawns), roadsides, disturbed land etc. 'T. officinale' is an aggregate name not used by national experts. 235 British microspecies, but few of these critically recorded after 1970, so rarity levels not assigned & extinctions not certain.	
Taraxacum aequilobum	A dandelion	Neo	1 record, B/m 1974	
Taraxacum alatum	A dandelion	Native	2 records, B/m 1974, Stockton 1980	
Taraxacum brachyglossum	A dandelion	Ext Native?	10 records 1956-65, S & mid Warks	
Taraxacum bracteatum	A dandelion	Native	3 sites 1952-1997	
Taraxacum britannicum	A dandelion	Ext Native?	1 record, Guy's Cliffe 1962	
Taraxacum coartatum	A dandelion	Neo	1 record, Bickmarsh 1997	

Scientific Name	Popular Name	Cat.	Notes	Rarity
Taraxacum dahlstedtii	A dandelion	Native	2 records, Crabbs Cross, near Redditch 1997, Farnborough 1953 (T. stenoglossum)	
Taraxacum duplidentifrons	A dandelion	Native	3 sites 1952-1985	
Taraxacum euryphyllum	A dandelion	Ext Native?	4 sites 1963-1964	
Taraxacum expallidiforme	A dandelion	Native	1 record, Lighthorne 1983	
Taraxacum faeroense	A dandelion	Native	20 sites, esp. N & mid Warks (includes 'T. spectabile')	
Taraxacum fulviforme	A dandelion	Native	3 sites, 1893-1982	
Taraxacum glauciniforme	A dandelion	Native	2 sites, Aston Cantlow 1963, Warwick 1982	
Taraxacum hamatum	A dandelion	Ext Native?	6 sites 1875-1957	
Taraxacum lacistophyllum	A dandelion	Native	16 sites 1893-1971	
Taraxacum laeticolor	A dandelion	Neo	1 record, Bickmarsh 1999	
Taraxacum leptodon	A dandelion	Neo	1 record, Crabbs Cross, near Redditch 1997	
Taraxacum nordstedtii	A dandelion	Native	12 sites 1896-1971, mainly N & mid Warks	
Taraxacum oxoniense	A dandelion	Native	13 sites 1954-1980, mainly S Warks	
Taraxacum piceatum	A dandelion	Neo	1 record Cheapside, Bidford on Avon 1996	
Taraxacum polyodon	A dandelion	Native	2 records, Crabbs Cross, Redditch 1997, Harbury 1971	
Taraxacum sagittipotens	A dandelion	Native	1 record, Guy's Cliffe 1986	
Taraxacum sahlinianum	A dandelion	Native	1 record, Major's Green, Solihull 2001	
Taraxacum sellandi	A dandelion	Native	1 record, Churchover 1988	
Taraxacum subhamatum	A dandelion	Ext Native?	1 record, nr. Harbury 1964	
Taraxacum trilobatum	A dandelion	Neo	1 record, Redditch 1997	
Taraxacum undulatiflorum	A dandelion	Neo	1 record, Warwick 1971	
Taraxacum unguilobum	A dandelion	Ext Native?	2 records, Merevale Park 1963, Sutton Park 1951	
Taxus baccata	Yew	Native	Widespread planted tree, esp. in churchyards and historic properties but bird-sown in some woods & other places	
Teesdalia nudicaulis	Shepherd's Cress	Ext Native	Extinct annual, last record Flecknoe 1961	NT
Tellima grandiflora	Fringecups	Neo	Garden escape perennial, 3 sites 1990-96	

Scientific Name	Popular Name	Cat.	Notes	Rarity
Tetragonia tetragonioides	New Zealand Spinach	Cas	Garden escape annual, L/Spa 1992 only record	
Tetragonolobus maritimus	Dragon's-teeth	Cas	Garden escape perennial, Bishop's Itchington 2000 only	
Teucrium chamaedrys	Wall Germander	Cas	Garden escape perennial, 2 sites, Ilmington 1962, Walsgrave 2003	
Teucrium scorodonia	Wood Sage	Native	Localised perennial, hedgerows, scrub, woods & disturbed land on acid soils, mostly N Warks	
Thalictrum aquilegiifolium	French Meadow-rue	Cas	Garden escape perennial, Baddesley Clinton 1998, Berkswell 2005	
Thalictrum flavum	Common Meadow-rue	Native	Localised perennial, marshes	WN
Thalictrum minus	Lesser Meadow-rue	Neo	Scarce garden escape perennial, tips, old gardens, hedges	
Thelypteris palustris	Marsh Fern	Ext Native	Extinct fern, marshes, last record Sutton Park 1877	NS
Thlaspi arvense	Field Penny-cress	Arch	Localised annual, mostly arable & disturbed land, declining	WN
Thymus polytrichus	Wild Thyme	Native	Scarce perennial, calc. grassland & quarries, S Warks (ssp. britannicus)	WN
Thymus pulegioides	Large Thyme	Native	Rare perennial, mostly calc. grassland & quarries, S Warks, 3 recent sites	WR
Tilia cordata	Small-leaved Lime	Native	As a native, a localised tree of ancient woods where often coppiced, also planted in parks, churchyards etc.	WN
Tilia platyphyllos	Large-leaved Lime	Neo?	Questionable native in Warks, 3 recent records of possibly naturalised trees 1983-92, widely planted, esp. in parks, a rare native in some other parts of Britain	(NS)
Tolmiea menziesii	Pick-a-back-plant	Neo	Garden escape perennial, woods, most recent record 1998	
Torilis arvensis	Spreading Hedge-parsley	Arch	Rare annual, mostly arable on calc. soils of S Warks, much declined, 7 recent sites	NE
Torilis japonica	Upright Hedge-parsley	Native	Widespread annual/biennial, mainly hedges & roadsides	
Torilis nodosa	Knotted Hedge-parsley	Native	Rare annual, grassland, roadsides, hedges etc., S & E Warks, 4 recent sites	WR
Trachystemon orientalis	Abraham-Isaac-Jacob	Neo	Garden escape perennial, Hatton 1983, Warwick 1986	
Tragopogon hybridus	Slender Salsify	Cas	Bird-seed annual, Rugby c.1960, Warwick 1989	

Scientific Name	Popular Name	Cat.	Notes	Rarity
Tragopogon porrifolius	Salsify	Neo	Scarce garden & allotment escape biennial, roadsides, allotments etc.	
Tragopogon pratensis ssp. minor	Goat's-beard ssp.	Native	Localised annual/perennial, roadsides, grassland, disturbed land etc., ssp. rarely given	
Tragopogon pratensis ssp. orientalis	Goat's-beard ssp.	Ext Neo	Only record, Burton Green 1892-4	
Tragopogon pratensis ssp. pratensis	Goat's-beard ssp.	Neo	Scarce ssp., disturbed ground, canalsides, v. similar to ssp. minor, possibly overlooked	
Trichophorum cespitosum	Deergrass	Native	V. rare perennial, wet heath & bogs, only site Sutton Park 1670-1990- (ssp. germanicum)	WR
Trifolium arvense	Hare's-foot Clover	Native	Localised annual, disturbed sandy ground, railways, roadsides etc.	
Trifolium aureum	Large Trefoil	Cas	Annual, only recent record Water Orton sidings 1984	
Trifolium campestre	Hop Trefoil	Native	Widespread but localised annual, disturbed ground, grassland, railways etc.	
Trifolium dubium	Lesser Trefoil	Native	Widespread & frequent annual, grassland, roadsides, disturbed ground, lawns etc.	
Trifolium fragiferum	Strawberry Clover	Native	Rare perennial, mainly roadsides & grassland on calc. soils of S & E Warks, 8 recent sites	WR
Trifolium hybridum	Alsike Clover	Neo	Widespread but localised perennial, roadsides, disturbed ground, grassland etc.	
Trifolium incarnatum	Crimson Clover	Neo	Scarce relic of cultivation annual, tips & disturbed ground, 4 recent sites (ssp. incarnatum)	
Trifolium medium	Zigzag Clover	Native	Localised perennial, esp. NW Warks, grassland, roadsides, railways, hedges, disturbed ground etc.	
Trifolium micranthum	Slender Trefoil	Native	Localised annual, lawns, grasslands & roadsides, esp. on lighter sandy soils	
Trifolium pratense	Red Clover	Native	Widespread & frequent perennial, grassland, roadsides, disturbed land, arable etc., often sown within grass leys	
Trifolium repens	White Clover	Native	Widespread & frequent perennial, grassland, roadsides, disturbed land, arable etc., often sown within grass leys	
Trifolium resupinatum	Reversed Clover	Ext Cas	Extinct casual, Oscott 1891 only	

Scientific Name	Popular Name	Cat.	Notes	Rarity
Trifolium scabrum	Rough Clover	Native	V. rare annual, long history from grasslands & quarries of the Burton Dassett area	WR
Trifolium striatum	Knotted Clover	Native	Rare annual, grasslands & roadsides, esp. on sandy soil, 7 recent sites	WR
Trifolium subterraneum	Subterranean Clover	Native	V. rare annual, dry grassland, only recent site Sherbourne, 1982-92-	WR
Triglochin palustre	Marsh Arrowgrass	Native	Scarce perennial, wetlands & watersides	WN
Trigonella caerulea	Blue Fenugreek	Ext Neo	Extinct annual, only record Shirley 1953	
Trigonella foenum-graecum	Fenugreek	Cas	Annual, spice-herb & bird-seed, L/Spa 1986	
Tripleurospermum inodorum	Scentless Mayweed	Arch	Widespread & frequent annual, arable, roadsides, disturbed ground, farmyards etc.	
Trisetum flavescens	Yellow Oat-grass	Native	Widespread perennial, esp. grassland & roadsides	
Triticum aestivum	Bread Wheat (Wheat)	Neo	Relic of cultivation & from bird-seed annual, arable, tips etc.	
Tropaeolum majus	Nasturtium	Cas	Garden escape annual, Elmdon 2007	
Tulipa sylvestris	Wild Tulip	Neo	Garden escape perennial, roadsides & meadows, 5 sites	
Tussilago farfara	Colt's-foot	Native	Widespread & frequent perennial, disturbed ground, roadsides, railways etc.	
Typha angustifolia	Lesser Bulrush	Native	Localised waterside perennial, ponds & lakes, sometimes planted	WN
Typha latifolia	Bulrush	Native	Widespread & frequent waterside perennial, ponds, lakes, rivers & canals	
Typha x glauca	Hybrid Bulrush	Native	V. rare, only site Edgbaston Pool 2006 (T. latifolia x T. angustifolia)	
Ulex europaeus	Gorse	Native	Widespread & frequent shrub, grassland, heath, hedges, roadsides, railways & disturbed land on acidic soils in N & W Warks, also hillsides in S & E Warks	
Ulex gallii	Western Gorse	Native	Scarce shrub, heathland, NW Warks	WN
Ulmus species	Elms		Large trees mostly eliminated by 1970's DED. Various hybrids (some seemingly involving 3 spp), ssp. & varieties complicate identification. Much disagreement over taxonomy & nomenclature - names used by	

Scientific Name	Popular Name	Cat.	Notes	Rarity
			CMF very out of date and some determinations probably dubious. Typically planted or suckering. Regrowth sometimes hard to identify. The following is a provisional assessment (the status of English and Wych Elms are the only certain ones).	
Ulmus glabra	Wych Elm	Native	Widespread as regrowth, esp. in hedges & woods, most of our few surviving large elms are this sp.	
Ulmus minor ssp. angustifolia	Cornish Elm	Unclear	A single questionable record for a hedge near Brinklow 1963	
Ulmus minor ssp. minor	Small-leaved (Field) Elm	Native?	Previously widespread in S & E Warks, very few recent records even for regrowth	
Ulmus minor ssp. sarniensis	Jersey Elm	Ext Neo?	Extinct tree once popular in urban streets, reported from 5 sites in hedges c.1960 (possibly all planted)	
Ulmus plotii	Plot's Elm	Native	Formerly localised in W & N Warks, 7 records in CMF c.1950-60, possibly a survivor in Warwick	WN
Ulmus procera	English Elm	Native?	Common in rural hedges as regrowth (our most frequent elm), though no large trees survived DED. Once known as the 'Warwickshire Weed'. Considered an archaeophyte in Britain by some experts.	
Ulmus x elegantissima	A hybrid elm	Native	Said to have been frequent in woods & hedgerows by CMF, 1 possible recent record, Wolston 1997 (U. glabra x U. plotii)	
Ulmus x hollandica	Dutch Elm group	Neo	Assorted hybrids once often planted. A large elm near Wellesbourne may be this hybrid (U. glabra x U. minor, apparently sometimes with U. plotii as a 3rd parent).	
Ulmus x vegeta	Huntingdon Elm	Neo	Probably always planted, one large tree survives, Humber Rd, Cov (U. glabra x U. minor)	
Ulmus x viminalis	A hybrid elm	Native	Unconfirmed records in CMF c.1950-60, a poorly defined hybrid (U. minor x U. plotii)	
Umbilicus rupestris	Navelwort	Native?	V. rare perennial, walls, only recent site Maxstoke Priory 1990-	WR

Scientific Name	Popular Name	Cat.	Notes	Rarity
Urtica dioica	Stinging Nettle	Native	Widespread & abundant perennial, woods, hedges, marshes, watersides, roadsides, gardens etc.	
Urtica membranacea	A nettle	Cas	Annual, Warwick pavement 2006-7, first GB record	
Urtica pilulifera	Roman Nettle	Ext Neo	Extinct annual, Warwick 1823	
Urtica urens	Small Nettle	Arch	Localised annual, mainly arable & disturbed ground	
Utricularia australis	Bladderwort	Native	Rare insectivorous aquatic perennial, mesotrophic pools & lakes, NW Warks, 3 sites 1988-2006	WR
Utricularia minor	Lesser Bladderwort	Ext Native	Extinct insectivorous aquatic perennial, boggy pools, last record Sutton Park 1934	
Vaccaria hispanica	Cowherb	Cas	Rare bird-seed annual, 3 recent sites 1977-2004	
Vaccinium myrtillus	Bilberry	Native	Scarce small shrub, ancient acid woods & heathland, NW & W Warks	WN
Vaccinium oxycoccos	Cranberry	Native	V. rare small shrub, wet heath & bog, NW Warks, only surviving at Sutton Park	WR
Vaccinium vitis-idaea	Cowberry	Native	V. rare local shrub, wet heath, only surviving at Sutton Park	WR
Vaccinium x intermedium	A hybrid Vaccinium	Ext Native	Extinct or possibly overlooked, Sutton Park 1889 (V. vitis-idaea x V. myrtillus)	
Valeriana dioica	Marsh Valerian	Native	V. rare perennial, mostly marshes & watersides, only recent records Tanworth-in-Arden & Dorridge 2005	WR
Valeriana officinalis	Common Valerian	Native	Localised perennial, marshes, watersides, wet grassland, hedges, ditches etc. mostly in NW Warks	WN
Valerianella carinata	Keeled-fruited Cornsalad	Arch	Localised but increasing annual, disturbed ground, walls, paths etc.	
Valerianella dentata	Narrow-fruited Cornsalad	Arch	V. rare arable annual weed, only recent records Combrook 1986, Ufton 1990	NE
Valerianella locusta	Common Cornsalad	Native	Localised annual, disturbed ground, walls, railways etc.	
Valerianella rimosa	Broad-fruited Cornsalad	Ext Arch	Extinct arable annual weed, last record Binton 1873	NE
Verbascum blattaria	Moth Mullein	Neo	Garden escape annual/biennial, 1 recent site, S/Avon c.1990	
Verbascum densiflorum	Dense-flowered Mullein	Neo	Garden escape biennial, Cranhill 1996, Beaudesert 1996	

Scientific Name	Popular Name	Cat.	Notes	Rarity
Verbascum lychnitis	White Mullein	Neo	Garden escape biennial, only record Kingsbury 1999, a scarce native in other parts of Britain	(NS)
Verbascum nigrum	Dark Mullein	Native	Localised biennial/perennial, grassland, roadsides, railways, disturbed ground, hedges etc.	
Verbascum phlomoides	Orange Mullein	Neo	Scarce garden escape biennial, disturbed land & railways	
Verbascum speciosum	Hungarian Mullein	Neo	Garden escape biennial, only recent record Great Alne 1983	
Verbascum thapsus	Great Mullein	Native	Widespread but localised biennial, roadsides, disturbed land, railways etc., the commonest mullein in Warks	
Verbascum virgatum	Twiggy Mullein	Neo	Scarce biennial, roadsides, disturbed ground, railways etc.	
Verbascum x lemaitrei	A hybrid mullein	Native	V. rare, last record Bearley sidings 1995-7 (V. virgatum x V. thapsus)	
Verbascum x semialbum	A hybrid mullein	Native	V. rare biennial usually found with both parents, Baginton Castle 1997 (V. thapsus x V. nigrum)	
Verbascum x thapsi	A hybrid mullein	Neo	V. rare biennial, Warwick 1968, Kingsbury 1999 (V. thapsus x V. lychnitis)	
Verbena bonariensis	Argentinian Vervain	Cas	Garden escape perennial, roadsides, L/Spa & B/m	
Verbena officinalis	Vervain	Arch	Scarce perennial, disturbed ground, railways, allotments, quarries etc.	
Veronica agrestis	Green Field-speedwell	Arch	Localised annual, arable, roadsides, gardens etc., declining	
Veronica anagallis-aquatica	Blue Water-Speedwell	Native	Rare perennial, watersides & wetlands, 3 recent sites	WR
Veronica arvensis	Wall Speedwell	Native	Widespread & frequent annual, arable, roadsides, disturbed land, grassland etc.	
Veronica beccabunga	Brooklime	Native	Frequent waterside perennial	
Veronica catenata	Pink Water-Speedwell	Native	Localised waterside perennial	
Veronica chamaedrys	Germander Speedwell	Native	Widespread but locally common perennial, roadsides, disturbed land, hedges, grassland, arable, woods etc.	
Veronica filiformis	Slender Speedwell	Neo	Widespread perennial, grassland, roadsides, disturbed land, garden lawns etc.	
Veronica hederifolia ssp. hederifolia	Ivy-leaved Speedwell ssp.	Arch	Widespread annual, arable, allotments, more often in rural habitats than ssp. lucorum	

Scientific Name	Popular Name	Cat.	Notes	Rarity
Veronica hederifolia ssp. lucorum	Ivy-leaved Speedwell ssp.	Arch	Widespread & frequent annual, arable, roadsides, disturbed land, gardens, hedges etc.	
Veronica longifolia	Garden Speedwell	Cas	Garden escape perennial, Rugby 1984, Dosthill 1997	
Veronica montana	Wood Speedwell	Native	Scarce perennial, esp. ancient woods & hedges	WN
Veronica officinalis	Heath Speedwell	Native	Localised perennial, grassland, roadsides, woodland, heaths etc., esp. W Warks	
Veronica persica	Common Field-speedwell	Neo	Widespread & frequent annual, arable, gardens, roadsides, farmyards etc.	
Veronica polita	Grey Field-speedwell	Neo	Scattered local annual, mainly arable & gardens, esp. on calc. soils of SE Warks	
Veronica scutellata	Marsh Speedwell	Native	Scarce perennial, marshes & watersides	WN
Veronica serpyllifolia	Thyme-leaved Speedwell	Native	Widespread & frequent perennial, grassland, arable, garden lawns, roadsides etc. (ssp. serpyllifolia)	
Veronica spicata	Spiked Speedwell	Cas	Garden escape perennial, easily confused with V. longifolia, roadside, B/m 2006	
Viburnum lantana	Wayfaring-tree	Native	Localised shrub, hedges, scrub & woods, mainly on calc. soils of S Warks	
Viburnum opulus	Guelder-rose	Native	Widespread but localised shrub, hedges, scrub, woods, watersides etc.	
Vicia cracca	Tufted Vetch	Native	Widespread & frequent perennial, hedges, roadsides, railway, disturbed ground, watersides etc.	
Vicia faba	Broad Bean	Cas	Relic of cultivation annual, Coleshill 2000	
Vicia hirsuta	Hairy Tare	Native	Widespread & frequent annual, roadsides, disturbed ground, grassland & hedges	
Vicia hybrida	Hairy Yellow-vetch	Ext Cas	Extinct casual, c. 1932, no location	
Vicia lathyroides	Spring Vetch	Native	V. rare annual, only recent record Piles Coppice 1996-2001	WR
Vicia lutea	Yellow-vetch	Cas	Rare escape annual, 3 recent sites 1997-2003, a scarce native of the coast	(NT)
Vicia parviflora	Slender Tare	Native	Rare annual, arable, rough grassland & disturbed land, only recent records Lighthorne 1992, Wellesbourne 1997	NV

Scientific Name	Popular Name	Cat.	Notes	Rarity
Vicia sativa ssp. nigra	Common Vetch ssp.	Native	Localised annual, dry grassland, roadsides, railways & disturbed land	
Vicia sativa ssp. sativa	Common Vetch ssp.	Arch	Fodder crop escape, arable land & disturbed ground, local status unclear	
Vicia sativa ssp. segetalis	Common Vetch ssp.	Arch	Widespread & frequent annual (the commonest ssp.), grassland, disturbed land, roadsides, hedges, arable etc.	
Vicia sepium	Bush Vetch	Native	Widespread & locally frequent perennial, roadsides, railways, disturbed land, hedges etc.	
Vicia sylvatica	Wood Vetch	Ext Native	Extinct perennial, last record Bentley Park 1836	
Vicia tenuifolia	Fine-leaved Vetch	Neo	V. rare perennial, roadsides & railways, only recent record Kineton 1985	WR
Vicia tetrasperma	Smooth Tare	Native	Widespread but localised annual, arable, roadsides, hedges, disturbed land, woods etc.	
Vicia villosa	Fodder Vetch	Neo	Scarce annual from bird-seen or grain, Cov tip 1974, S/Avon roadside 1992-4	
Vinca major	Greater Periwinkle	Neo	Localised garden escape, roadsides, railways, hedges, urban & rural	
Vinca minor	Lesser Periwinkle	Arch	Occasional garden escape perennial, roadsides, railways, woods, hedges etc.	
Viola arvensis	Field Pansy	Arch	Widespread but localised annual, mainly arable & disturbed ground	
Viola canina	Heath Dog-violet	Native	V. rare perennial, acid grassland, recent records Coombe Park 1982, Brandon 2005 (ssp.canina)	NNT
Viola cornuta	Horned Pansy	Ext Neo	Extinct garden escape perennial, Emscote 1966	
Viola hirta	Hairy Violet	Native	Localised perennial, roads, banks, hedges, grassland on calc. soils, S Warks	WN
Viola lactea	Pale Dog-violet	Ext Native	Extinct perennial, only record Keresley 1857	NV
Viola odorata	Sweet Violet	Native	Widespread & frequent native & garden escape perennial, mainly hedges & woods on calc. soils	
Viola palustris	Marsh Violet	Native	Rare perennial, mire & bog, NW Warks, 4 sites 1985-2000 (ssp. palustris)	WR
Viola reichenbachiana	Early Dog-violet	Native	Scarce perennial, ancient woods, hedges, roadsides, gardens etc.	WN

Scientific Name	Popular Name	Cat.	Notes	Rarity
Viola riviniana	Common Dog-violet	Native	Frequent perennial of NW Warks, scarcer in S, hedges, woods, roadsides, gardens etc.	
Viola tricolor	Wild Pansy	Native	Rare & declined annual, mainly arable & disturbed ground (ssp. tricolor)	NNT
Viola x bavarica	A hybrid dog-violet	Native	Rare perennial, 2 recent sites, gardens, L/Spa 2007 (V. riviniana x V. reichenbachiana)	
Viola x intersita	A hybrid dog-violet	Ext Native	Extinct perennial, only record Coleshill Bog 1954 (V. riviniana x V. canina)	
Viola x scabra	A hybrid violet	Ext Native	Extinct perennial, last records Houndshill, Bidford, Exhall 1959, but possibly overlooked (V. odorata x V. hirta)	
Viola x wittrockiana	Garden Pansy	Cas	Garden escape annual, often 'miniature', B/m 2006-7, L/Spa 2006-7 (V. lutea x V. tricolor x V. altaica)	
Viscum album	Mistletoe	Native	Localised tree & shrub epiphytic parasitic, local hosts include Apple, Hawthorn, Common Lime, Hybrid Black Poplar and False Acacia	
Vitis vinifera	Grape-vine	Cas	Perennial climber, Walsgrave Hospital 1990 (probably from discarded pips!)	
Vulpia bromoides	Squirreltail Fescue	Native	Localised annual, disturbed ground, roadsides, railways, dry grassland, walls etc.	
Vulpia myuros	Rat's-tail Fescue	Arch	Localised annual, railway, roadsides, disturbed ground etc., increasing	
Wahlenbergia hederacea	Ivy-leaved Bellflower	Ext Native	Extinct perennial, wet heath & bog, last record Arbury Hall 1847-72	NT
Xanthium spinosum	Spiny Cocklebur	Ext Cas	Extinct annual, skinyards K/worth 1873, tip Bedworth 1964	
Zannichellia palustris	Horned Pondweed	Native	Localised submerged aquatic perennial, ponds, rivers & canals	

Appendix 1

Extinct native and archaeophyte plant species and subspecies

These are arranged in order of last recorded year. Hybrids, casuals & microspecies are excluded.

- Great Fen-sedge *Cladium mariscus* (1670)
- Rough Horsetail *Equisetum hyemale* (1695)
- Black Bog-rush *Schoenus nigricans* (1817)
- Smooth Cat's-ear *Hypochaeris glabra* (1830)
- Small Fleabane *Pulicaria vulgaris* (1830)
- Deptford Pink *Dianthus armeria* (1832)
- Wood Vetch *Vicia sylvatica* (1836)
- Marsh Clubmoss *Lycopodiella inundatum* (1842)
- Fir Clubmoss *Huperzia selago* (1846)
- Greater Broomrape *Orobanche rapum-genistae* (1847)
- Beech Fern *Phegopteris connectilis* (1848)
- Lesser Calamint *Clinopodium calamintha* (1851)
- Rampion Bellflower *Campanula rapunculus* (1851)
- Narrow-leaved Water-dropwort *Oenanthe silaifolia* (1854)
- Least Bur-reed *Sparganium natans* (1854)
- Loddon Pondweed *Potamogeton nodosus* (1856)
- Green-flowered Helleborine *Epipactis phyllanthes* (1857)
- Pale Dog-violet *Viola lactea* (1857)
- Sharp-leaved Pondweed *Potamogeton acutifolius* (1859)
- Wood Crane's-bill *Geranium sylvaticum* (1866)
- Pennyroyal *Mentha pulegium* (1866)
- Ivy-leaved Bellflower *Wahlenbergia hederacea* (1872)
- Round-leaved Mint *Mentha suavolens* (1873)
- Common Wintergreen *Pyrola minor* (1873)
- Autumn Lady's-tresses *Spiranthes spiralis* (1873)
- Broad-fruited Cornsalad *Valerianella rimosa* (1873)
- Green Hound's-tongue *Cynoglossum germanicum* (1875)
- Hairy Dog-rose *Rosa caesia* ssp. *caesia* (1876)
- Marsh Fern *Thelypteris palustris* (1877)
- Frog Orchid *Coeloglossum viride* (1878)
- Water-violet *Hottonia palustris* (1878)
- Stag's-horn Clubmoss *Lycopodium clavatum* (1884)
- Marsh Stitchwort *Stellaria palustris* (1884)

- White Beak-sedge *Rhynchospora alba* (1885)
- A hawkweed *Hieracium eboracense* (1886)
- White Helleborine *Cephalanthera damasonium* (1887)
- Small-leaved Sweet-briar *Rosa agrestis* (1889)
- Bur Chervil *Anthriscus caucalis* (1891)
- Green Spleenwort *Asplenium viride* (1893)
- Blue Fescue *Festuca longifolia* (1897)
- Upright Chickweed *Moenchia erecta* (1898)
- Pillwort *Pilularia globulifera* (1898)
- Chamomile *Chamaemelum nobile* (1901)
- Slender Bedstraw *Galium pumilum* (1904)
- Royal Fern *Osmunda regalis* (1908)
- Meadow Clary *Salvia pratensis* (1908)
- Pheasant's-eye *Adonis annua* (1920)
- Lesser Bladderwort *Utricularia minor* (1934)
- Many-stalked Spike-rush *Eleocharis multicaulis* (1945)
- Fragrant Orchid *Gymnadenia conopsea* (1948)
- Corn Parsley *Petroselinum segetum* (1950)
- Corncockle *Agrostemma githago* (1955)
- Wood Barley *Hordelymus europaeus* (1955)
- Whorled Water-milfoil *Myriophyllum verticilllatum* (1955)
- Knapweed Broomrape *Orobanche elatior* (1957)
- Lesser Water-plantain *Baldellia ranunculoides* (1957)
- Dodder *Cuscuta epithymum* (1959)
- Stinking Goosefoot *Chenopodium vulvaria* (1960)
- Marsh Hawk's-beard *Crepis paludosa* (1960)
- Creeping Willow *Salix repens* (1960)
- An eyebright *Euphrasia micrantha* (c.1960)
- Long-stalked Pondweed *Potamogeton praelongus* (c.1960)
- Shepherd's Cress *Teesdalia nudicaulis* (1961)
- A Lady's-mantle *Alchemilla xanthochlora* (1961)
- Chaffweed *Anagallis minima* (1961)
- Burnet Rose *Rosa spinossisima* (1962)
- Greater Dodder *Cuscuta europaea* (1962)
- Bog Asphodel *Narthecium ossifragum* (1962)
- Lesser Skullcap *Scutellaria minor* (1962)
- Hairy Rock-cress *Arabis hirsuta* (1963)
- Narrow-leaved Bittercress *Cardamine impatiens* (1963)
- An eyebright *Euphrasia arctica* (1964)
- Yellow Star-of-Bethlehem *Gagea lutea* (1965)
- A hawkweed *Hieracium vulgatum* (1965)
- Grass-wrack Pondweed *Potamogeton compressus* (1965)
- Red Pondweed *Potamogeton alpinus* (1967)
- Alternate Water-Milfoil *Myriophyllum alternifolium* (1968)

Extinctions of native and naturalised habitat specialists

- Woodland – 7 species
- Hedgerows – no species
- Permanent grassland – 19 species
- Water courses and wetlands – 19 species
- Arable land – 12 species
- Heathland and mire – 16 species
- Disturbed ground – 4 species
- The built environment – no species

Appendix 2

Red Data List plants recorded since 1970

A new list of rare British plants was published in 2005, *The Vascular Plant Red Data List for Great Britain* (Cheffings & Farrell, Eds). The following categories were used and the British totals and totals for Warwickshire are given, excluding casual records of species not native to VC38 and those native species not recorded since 1970. Names of species are also given for each category.

Critically Endangered Species (annotated NC in checklist)
Total of NC species in Britain   35
Total of NC species in VC 38   4

* *Bupleurum rotundifolium* (Thorow-wax)
* *Galeopsis angustifolia* (Red Hemp-nettle)
* *Ranunculus arvensis* (Corn Buttercup)
* *Scandix pecten-veneris* (Shepherd's-needle)

NB: All these 4 species are arable annuals.

Endangered Species (annotated NE in checklist)
Total of NE species in Britain   90
Total of NE species in VC 38   11

* *Aceras anthropophorum* (Man Orchid)
* *Anthemis arvensis* (Corn Chamomile)
* *Campanula patula* (Spreading Bellflower)
* *Gnaphalium sylvaticum* (Heath Cudweed)
* *Lithospermum arvense* (Corn Gromwell)
* *Minuartia hybrida* (Fine-leaved Sandwort)
* *Monotropa hypopitys* ssp. *hypophegea* and ssp. *hypopitys* (Yellow Bird's-nest)
* *Scleranthus annuus* (Annual Knawel)
* *Torilis arvensis* (Spreading Hedge-parsley)
* *Valerianella dentata* (Narrow-fruited Cornsalad)

NB: 5 of the 11 species are arable annuals.

Vulnerable Species (annotated NV in checklist)
Total of NV species in Britain   220
Total of NV species in VC 38   22

- *Allium oleraceum* (Field Garlic)
- *Anthemis cotula* (Stinking Chamomile)
- *Blysmus compressus* (Flat-sedge)
- *Bromus secalinus* (Rye Brome)
- *Cephalanthera longifolia* (Narrow-leaved Helleborine)
- *Chenopodium bonus-henricus* (Good-King-Henry)
- *Chrysanthemum segetum* (Corn Marigold)
- *Clinopodium acinos* (Basil Thyme)
- *Galeopsis speciosa* (Large-flowered Hemp-nettle)
- *Groenlandia densa* (Opposite-leaved Pondweed)
- *Hyoscyamus niger* (Henbane)
- *Myosurus minimus* (Mousetail)
- *Nepeta cataria* (Cat-mint)
- *Oenanthe fistulosa* (Tubular Water-dropwort)
- *Ophrys insectifera* (Fly Orchid)
- *Papaver argemone* (Prickly Poppy)
- *Persicaria minor* (Small Water-pepper)
- *Platanthera bifolia* (Lesser Butterfly-orchid)
- *Rorippa x erythrocaulis* (Thames Yellow-cress)
- *Silene noctiflora* (Night-flowering Catchfly)
- *Spergula arvensis* (Corn Spurrey)
- *Vicia parviflora* (Slender Tare)

NB: 8 of the 22 species are arable annuals.

Near Threatened Species (annotated NNT in checklist)
Total of NNT species in Britain 98
Total of NNT species in VC 38   15

- *Carex diandra* (Lesser Tussock-sedge)
- *Colchicum autumnale* (Meadow Saffron)
- *Cynoglossum officinale* (Hound's-tongue)
- *Euphorbia exigua* (Dwarf Spurge)
- *Filago vulgaris* (Common Cudweed)
- *Genista anglica* (Petty Whin)
- *Juncus compressus* (Round-fruited Rush)
- *Neottia nidus-avis* (Bird's-nest Orchid)
- *Orchis morio* (Green-winged Orchid)
- *Platanthera chlorantha* (Greater Butterfly-orchid)
- *Potamogeton friesii* (Flat-stalked Pondweed)
- *Potentilla argentea* (Hoary Cinquefoil)
- *Stachys arvensis* (Field Woundwort)
- *Viola canina* (Heath Dog-violet)
- *Viola tricolour* (Wild Pansy)

NB: 3 of the 15 species are arable annuals.

Glossary

Acidic – vegetation growing on ground with a pH in the range of 3.5-5.5 (i.e. bog, heath, poor-fen, acid grassland and acid woodland).

Acidophile – a plant that prefers acidic ground.

Aggregate (in the botanical sense) – a collection of plants within the same genus when treated collectively. This often happens with very difficult groups such as brambles and dandelions.

Aggregate (in the geological sense) – refers to gravel, sand and crushed rock which are excavated at sites that may have botanical value, or acquire it once quarrying is finished.

Alien – a non-native plant.

Ancient Countryside – the lowland British landscape type characterised by small irregular field systems of Anglo-Saxon origin or older, bounded by ancient banked hedges, and with a high density of small ancient woods, veteran trees, ponds, hamlets and old timber-framed farmhouses. Arden is the Ancient Countryside of Warwickshire.

Ancient hedge – a hedge that predates the Parliamentary Enclosure Acts of the eighteenth and nineteenth centuries, and often much older than this.

Ancient woodland – woodland that was established before 1600AD, and often long before this (see entry for 'Primary woodland').

Anglo-Saxon – pertaining to the period that immediately follows the end of the Romano-British period (410AD) until the Norman invasion of 1066.

Annual – a plant that completes its life-cycle within a year (and often much less).

Apomixis – propagation by unfertilised seeds, resulting in progeny that are genetically identical to the parent (the plant equivalent of animal parthogenesis). Over millennia it can result in 'apomictic' microspecies.

Aquatic – a plant associated with water.

Arable – land used for the growing of crops.

Archaeophyte – a species that arrived in Britain through the agency of people before 1500AD and is not native.

Area of Outstanding Natural Beauty (AONB) – a designated landscape area of national significance (Warwickshire has a northern section of the Cotswolds AONB).

Arden – the north-west and west of Warwickshire featuring 'Ancient Countryside' (see that entry). Mostly overlying acidic soils which supported numerous areas of heathland and mire in the past.

Assarting – the process by which fields were carved out of woodland or other land types, usually producing small irregular field systems with banked ancient hedges.

Avon Valley – as a landscape zone, the broader part of the River Avon's flood plain running from Warwick towards the Vale of Evesham, one of the first parts of Warwickshire to support human settlement and with most of its woodland cleared long ago.

Back-cross – a hybrid that interbreeds with one of its parents.

Base-poor – rocks, soils or waters that are deficient in calcium carbonate or other alkaline minerals.

Biennial – a plant that completes its life cycle in two years, typically flowering in the second year.

Biodiversity – the variety of wildlife species and habitats.

Bird-sown – a plant that has spread as a result of birds spreading its seeds, usually in their droppings: a form of spread that has strongly influenced our flora.

Bog – a type of mire wetland featuring highly acidic and mineral-poor conditions, usually on very pure peat and featuring much Sphagnum moss.

Bronze Age – the period 2000 to 700BC, characterised by bronze tools and weapons and various other technological developments, some of which impacted plant communities.

BSBI – the Botanical Society of the British Isles, the official organisation for plant recorders and researchers, amateur and professional alike, responsible for many important publications.

Calcareous (e.g. grassland) – vegetation growing on ground containing relatively high levels of calcium carbonate and with a pH in the range of 6.5-8.5, i.e. lime-rich.

Calcicole – a plant that prefers calcareous ground.

Canals – artificial linear water features (with mostly standing water) originally constructed to aid transportation of goods, and with a footpath (towpath) on at least one side.

Carboniferous – the period of geological time between approximately 350 to 290 million years before present.

Carr – scrub and young woodland that develops within wetlands, typically dominated by various willows, Alder or Downy Birch, as part of the transition to mature wet woodland (some definitions include more mature wet woodland within carr).

Casual – a species of plant that becomes temporarily wild but does not persist to become 'naturalised' (see that entry).

Catchment – the land that feeds water into all the streams and tributaries that feed into a major river, e.g. the River Avon catchment that dominates southern Warwickshire and the River Trent catchment which includes the Tame and its tributaries.

Channelisation – the engineering of rivers and streams, usually involving deepening, straightening and steepening/strengthening of the banks – generally a bad thing for aquatic and marginal plant communities.

Climber – a plant that scrambles up other plants to gain height, most typically shrubs and trees, e.g. Ivy, Honeysuckle and bindweeds.

Community – an association of plant species brought together by one or more environmental factors, e.g. soil type or land-use.

Coppicing – the regular cutting of a tree or shrub at its base so that it produces a regular crop of stems (poles) rather than a single trunk.

Cotswolds – the hilly, limestone and ironstone districts in the south of Warwickshire

County Wildlife Site – the name given to a SINC in some parts of Warwickshire (see SINC).

Cultivar – a variety of a plant species deliberately bred to be different to the wild form, either in appearance, growth or some other attribute (especially in plants favoured by agriculture or horticulture).

Cultivated – a plant deliberately grown to provide a specific resource.

Culverting – the covering up of watercourses, typically through a large pipe or tunnel, e.g. section of the River Sowe where it passes through Coventry.

Crop – cultivated plants grown for an agricultural or commercial purpose (can refer to trees or herbaceous species such as grains and vegetables).

Derelict land – land not being specifically used for any purpose (though often rich in biodiversity).

Disturbed – a piece of land that is, or has recently been, subject to substantial disturbance such as demolition, dumping, vehicle movement or construction.

Ditches – artificial, linear drainage features designed to speed up the drying of land, and often associated with hedges, field margins and woods.

Dominant – a plant or plant community that outcompetes or outnumbers another.

Drainage – the removal of water from the land, especially wetlands.

Dunsmore – the plateau between Coventry, Rugby and Leamington that tends to feature acidic soil overlying sand and gravel and which once supported much heathland.

Dutch elm disease – a wilting disease of most elms and some closely related trees, caused by a fungus that is spread by bark beetles.

Emergent – a plant that grows partly underwater and partly above the water surface e.g. Common Reed or Bulrush.

Enclosure – the hedging of open field systems and commons to create large, regular fields, mostly through the Parliamentary Enclosure Acts of the eighteenth and nineteenth centuries.

Endemic – a plant that is only found in one region/country and nowhere else in the world.

Enrichment (of soil) – increasing fertilisation of the soil, typically by nitrogen and phosphorus (which can facilitate plant growth but allows competitive plants to outcompete less competitive but rarer ones), and also by calcium carbonate (which can make a wetland become fen rather than mire).

Environmental Impact Assessment – see 'Impact Assessment'.

Escape – a cultivated plant found outside of cultivation (e.g. a garden escape).

Eutrophic (waterbody) – a pool or lake with relatively high nutrient levels (such as nitrates and phosphates), the usual state in Warwickshire especially in waterbodies overlying neutral or calcareous geology. At its most extreme (typically following a pollution incident involving slurry or sewage) it can badly damage the aquatic and wetland flora, but at moderate levels it can support a good variety of species.

Extinct – a species that has completely disappeared from an area, at least as a wild species (though some 'extinct' plants may still turn up as short-lived casuals or be rediscovered).

Fallow – agricultural land that is being rested for one or more years between crops, often quite good for wildflowers.

Feldon – the southern and eastern part of Warwickshire, gently rolling claylands that are typically calcareous, bounded by the Dunsmore to the north, Northamptonshire Wolds to the east, Cotswolds to the south and Avon Valley to the west.

Fen – well-vegetated open wetland on peaty soil where the water level fluctuates around ground level, It ranges from mildly acidic through to moderately calcareous (i.e. there is more mineral enrichment and less acidity than bog).

Fertilizer – a substance that increases fertility of the land (see entry for 'Enrichment').

Floodplain – the lowest-lying part of a river or stream valley that can be subject to flooding.

Form (of a species, also known as a variety) – low-ranking variation of a species, perhaps due to genetics or growth conditions, but not as significant as a subspecies which usually has a much more ancient origin.

Free-floating – a plant that floats on the water surface without any attachment to the waterbed.

Garden escape – a plant grown for horticulture (gardens, parks etc) that escapes into the wild, sometimes for a very short period (as a casual) but occasionally with greater frequency and persistence (usually as a neophyte). This can be through the spread of viable seed (variously by wind, water, birds, mammals & ants), dumping of garden waste or suckering from roots.

Genus (*pl.* genera) – typically, a collection of closely-related species. For example, willows which belong in the genus *Salix*, e.g. *Salix caprea* (Goat Willow) and *S. alba* (White Willow). Also used for just one species if it is too distinct to be placed in any other genus.

Germination – when a young plant emerges from a seed.

Glaciation – the formation or expansion of a glacier or ice sheet, during an ice age.

Grass ley – deliberately-sown grassland for stock-grazing and silage production usually dominated by ryegrasses and fescues, often with added clovers but with few wildflowers (i.e. a type of 'improved' grassland).

Gymnosperm – the group of trees that includes conifers and yews.

Habitat Biodiversity Audit (HBA) – a partnership project that maintains up-to-date habitat information in the form of a computerised map for all of Warwickshire, Solihull and Coventry.

Halophyte – a plant that tolerates salty (saline) ground such as salt-sprayed road verges.

Headlands – sections of fields exempt from cultivation to encourage wild flowers and other wildlife.

Hedge/hedgerow – the narrow strips of shrubs and trees that surround fields, properties and sometimes woods.

Hedgebank – the raised ground beneath a hedge that usually indicate an ancient hedge of Anglo-Saxon age or older.

Hedgelaying – the process in which the main stems in a neglected hedge are partially cut and then anchored at about 45 degrees to create a new stockproof hedge with invigorated growth.

Hedge-tree – a tree that grows up from a hedge.

Hemi-parasite – a species that gains some of its nutrients from other plants, but still retains chlorophyll for photosynthesis, e.g. louseworts, bartsias and Yellow-rattle.

Herbicide – a substance that kills plants, typically the ones considered weeds.

Herbs – non-woody plants (not to be confused with culinary herbs).

Higher plant – a 'vascular' plant, i.e. one that has vascular tissue for transporting water and nutrients around the plant and usually well-developed foliage comprising leaves (includes ferns, horsetails and their relatives, and all flowering plants including trees, shrubs and grasses).

Humus – soil with a high organic content, typically foliage that is being recycled by invertebrates, fungi and microbes.

Hybrid – a plant that has two or more species (typically very closely related) as parents.

Hybrid swarm – a population of hybrids that have back-crossed with one or both of the parents on numerous occasions so that a colony of plants exhibits a variable mixture of traits from each parent.

Hydrology – the status, quality and movement of water at a site or in the ground below it.

Hydrosere – the habitat transition of open water, through swamp and marsh/fen/mire either to wet woodland or to another drier habitat

Ice age – cold periods that intermittently affect Britain and other parts of the temperate world and resulted in Warwickshire either being covered in a thick sheet of ice or (in the last ice age) developing tundra over ground that was permanently frozen below the surface (permafrost).

Impact Assessment – a technique for predicting the type and magnitude of the impacts (good or bad) on a wildlife site. Frequently requested by a local authority when planning applications are submitted. Also known as an Environmental Impact Assessment.

Improved (e.g. grassland) – vegetation that has been improved for agriculture, typically by increasing soil fertility and trying to replace wild flowers with favoured grasses or crops. This is usually very damaging to natural plant communities.

Indigenous – native, originating or occurring naturally in Warwickshire and not introduced by people.

Intergeneric hybrid – a hybrid which has parents that belong to two different genera (a fairly unusual situation exhibited by a few Warwickshire plants).

Introduction (in the plant sense) – a species that has been introduced to Britain or Warwickshire, i.e. an archaeophyte, neophyte or casual.

Iron Age – the period 700BC to the Roman invasion of 43AD, characterised by the appearance of iron tools and weapons and various other technological and agricultural developments some of which impacted plant communities.

Jurassic – the period of geological time between approximately 205 and 140 million years before present. Calcareous rocks such as oolitic limestone, the Marlstone and those of the Blue Lias formed during this Period. They support important calcicolous plant communities.

Lake – a large standing water feature, nominally more than one hectare in surface area and often considerably larger.

Leached – soil and other ground that has had its minerals removed by the downward percolation of rainwater, leaving upper layers of the ground very infertile and acidic.

Lime-rich – see entry for calcareous.

Local Biodiversity Action Plan (LBAP) – a local partnership project that sets targets for the conservation of wildlife habitats and various key wildlife species including scarce plants.

Local Nature Reserve (LNR) – a type of statutory nature reserve, designated by local authorities both for people and wildlife.

Marsh – well-vegetated open wetland on mineral soils, e.g. silts, clays and gravels, where the water level fluctuates around ground level.

Meander – the natural curves of a river (less often a stream) which affects the depth, waterflow and other aspects of this habitat.

Medieval – of the Middle Ages (see that entry).

Mesolithic – the 'Middle Stone Age' period from about 10,000 to 4,000BC during which people were nomadic hunter-gatherers and made relatively little impact on the wildwood.

Mesotrophic (waterbody) – a pool or lake with relatively low nutrient levels, a state found in a number of Warwickshire waterbodies that overlie base-poor rocks (e.g. sandstone) in what are or once were heathland districts (e.g. at Sutton Park and Alvecote Pools).

Microhabitat – a narrowly defined habitat or habitat feature, e.g. a patch of bare ground within a more broadly-defined habitat, e.g. woodland or grassland.

Microspecies – a very subtle or poorly-defined species, e.g. an apomictic species (see that entry) with tiny but regular differences from similar, closely related species.

Middle Ages – the period from 1154 to 1485AD which saw massive social change that impacted on land-use and therefore wildflowers.

Mire – well-vegetated wetland on waterlogged peat or peaty soil that is moderately (poor-fen) to strongly (bog) acidic due to a lack of minerals and the leaching effect of rainwater.

Mobile – a plant capable of quickly moving to new areas and new sites, typically because of seeds that can be carried by the wind, animals or birds.

Mycorrhiza – the network of fungal filaments that exist in most soils, usually in connection with plant roots, and periodically give rise to fruiting bodies (fungi and mushrooms). Many plants cannot exist without associated fungi, though it is a largely invisible relationship.

National Nature Reserve (NNR) – a 'Site of Special Scientific Interest' (see that entry) of the very highest national significance. Sutton Park is the only one in Vice-county Warwickshire.

National Vegetation Classification (NVC) – a project that has classified all the vegetation types of Great Britain using the presence and abundance of different plant species. The classifications help us to understand the subtle environmental, geographical and historical factors that influence habitats.

Native – a plant that has come to grow in an area without human intervention (though its distribution and status may heavily influenced by human activity).

Naturalised – a non-native plant that has become established and now grows as a fully wild species (as opposed to a casual, which forms short-lived populations).

Neolithic – the 'New Stone Age' period from about 4,000 to 2,000BC during which people formed settled agricultural communities and started to clear and modify the wildwood.

Neophyte – a species that arrived in Britain through the agency of people after 1500AD and is not native.

Neutral (e.g. grassland) – vegetation growing on ground with a pH in the range of 5-6.5.

Nitrate – a nitrogen-based molecule which contributes to the fertility of soil and water (especially that which is 'eutrophic') but can be damaging to plants where its levels become too high.

NVC – see 'National Vegetation Classification'.

Open field systems – see 'Strip farming'.

Palaeozoic – the period of geological time between approximately 550 and 250 million years before present. Responsible for much of the solid geology in central and north Warwickshire and subject to quarrying throughout this area.

Pasture – land subject to regular grazing by stock animals e.g. cattle, sheep and horses.

Perennial – a plant that lives for three or more years (often many years).

Permian – the period of geological time between approximately 290 and 250 million years before present.

Phosphate – a phosphorus-based molecule which contributes to the fertility of soil and water (especially that which is eutrophic) but can be damaging to plants where its levels become too high.

Pioneer – a plant that is one of the first species to colonise a new or bare piece of ground or other habitat feature (e.g. a pool), often as part of a ruderal community.

Planned Countryside – the lowland British landscape type that gains much of its modern character from the enclosure (by hedging) of open field systems following the Parliamentary Enclosure Acts of the eighteenth and early nineteenth century. Typified by the Feldon, Cotswolds, Avon Valley and Dunsmore (see those entries).

Plantation woodland – deliberately-planted woodland on a piece of land that was not previously wooded (though the term is often used for blocks of conifers or commercial broadleaves planted in cleared old woodland which, strictly-speaking, is 'replanted woodland' and tends to have many more woodland plants).

Pollarding – the regular cutting of a tree, typically at a height of 2-3 meters, so that it produces a regular supply of new growth. The tree is called a 'pollard'.

Pollution – the introduction of harmful contaminants into the environment. This can include water-borne substances, e.g. sewage or fertilisers, or airborne substances, e.g. dust and gases.

Pond – a small standing water feature, nominally less than one hectare in surface area.

Poor-fen – a type of mire wetland with less acidity and more mineral enrichment than bog, making it transitional between bog and rich-fen.

Post-industrial – land that has had an industrial use in the past such as quarrying and associated dumping, or following the demolition of a factory or warehouse.

Precambrian – geological time before about 550 million years before present, responsible for some of the rocks quarried in the Nuneaton area

Primary woodland – the oldest ancient woodland; that which has remained wooded since the wildwood.

Propagate – to reproduce or multiply, either sexually or by vegetative means, e.g. budding, fragmenting and re-rooting.

Pteridophytes – the relatively primitive group of higher plants that contains ferns and clubmosses.

Race – see 'Subspecies'.

Relic of cultivation – a crop plant that escapes into the wild, usually for a very short period (as a casual) but occasionally with greater frequency and persistence (usually as archaeophytes and neophytes).

Ridge-and-furrow – the parallel earth features that represent the old plough marks associated with open field systems (strip farming) of the Anglo-Saxon and medieval periods.

Riverbank – the elevated sides of a river (as opposed to the riveredge, which is at water level or below).

Romano-British – pertaining to the period 43 to 410AD, during which much of Britain was ruled by Rome and saw various technological and agricultural developments, some of which impacted plant communities.

Ruderal – the habitats and vegetation that are associated with disturbance or the period of recolonisation that follows it, characterised by lots of pioneer species.

Saline – soil or water that has a high salt content, typically due to contamination with road salt but also due to the natural seepage of salty water from some rocks in Warwickshire (hence the development of Leamington Spa and the presence of Sea Club-rush at two Warwickshire sites).

Scrub – vegetation dominated by shrubs and young trees, typically developing on grassland, heathland or within woodland rides and clearings as part of the transition/succession to woodland.

Secondary woodland – woodland that has arisen from non-wooded land (as opposed to primary woodland) either before 1600AD (ancient secondary woodland) or since 1600AD (non-ancient secondary woodland which includes much plantation woodland).

Seepage (flush) – a place where water emerges directly from the ground, often creating a small wetland feature or a patch of wet woodland.

Semi-improved (e.g. grassland) – vegetation that has been partially improved for agriculture, typically by increasing soil fertility and trying to replace wildflowers with favoured grasses or crops, though to a lesser extent than fully improved vegetation.

Semi-natural – vegetation that has a strong natural character but has been influenced by human activity to some extent. There is arguably no genuine fully natural habitat left in Warwickshire – it disappeared with the wildwood, though some places are more natural than others.

Set-aside land – agricultural land temporarily taken out of production. It can sometimes enable wildflowers to flourish, but is often treated regularly with herbicide, so preventing this.

Site of Importance for Nature Conservation (SINC) – typically a wildlife site of high county or local importance that receives a level of protection against development, but less protection than that enjoyed by a SSSI (see that entry). Also known as a non-statutory or second-tier wildlife site.

Site of Special Scientific Interest (SSSI) – a nationally important wildlife site designated by Natural England (formerly English Nature) under their statutory powers.

Soil – a substrate comprised of weathered mineral matter combined with organic matter (decaying or decomposed plant remains, animal remains and faeces). It can be absent from some plant habitats, e.g. bare rocks, pure sand and gravel, and various features of the built environment.

Species – a genetically-defined type of plant that usually breeds true with itself and under natural circumstances tends not to hybridise with other species. The complication arises where subspecies develop or where closely-related species that would not naturally grow together find themselves in close proximity and hybridise with varying degrees of success (an increasingly frequent phenomenon).

Species-rich (vegetation) – vegetation featuring a relatively high number of plant species (as opposed to species-poor).

Standing water – still (non-flowing) water.

Strip farming – an Anglo-Saxon and medieval form of arable agriculture that involved dividing hedgeless 'open field' land into numerous strips of about 0.5 hectares, and rotating crops around these typically on a four-year basis. The ancient plough marks associated with this are called 'ridge-and-furrow' (see that entry).

Submerged – growing underwater.

Subsidence pool – a waterbody that forms where the land has sunk; in Warwickshire usually because of underlying coalmines (e.g. Alvecote Pools, Stoke Floods, Wyken Slough).

Subspecies (also known as a race) – variation within a species that usually has a strong genetic basis stemming from the breaking up and subsequent isolation of populations (e.g. during the ice ages). This can eventually produce populations of a plant that differ in appearance or ecology, or both, but not sufficiently so to justify splitting them into separate species (e.g. Scarlet Pimpernel *Anagallis arvenis* ssp. *arvensis* and Blue Pimpernel ssp. *foemina*).

Substrate – the material upon which a plant is growing and usually rooted into. It can be soil, rock, sand, gravel and a variety of waste materials or building materials.

Succession – the process by which one vegetation type or plant community turns into another over time, e.g. ruderal into grassland, grassland into scrub, and scrub into woodland. Succession can be prevented by management such as grazing, hay cutting, nature conservation management or disturbance.

Suckering – the process by which a plant produces new aerial growth from its root system, resulting in a patch of genetically identical plants that may divide to become new individuals (e.g. trees like Aspen and English Elm).

Swamp – well-vegetated open wetland where the plant bases are more or less permanently under water.

Tall-herb – herbaceous, non-woody vegetation dominated by tall robust herbs such as nettles, thistles, Hogweed, Teasel, etc.

Transitional (vegetation) – vegetation that is either intermediate between two well recognised states, e.g. bog and fen, or in the process of changing from one state to another as part of the succession process. Some plants favour transitional states e.g. the plants of poor-fen.

Triassic – the period of geological time between approximately 250 and 205 million years before present, responsible for the calcareous White Lias which supports important calcicolous plant communities.

Triple hybrid – a hybrid with three species in its parentage, e.g. willows such as *Salix* x *calodendron* and some hybrid evening-primroses.

Unimproved (e.g. grassland) – vegetation that has not been subject to any agricultural activity that improves its productivity (e.g. ploughing, fertilising or re-seeding). Often incorrectly used to refer to species-rich grassland that has experienced relatively little improvement (Warwickshire is unlikely to have any truly unimproved grassland: see entry for 'semi-improved').

Variety – see entry for 'Form'.

Vascular plant – see entry for 'Higher plant'.

Vegetation – a habitat featuring plants, including grassland, heathland, wetland, etc.

Vernal – of the spring, i.e. plant growth or flowering that takes place in spring.

Vice-county (Warwickshire) – the biological or Watsonian County, which resembles the old County and tends to use stable natural features such as watercourses and ridges to define its boundary. It never changes, unlike modern administrative counties.

Voucher specimen – an actual specimen that provides hard evidence for a record.

Wasteland – essentially the same as 'derelict land' (see that entry).

Waterbody – a discrete area of open water such as a pond, pool, lake or reservoir. Often permanent, but not necessarily so. (Temporary or fluctuating water bodies can harbour considerable botanical interest.)

Water course – a river, stream, canal or water-filled ditch.

Watsonian (Warwickshire) – the same as 'Vice-county' (see that entry).

Weed – a plant growing where it is not wanted, e.g. a wildflower (arable weed) growing within a crop. Not automatically derogatory if considered from a botanical point of view.

Wetland – a habitat subject to a high water table or prolonged flooding such that the ground is covered by shallow water for some or all of the year.

Wildwood – the primeval and totally natural woodland that covered much of Britain after the last ice age before the Neolithic period, at which point it started to be cleared or modified by cutting, grazing and management.

Withy beds (osier beds) – damp areas where certain willows, notably Osier, were grown as a source of twigs for basketry.

Woody species – perennial plants that lay down lignin in their stems to make them larger, more robust and winter-hardy, typically shrubs and trees (but also some climbers).

Further Reading

Key Warwickshire botanical publications

Allen, D.E. 1957. *The Flora of the Rugby District*. Rugby School Natural History Society.

Bagnall, J.E. 1891. *Flora of Warwickshire*. London and Birmingham.

Cadbury, D.A., Hawkes, J.G. & Readett, R.C. 1971. *A Computer-Mapped Flora. A Study of the County of Warwickshire*. Academic Press, London.

Clark, M.C. 1978. Additions to the Flora of Warwickshire. *Proceedings of the Birmingham Natural History Society* 23 (4): 238.

Copson, P.J. 1979. Additions to the Flora of Warwickshire. *Proceedings of the Birmingham Natural History Society* 24 (1): 33-36.

Copson, P.J. 1980. Additions to the Flora of Warwickshire. *Proceedings of the Birmingham Natural History Society* 24 (2): 66-74.

Copson, P.J. 1981. Additions to the Flora of Warwickshire. *Proceedings of the Birmingham Natural History Society* 24 (3): 153-156.

Copson, P.J. 1982. Additions to the Flora of Warwickshire. *Proceedings of the Birmingham Natural History Society* 24 (4): 199-202.

Copson, P.J. 1983. Additions to the Flora of Warwickshire. *Proceedings of the Birmingham Natural History Society* 25 (1): 2-4.

Copson, P.J. 1984. Additions to the Flora of Warwickshire. *Proceedings of the Birmingham Natural History Society* 25 (2): 62-64.

Copson, P.J. 1985. Additions to the Flora of Warwickshire. *Proceedings of the Birmingham Natural History Society* 25 (3): 146-149.

Copson, P.J. 1987. Additions to the Flora of Warwickshire. *Proceedings of the Birmingham Natural History Society* 25 (4): 187-192.

Copson, P.J. 1989. Additions to the Flora of Warwickshire. *Proceedings of the Birmingham Natural History Society* 26 (1): 29-36.

Copson, P.J. 1991. Additions to the Flora of Warwickshire. *Proceedings of the Birmingham Natural History Society* 26 (2): 69-77.

Copson, P.J. 1994. Additions to the Flora of Warwickshire. *Proceedings of the Birmingham Natural History Society* 27 (1): 36-50.

Copson, P.J. 1996. Additions to the Flora of Warwickshire. *Proceedings of the Birmingham Natural History Society* 27 (2): 84-90.

Copson, P.J. 1998. Additions to the Flora of Warwickshire. *Proceedings of the Birmingham Natural History Society* 27 (3): 146-154.

Copson, P.J. 2000. Additions to the Flora of Warwickshire. *Proceedings of the Birmingham Natural History Society* 27 (4): 205-211.

Copson, P.J. 2002. Additions to the Flora of Warwickshire. *Proceedings of the Birmingham Natural History Society* 28 (1): 24-26.

Copson, P., Partridge, J. & Roberts, J. 2008. *A New Checklist of the Flora of Warwickshire*. Warwickshire Publications, Warwick (informally published report).

Hawkes, J.G., Williams, J.T., Clark, M.C., Fowkes, H.H. & Laflin, T. 1973. Additions to the Flora. *Proceedings of the Birmingham Natural History Society* 22 (3): 169-173.

Langley, D.C.D. 1977. Additions to the Flora of Warwickshire. *Proceedings of the Birmingham Natural History Society* 23 (3): 162-163.

Partridge, J. 2005. *Sonchus tenerrimus* – first cytologically confirmed British record. *BSBI News* 99: 77.

Partridge, J. 2006a. The Changing Flora of Warwickshire: local change 2003/4. *Proceedings of the Birmingham Natural History Society* 28 (3): 160-163.

Partridge, J. 2006b. Additions to the Flora of Warwickshire. *Proceedings of the Birmingham Natural History Society* 28 (3): 164-166.

Price, J.M. 1980. Memories of Bagnall and his flora. *Proceedings of the Birmingham Natural History Society* 24 (2): 75-92.

Price, J.M. 2002. *Stratford-upon-Avon – A Flora and Fauna*. Gem, Wallingford.

Price, J.M. & Partridge J.W. 2007. *Bupleurum longifolium* L.: another new British record for Warwickshire (v.c. 38)? *BSBI News* 105: 31.

Purton, T. 1817. *The Midland Flora*. London (2 vols).

Readett, R.C., Hawkes, J.G., Cadbury, D.A. & Laflin, T. 1965. Check lists of the vascular plants and bryophytes of Warwickshire (VC38) and surrounding vice-counties. *Proceedings of the Birmingham Natural History and Philosophical Society* (special number) 20 (4).

Williams, J.T. 1974. Corrections and Additions to the Flora. *Proceedings of the Birmingham Natural History Society* 22 (4): 242-246.

Williams, J.T. 1975. Additions to the Flora of Warwickshire. *Proceedings of the Birmingham Natural History Society* 23 (1): 4-10.

Williams, J.T. 1976. Additions to the Flora of Warwickshire. *Proceedings of the Birmingham Natural History Society* 23 (2): 91-94.

Warwickshire's landscape and wildlife

Anon. 1991. *Assessment and conservation of landscape character. The Warwickshire Landscapes Project approach*. Countryside Commission.

Anon. 1993. *Warwickshire Landscape Guidelines: Arden*. Warwickshire County Council Planning & Transportation Department.

Anon. 1993. *Warwickshire Landscape Guidelines: Dunsmore, High Cross Plateau, Mease Lowlands*. Warwickshire County Council Planning & Transportation Department.

Anon. 1993. *Warwickshire Landscape Guidelines: Avon Valley, Feldon, Cotswolds*. Warwickshire County Council Planning & Transportation Department.

Dix, H.M. & Hughes, D.R.(Eds.) 1960. *The Coventry District – A Naturalist's Guide*. The Coventry & District Natural History and Scientific Society, Coventry.

Tasker, A. (Ed.) 1990. *The Nature of Warwickshire*. Barracuda Books, Buckingham.

Vigor, P. & Roberts, J. (Eds.) 2007. *Discover wild Warwickshire – a guide to local nature reserves*. Warwickshire Wildlife Trust, Coventry.

Woodland

Anon. 1985. *Inventory of Ancient Woodland (Provisional) – Warwickshire*. Nature Conservancy Council.

Lean R. & Robinson, D.P. 1989. *West Midlands Inventory of Ancient Woodland (Provisional)*. Nature Conservancy Council.

Peterken, G.F. 1981. *Woodland Conservation and Management*. Chapman & Hall, London.

Rackham, O. 1976. *Trees and Woodland in the British Landscape*. Dent, London (and subsequent editions).

Rackham, O. 2003. *Ancient Woodland – Its History, Vegetation and Uses in England*. Castlepoint Press.

Rackham, O. 2006. *Woodlands*. Collins (New Naturalist Library, No. 100).

Rodwell, J.S. (Ed.) 1991. *British Plant Communities, Volume 1: Woodland and Scrub*. Cambridge University Press, Cambridge.

Wager, S.J. 1998. Woods, Wolds and Groves. *The woodland of medieval Warwickshire*. British Archaeological Reports (No. 269). J&EH.

Hedgerows

Pollard, E. Hooper, M.D. & Moore. N.W. 1974. *Hedges*. Collins (New Naturalist Library, No. 58).

Rackham, O. 1986. *The History of the Countryside*. Dent, London (and subsequent versions and editions).

Wilkinson, G. 1978. *Epitaph for the Elm*. Hutchinson, London.

Permanent grassland

Anon. 1995. *Grassland Inventory – Warwickshire*. English Nature.

Anon. 1996. *Grassland Inventory – West Midlands*. English Nature.

Duffey, E. (Ed.) 1974. *Grassland ecology and wildlife management*. Institute of Terrestrial Ecology. London.

Lousley, J.E. 1969. *Wildflowers of Chalk and Limestone*. Collins (New Naturalist Library, No.16; reprinted by Bloomsbury Books, 1990).

Rodwell, J.S. (Ed.) 1991. *British Plant Communities, Volume 3: Grassland and montane communities*. Cambridge University Press, Cambridge.

Water courses and wetlands

Haslam, S.M. 1978. *River Plants*. Cambridge University Press, Cambridge.

Haslam, S.M., Sinker, C.A. & Wolseley, P.A. 1975. British Water Plants. *Field Studies* 4: 243-351 (available as a stand-alone reprint).

Preston, C.D. 1995. *Pondweeds of Great Britain and Ireland*. BSBI (BSBI Handbook No. 8).

Preston, C.D. & Croft, J. 2001. Aquatic plants in Britain and Ireland. Harley Books.

Rodwell, J.S. (Ed.) 1995. *British Plant Communities, Volume 4: Aquatic communities, swamps and tall-herb fens*. Cambridge University Press, Cambridge.

Arable and other cultivated land

Ammerman, A.J. & Cavalli-Sforza, L.L. 1971. Measuring the rate of spread of early farming in Europe. *Man* 6: 674-688.

Byfield, A.J. & Wilson, P.J. 2005. *Important Arable Plant Areas: identifying priority sites for arable land plant conservation in the United Kingdom*. Plantlife International, Salisbury (available on the web).

Chancellor, R.J. 1977. A preliminary survey of arable weeds in Britain. *Weed Research* 17: 283-287.

Copson, P.J. & Roberts, H.A. 1991. Garden weeds – a survey in Warwickshire. *Professional Horticulture* 5: 71-73.

Hanf, M. 1983. *The Arable Weeds of Europe with their seedlings and seeds.* BASF, Ludwigschafen, Germany.

Lockton, A. 2002. *BSBI Arable Weed Survey.* BSBI.

Partridge, J. 2007. *Viola* x *bavarica*: the punctual Dog-violet? *BSBI News* 106: 8-9.

Price, J.M. & Partridge J.W. 2007. *Bupleurum longifolium* L.: another new British record for Warwickshire (v.c. 38)? *BSBI News* 105: 31.

Rackham, O. 1986. *The History of the Countryside.* Dent, London (and subsequent versions and editions).

Wilson, P, J. 1992. Britain's Arable Weeds. *British Wildlife* 3: 149-161.

Wilson, P. & Miles, K. 2003. *Arable Plants – a field guide.* English Nature and WILDGuides (also available in an interactive, searchable version on the web).

Heathland and mire

Anon. 1996. *The Lowland Heathland inventory.* English Nature & RSPB.

Coxhead, P. 1994. Changes in the Vascular Plant Flora of Sutton Park. *Proceedings of the Birmingham Natural History Society* 27(1): 2-12.

Coxhead, P. 2000. Recent Changes and Additions to the Flora of Sutton Park. *Proceedings of the Birmingham Natural History Society* 27(4): 246-247.

Coxhead, P. & Fowkes, H.H. (Eds.) 1998. *A Natural History of Sutton Park - Part 1: Vascular Plants.* Sutton Coldfield Natural History Society, 2nd edition.

Fowkes, H.H. & Coxhead, P. 1991. *The Natural History of Sutton Park – Part 1: The Vascular Plants.* Sutton Coldfield Natural History Society.

Readett, R.C. 1971. A Flora of Sutton Park, Warwickshire. *Proceedings of the Birmingham Natural History Society* 22: 2-75.

Rodwell, J.S. (Ed.) 1991. *British Plant Communities, Volume 5: Mires and Heaths.* Cambridge University Press, Cambridge.

Webb, N.R. 1986. *Heathlands. A natural history of Britain's lowland heaths.* Collins (New Naturalist Library, No. 72).

Disturbed ground

Bowra, J.C. 1999. *Oenothera*, (evening-primroses) – the way forward. *BSBI News* 81: 24-26.

Bowra, J.C. 2001. *Oenothera* (evening-primroses) in Britain: the effects of essential clonalism and hybridisation. *BSBI News* 87: 60-61.

Gilbert, O. 1989. *The Ecology of Urban Habitats.* Chapman and Hall, London.

Gilbert, O. 1992. *The flowering of the cities: The natural flora of 'urban commons'.* English Nature, Peterborough.

Partridge, J. 2005. *Sonchus tenerrimus* – first cytologically confirmed British record *BSBI News* 99: 77.

Rodwell, J.S. (Ed.) 2000. *British Plant Communities, Volume 5: Maritime communities and vegetation of open habitats.* Cambridge University Press, Cambridge.

Salisbury, E.J. 1961. *Weeds & Aliens*. Collins (New Naturalist Library, No. 43).
Teagle, W.G. 1978. The Endless Village. Nature Conservancy Council, Shrewsbury.

The built environment
Boucher, A. & Partridge, J. 2006. *Urtica membranacea*, an annual nettle, in Warwick: a first British record? *BSBI News* 103: 29-3.
Darlington, A. 1981. *Ecology of Walls*. Heinemann, London.
Gilbert, O. 1992. *Rooted in stone: The natural flora of urban walls*. English Nature, Peterborough.
Scott, N.E. & Davison, A.W. 1982. De-icing salt and the invasion of road verges by maritime plants. *Watsonia* 14: 41–52.
Scott, N.E. (1985). The updated distribution of maritime species on British roadsides. *Watsonia* 15: 381-386.

Plant identification

General wildflower guides
Blamey, M., Fitter, R. & Fitter, A. 2003. *The Wild Flowers of Britain and Ireland*. A. & C. Black.
Blamey, M. & Grey-Wilson, C. 2003. *Cassell's Wildflowers of Britain and Northern Europe*. Cassell.
Garrard, I. & Streeter, D. 1998. *The Wild Flowers of the British Isles*. Midsummer Books, London.
Phillips, R. 1994. *Wild Flowers of Britain*. Pan MacMillan, 2nd edition.
Rich, T.C.G. & Jermy, A.C. 1998. *Plant Crib 1998*. BSBI.
Rose, F. & O'Reilly, C. 2006. *The Wild Flower Key*. Frederick Warne Books.
Stace, C.A. 1997. *New Flora of the British Isles*. Cambridge University Press, 2nd edition.

Guides to trees
Johnson, O. & More, D. 2004. *Collins Tree Guide*. HarperCollins. London
Meikle, R.D. 1984. *Willows and Poplars of Great Britain and Ireland*. BSBI (BSBI Handbook No. 4).
Panter, J. & May, A. 2000. *A Guide to the Identification of Deciduous Broad-leaved Trees and Shrubs in Winter*. Field Studies Council.
Phillips, R. 1978. *Trees in Britain, Europe and North America*. Macmillan

Guides to aquatic plants
Haslam, S.M. 1978. *River Plants*. Cambridge University Press, Cambridge.
Haslam, S.M., Sinker, C.A. & Wolseley, P.A. 1975. British Water Plants. *Field Studies* 4: 243-351 (available as a stand-alone reprint).
Preston, C.D. 1995. *Pondweeds of Great Britain and Ireland*. BSBI (BSBI Handbook No. 8).

Guides to ferns and other pteridophytes

Fitter, R., Fitter, A. & Farrer, A. 1984. *Collins Guide to the Grasses, Sedges, Rushes and Ferns of Britain and Northern Europe*. Collins. London.

Jermy, C. & Camus, J. 1991. *The Illustrated Guide to Ferns and Allied Plants of the British Isles*. The Natural History Museum. London

Merryweather, J. & Hill, M. 2007. *The Fern Guide. An introductory guide to the ferns, clubmosses, quillworts and horsetails of the British Isles*. Field Studies Council, 3rd edition.

Page, C.N. 1997. *Ferns of Britain and Ireland*. Cambridge University Press, 2nd edition.

Phillips, R. 1980. *Grasses, Ferns, Mosses & Lichens of Great Britain and Ireland*. Pan Books, London.

Rose, F. 1989. *Colour identification Guide to the Grasses, Sedges, Rushes and Ferns of the British Isles and North Western Europe*. Viking Books.

Guides to grasses, sedges and rushes

Fitter, R., Fitter, A. & Farrer, A. 1984. *Collins Guide to the Grasses, Sedges, Rushes and Ferns of Britain and Northern Europe*. Collins. London.

Hubbard, C. 1984. *Grasses*. Penguin Books, 3rd edition.

Jermy, A.C.J., Simpson, D.A., Foley, M.J.Y. & Porter, M.S. 2007. *Sedges of the British Isles*. BSBI (BSBI Handbook No. 1), 3rd edition.

Phillips, R. 1980. *Grasses, Ferns, Mosses & Lichens of Great Britain and Ireland*. Pan Books, London.

Rose, F. 1989. *Colour identification Guide to the Grasses, Sedges, Rushes and Ferns of the British Isles and North Western Europe*. Viking Books.

Guides to other specific plant groups

Clement, E.J., Smith, D.P.J. & Thirlwell, I.R. 2005. *Illustrations of Alien Plants in the British Isles*. BSBI

Dudman, A.A. & Richards, A.J. 1997. *Dandelions of Great Britain and Ireland*. BSBI (BSBI Handbook No. 9).

Edees, E.S. & Newton, A. 1988. *Brambles of the British Isles*. The Ray Society, London.

Foley, M. & Clarke, S. 2005. *Orchids of the British Isles*. Griffin Press.

Graham, G.G. 1993. *Roses of Great Britain and Ireland*. BSBI (BSBI Handbook No. 7).

Harrap, A. & Harrap, S. 2005. *Orchids of Britain and Ireland*. Christopher Helm.

Lang, D. 2004. *Britain's Orchids*. English Nature and WILDguides (also available in an interactive, searchable version on the web).

Lousley, J.E. & Kent, D.H. 1981. *Docks and Knotweeds of the British Isles*. BSBI (BSBI Handbook No. 3).

Rich, T.C.G. 1991. *Crucifers of Great Britain and Ireland*. BSBI (BSBI Handbook No. 6).

Tutin, T.G. 1980. *Umbellifers of the British Isles*. BSBI (BSBI Handbook No. 2).

Wilson, P. & Miles, K. 2003. *Arable Plants – a field guide*. English Nature and WILDGuides (also available in an interactive, searchable version on the web).

Atlases and checklists

Clement, E.J. & Foster, M.C. 1995. *Alien Plants of the British Isles*. BSBI.

Clement, G., Ryves, T.B. & Foster, M.C. 1996. *Alien Grasses of the British Isles: A Provisional Catalogue*. BSBI.

Kent, D.H. 1992. *List of Vascular Plants of the British Isles*. BSBI.

Newton, A. & Randall, R.D. 2004. *Atlas of the British and Irish Brambles*. BSBI.

Preston, C.D., Pearman. D.A.& Dines, T.D. (Eds.) 2002. *New Atlas of the British & Irish Flora*. Oxford University Press. Oxford.

Stace, C.A. et al. (Eds.) 2003. *Vice-county Census Catalogue of Vascular Plants of Great Britain*. BSBI.

Wardlaw, A.C. & Leonard, A. (Eds.) 2005. *New Atlas of the Ferns & Allied Plants of Britain & Ireland*. British Pteridological Society.

Literature on scarce plants and changing statuses

Braithwaite, M.E., Ellis, R.W. & Preston, C.D. 2006. *Change in the British Flora 1987 -2004*. BSBI.

Cheffings, C.M. & Farrell, L. (Eds.) 2005. The Vascular Plant Red Data List for Great Britain. *Species Status* 7. JNCC, Peterborough (downloadable from the JNCC web site).

Preston, C.D., Pearman. D.A. & Hall, A.R. 2004. Archaeophytes in Britain. *Botanical Journal of the Linnaean Society* 145: 257-294.

Rich, T.C.G. & Woodruff, E.R. 1996. Changes in the vascular plant floras of England and Scotland between 1930-60 and 1987-88: the BSBI monitoring scheme. *Biological Conservation* 75: 217-229.

Index of Plant Names

INDEX OF PLANT NAMES

Index of Place Names

(Warwickshire area only)